THE TRIUMPH OF SURGERY

THE
TRIUMPH
OF SURGERY

BY JÜRGEN THORWALD

TRANSLATED BY RICHARD AND CLARA WINSTON

PANTHEON BOOKS

Grateful acknowledgment is made to the following for granting permission to reproduce pictures from their collections: Steingrüben Archiv, Stuttgart, for all illustrations except the following: Abelard-Schuman Limited, New York, for an illustration from Robinson, *Victory Over Pain*, copyright 1946: Carl Koller / Basic Books, Inc., New York, for an illustration from Jones, *The Life and Work of Sigmund Freud:* Sigmund Freud with Martha Bernays / The Bettmann Archive, New York, for the illustration on the title page / Dr. Webb Haymaker, Washington, for three illustrations from *The Founders of Neurology*, edited by Webb Haymaker, M.D., and published by Charles C. Thomas: Sir David Ferrier, Jean Martin Charcot, John Hughlings Jackson / Institut für Geschichte der Medizin, Vienna: Eduard Zirm / University of Minnesota Press, Minneapolis, for two illustrations from Clapesattle, *The Doctors Mayo*, copyright 1941: Charles Mayo, William Mayo / The Williams and Wilkins Company, Baltimore, for an illustration from *History of Neurological Surgery*, edited by Earl A. Walker: William Macewen

AUTHOR'S NOTE

The Century of the Surgeon, a volume devoted to the crucial moments in the pioneering age of surgery, used the device of an eyewitness as narrator, an American physician whom I have named after my maternal grandfather, Henry Steven Hartmann. In 1846, Hartmann, then a medical student, witnessed the revolutionary discovery of anesthetics, demonstrated at the Massachusetts General Hospital in Boston, which changed surgery from butchery to a fine art. Hartmann was presented as a man of the liveliest curiosity, rich enough to devote his life to the witnessing and chronicling of decisive new advances in the field of surgery. Two decades after the discovery of anesthesia, he assisted at the birth of antisepsis, another crucial step in the development of surgery, since it eliminated one of its main obstacles, the frequently fatal infection of surgical wounds.

In *The Triumph of Surgery*, the same narrator is shown continuing his quest, at a time when surgery had got beyond its initial explorations in anesthetics and antisepsis, and advanced into new territories demanding more complicated means and skills.

As in *The Century of the Surgeon*, all medical and historical facts presented in this book are based on scholarly and reliable documents, a list of which is given in the Bibliography at the end of this volume.

CONTENTS

ILLUSTRATIONS

showing inguinal hernia – Carl Koller (1857–1944) – Sigmund Freud (1856–1939) with Martha Bernays – Paul Reclus (1847–1914) – William Stewart Halsted (1852–1922) – Halsted shown during an operation in 1904 – Carl Ludwig Schleich (1859–1922) – August Hildebrandt – August Bier (1861–1949) and F. Sauerbruch – John B. Murphy (1857–1916) – Christian Fenger (1840–1902) – Carlo Forlanini (1847–1918) – Nicholas Senn (1840–1908)

Uncharted Territory

Dr. Ferrier's Monkeys

When I set foot in London on Tuesday, August 2, 1881, I was visiting that city for the thirtieth or fortieth time. The following day the Third International Medical Congress was to open in St. James's Hall.

Three thousand physicians from all over the globe, among them the bearers of the most famous names in medicine, had already arrived in London as I drove in late that evening from Piccadilly to Berkeley Street and got out at the St. James Hotel. Back at the station I had spied Virchow, Langenbeck, and Robert Koch from Berlin, Pasteur from Paris, Rauchfuss and Kolomnin from St. Petersburg, Henry Bigelow from Boston, and William Keen from Philadelphia. These were but a few of the noted physicians who had gathered in the British capital for a congress which I personally have since remembered as marking the beginning of the second great epoch in the history of surgery.

The actual birth date of this new era replete with so many struggles and discoveries, defeats and triumphs, is hard to set. The elimination of surgical pain as the result of the development of anesthesia during the fifties, and the conquest of surgical infection through antisepsis and asepsis during the eighties, had liberated surgery from its fetters. For throughout the first half of the century surgery had been essentially a cruel, murderous business—and restricted, moreover, to a few superficial operations. The great discoveries had set the stage for the new era in which surgery proceeded to apply its technical achievements and extended its domain to the entire human body. To some extent one era passed imperceptibly into the other. Thus, even before the universal acceptance of anesthesia and antisepsis a few audacious, or perhaps desperate, surgeons had attempted to penetrate into the interior

3

of the human body, into the abdominal, thoracic, and cerebral cavities, and to repair afflicted organs which for thousands of years had been regarded as untouchable. Sometimes luck favored them, sometimes it did not. Their successes were feats, and remained at best the province of a few exceptional surgeons. Only a very few could claim to have laid cornerstones of the new era. Nevertheless, their work had been done, and for this very reason the dating of the turning point cannot be definite. That is why I must select the particular moment in time which to me represented a turning point, and which afforded me a glimpse of the tremendous conquests to come.

Nowadays I frequently ask myself why this particular congress registered so deeply upon my consciousness as a special milestone. The question seems all the sharper since the congress was not distinguished by any great event in *surgery*. Rather, its attention was focused on an auxiliary science, that of physiology and specifically the physiology of the brain. It was a discovery in this field which emboldened surgery to extend its domain to the human brain. Even to this day there is a strange thrill about the idea of brain surgery. At that time the very thought of attacking this organ surgically was a portentous thing. For was not the brain then, and is it not still to some extent, the most mysterious part of our bodies, the apparently unfathomable and inviolable center of all our feeling, thinking, and acting, perhaps of our souls? To me, at any rate, it seems logical that the discovery immediately antecedent to brain surgery should be appointed the opening of that new era which is the subject of this book.

The St. James Hotel, where I stayed during the congress, was scarcely one of the most magnificent hotels in the London of the eighteen-eighties. However, it used to be the favorite hotel of Charles Dickens, and consequently enjoyed a certain cultural aura.

Conferring in the rather dusky lobby with the spare-bodied, white-haired desk clerk, I followed a practice which had served me well in my many years of stopping at hotels, especially in towns where congresses were being held. I asked for the register, and scanned the recent entries for the names of doctors and surgeons I might know. I had run down the list of four or five French and English names which meant little or nothing to me when my eye was caught by a curt, somewhat curlicued, but perfectly legible and precise signature: Friedrich Goltz—Strassburg. The clerk, who had been watching me attentively, noticed that my finger stopped at Goltz's name. "A German," he volunteered. "Funny codger. I beg your pardon," he amended, "but he really is a queer fish. Got a sick dog with him, and treats it like a baby."

"A sick dog?" I asked, my attention caught.

"Yes, sir," the clerk said. "Carries it around in a kind of portable doghouse. It's a poor mutt with its head squashed in and the most mournful eyes I've ever seen on a dog. Guess it had an accident somewhere. Maybe run over by a carriage. Mr. Goltz didn't bother to say anything about it. . . . Beg your pardon again, sir, for running on about the dog. I'm an animal lover, I am."

"Is the dog in the hotel?" I asked.

The clerk nodded.

"And is Professor Goltz here too?"

The clerk showed surprise. "You know the gentleman?" he asked. I nodded, somewhat hesitantly. "He went out about half an hour ago, sir, leaving a servant behind with the dog."

"And the animal's head is injured, you say?"

"That it is," the clerk replied. "It looks as if part of his head is missing." He hesitated, throwing me a probing, almost suspicious look. "Would you mind telling me," he said, "but is Professor Goltz really one of these experimenters, I mean vivisectionists?" He paused, obviously constrained. "I should have thought of that sooner. Don't misunderstand me, sir, but here in London we're rather touchy about inflicting pain on animals, you know. Just five years ago Parliament passed the Vivisection Act, so not even scientists can torture animals, pretending it's all for the good of medicine. You see, sir, I thought this German chap's dog was really sick and he was a kind-hearted gentleman who just didn't want to part with his pet. But if it's some poor beast who's being hacked up on the pretext that science will benefit, why, our Society for the Protection of Animals will . . ."

"I'm sure it's nothing of the sort," I put in quickly. "Incidentally, I am a physician myself."

A fanatical gleam came into the clerk's eyes. A sluice gate seemed to have opened somewhere inside him. "Begging your pardon, sir," he said. "I don't mean to offend you, you being a doctor and all, but what some of these doctors are up to is nothing more nor less than cruelty to living creatures. The whole country is outraged over it. We don't want our pets falling into the hands of so-called scientists. Unfortunately we haven't been able to persuade Her Majesty and Parliament to forbid all experiments on living animals. There are still loopholes in our laws, but we mean to close them. Just a month ago a meeting was held on the matter in the Chief Lord Justice's home on Sussex Square. Cardinal Manning, Lady Bunbury, and Lady Mount-Temple were present and called for a complete ban on all kinds of vivisection. You see, sir, I happen to be a member of the Society for . . ."

"That's fine," I said, my thoughts still revolving about the name of Goltz. "But really, I am very tired. May I see my room?"

"Yes, sir," the clerk said. "Incidentally your room happens to be . . ." He broke off, but I guessed that he wanted to tell me Goltz's room was near mine.

I felt rather done in after the voyage across the Atlantic. Dressed as I was, I threw myself down on the bed, and wondered how I ought to finish off the evening. Just as I stretched out my weary limbs, I heard from some distance away the faint whimpering of an animal. The sound was barely audible, and did not continue long. But involuntarily I listened to the silences in the hotel. The whimpering was not repeated, but I felt certain that it had come from the mysterious dog of which the clerk had spoken. This, and the clerk's remarks, combined not only to keep me awake, but to banish my weariness.

The events of the subsequent hours and days would signify little to people today if I did not at this point sketch in the background which resulted in Goltz's becoming a key figure in my imagination and in the whole development of surgery.

During those years Goltz stood in the van of an international group of leading physiologists who were probing the secrets of the brain. At this time the brain was generally considered to be a unitary organ, whose functioning was governed by mysterious higher influences. From experiments with frogs, the French scientist Pierre Flourens came to the conclusion that the functions of the brain were evenly distributed throughout the entire organ. Hence, even the greater part of the brain could be excised without impairment of functions; the portion remaining would be able to assume all the mental and somatic functions formerly borne by the whole brain. Despite the fact that ancient Greek physicians had observed that injuries to the head, and diseases attacking one side of the brain, had resulted in paralyses and convulsions on the opposite side of the body, Flourens's doctrine of the equality of all parts of the brain was held as sacrosanct.

In 1861 Paul Broca, the Parisian surgeon and anthropologist, revolted against this dogma. On the dissecting table, Broca had opened the brain of a dead woman who had lost her powers of speech a few years before her demise. In the course of his autopsy Broca found a clearly defined morbid softening in the left frontal lobe of the brain, between the second and third frontal convolutions. He came to the conclusion that this softened portion constituted a functional center which "controlled human speech and above all the capacity for word formation." His patient's loss of speech had been caused by the damage to this center, he argued, and he further advanced the thesis that the brain probably was composed of many such centers, each of which governed specific functions of the body. Thus there would be centers for the muscles, for the senses, and so on.

Broca's hypothesis was accorded almost unanimous and frequently intemperate rejection. A few years later, however, a young doctor at the then tiny National Hospital for the Paralysed and Epileptic in London, Hughlings Jackson by name, followed the trail Broca had blazed. Jackson, who became a good friend of mine in the years to come, was neither a surgeon nor an anatomist. He was a specialist in clinical medicine with a remarkable gift for deducing from the visible symptoms of his hospital patients the nature of unknown processes in the brain. Jackson had the obsessiveness of a true scientific eccentric. For example, he would fly into a rage if anyone disturbed him while he was observing the symptoms of his own severe attacks of migraine. His wife Elizabeth had died of a disease of the cerebral cortex, in the course of which she had suffered from convulsions similar to those of epilepsy. Much as I esteemed Jackson, I felt sure that he had used even his wife's disease as a subject for dispassionate observation.

By 1864 Jackson had described numerous cases of right-side paralysis caused by cerebral hemorrhage which led simultaneously to loss of speech. That such conditions of paralysis almost always appeared on the side of the body opposite to the affected part of the brain lent support to Broca's theory that the speech center was located in the left half of the brain. A few years later Jackson published a new series of observations. He had noticed a certain consistent pattern in the attacks of patients suffering from convulsions on one side of the body. The hand and foot were first affected; then the spasms extended to the leg and arm, just as if there existed "motor" centers in the brain responsible for the individual limbs, centers lying so close together that a stimulus passing through them affected the limbs in a regular order. Subsequently Jackson maintained that such motor centers did indeed exist, and governed individual muscular movements. Without having performed a single autopsy, solely on the basis of clinical observation, he claimed that the centers for various types of movement lay within the area of ramification of the middle cerebral artery. A year later—in 1871 —the amazing report reached London from Berlin that such motor centers had actually been demonstrated in the brains of dogs. Two young Berlin physicians, Gustav Theodor Fritsch and Eduard Hitzig (later a prominent neurologist), were the authors of this report. During the Prusso-Danish War Fritsch had attended a soldier with such severe head wounds that parts of the brain were exposed. By chance he observed that touching certain parts of the brain produced specific twitching movements in certain parts of the body on the opposite side. Some time later he joined with Hitzig, who was working at the Berlin Physiological Institute, to test his observations by experiments on animals. Fritsch and Hitzig removed sizable segments from the skulls of dogs, exposing the meninges. The first dog bled to death as soon as the cranium was opened. Subsequent operations proved more successful. Fritsch and Hitzig applied feeble electric currents to the cortex and determined that contact with specific points in the brain indeed produced movements in the right or left half of the body—the opposite half in each case. Pins were inserted as markers, the dogs killed, and the brain opened up. In every case the points of the pins were found to be in precisely the same location in the central convolutions of the brain. After some experimentation Fritsch and Hitzig were able to find almost immediately the spots which produced particular movements when stimulated; they no longer needed to fumble about for these "motor centers," as they came to call these places. Like Jackson, they now maintained that all muscular movements were governed by such centers and that the brain was not at all a unitary body. Rather, it was a "well-articulated sum of several functional centers."

About this time I had attended an autopsy conducted by Paul Broca in Paris. The subject was a patient who had died after symptoms of intense headache and of progressive paralysis of the left arm and the left foot. In the right hemisphere of the brain Broca found an encapsulated tumor about the size of a chestnut, which could easily be peeled away from the mass of cranial matter. There seemed no doubt that this had been the cause of the paralysis and pain. As I looked on, the thought for the first time struck me: How easily this man could have been helped if his skull had been opened and the tumor removed. Opening of the skull—trepanation—was, after all, one of the oldest operations known to surgery. In fact, Broca himself had studied the history of this operation with particular care, and had unearthed a number of amazing facts.

In 1873 Broca had attended a congress of anthropologists at Lyons. There he had met a country doctor, one Dr. Prunières, who had taken part in the excavation of certain Stone Age graves in his native village. In the course of this work Dr. Prunières had come upon skulls with large circular openings. Prunières's explanation was that the Stone Age primitives had cut amulets from the skulls of dead men who had been known for exceptional prowess. Broca demonstrated, however, that the holes in the skulls must have been made while the men were still living. With few exceptions, the edges of the openings showed signs of the bony regeneration which takes place after bone injuries in living persons. From the extent of regeneration he concluded that many patients had survived the operation for considerable periods of time. Since only a few of the skulls also showed wounds received in battle, Broca was justified in assuming that only some of the trepanations had been performed to remove splintered portions of skull bone. Perhaps such emergency operations had taught Stone Age surgeons that removal of bone splinters could eliminate paralyses or headaches, and they had then proceeded to open the skull even when no wounds were present, as a cure for persistent headache, paralysis, epilepsy, or other symptoms of disease. Another possibility was that the skull had been opened for medico-religious reasons, to allow evil spirits to escape from the head. This was all in the realm

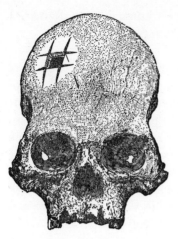

Inca skull found by George
Squiers in Cuzco, Peru.

of hypothesis, of course. On the other hand, Broca had demonstrated beyond the shadow of a doubt that a Stone Age medicine man could have performed trepanations with the instruments at his disposal. For Broca himself had no trouble trepanning the skulls of living dogs with flint knives and splinters of obsidian. Subsequently he performed the same experiment upon human cadavers. It took him only four minutes to scrape an opening in a child's skull with stone tools. A similar operation upon an adult required an hour.

Somewhat later, Ephraim George Squiers, a New York archaeologist and writer, came across a remarkable Indian skull in a private collection in Cuzco, Peru. The skull had been found in an ancient Peruvian grave dating from the Inca period, and likewise showed signs of trepanning. Here, however, the operation had been carried out in a manner different from that in Broca's skulls. On the left side of the frontal bone a rectangular piece of bone had been removed by means of four straight incisions meeting at the corners. From the nature of the cuts it was apparent that a stone instrument had been employed to cut through the skull to the meninges and to break out the rectangle of bone. Here, too, clear signs of bony regeneration indicated that the operation had been performed during the lifetime of the patient, and that he had survived it.

Word of these discoveries had made a profound impression upon both Broca and myself. They heightened our feeling that it should be possible to treat cerebral illnesses of various types, above all cerebral tumors, by opening the skull and surgically removing the morbidity. If men of the Stone Age had commanded the technique of trepanation without anesthesia or antisepsis, we, with our modern achievements, should surely be able to perform such operations successfully and thus attack the hidden focus of cerebral diseases. Delving into medical literature revealed that trepanation had also been practiced in classical antiquity, during the Middle Ages, and in as recent times as the first half of the nineteenth century.

In the writings traditionally ascribed to Hippocrates, trepanation is recommended in cases of concussion of the brain, in order to alleviate the effects of hemorrhage and secretion in the cranial cavity. Greek surgeons had employed the selfsame instrument which reappeared during the Middle Ages and still—with a few superficial improvements—took its place among the surgical instruments of my youth: the coronal trepan. This was a sharp band-saw bent into a circle, and fitted with handles. Another form of it consisted of a simple pipe with one end filed into saw teeth. These instruments were placed upon the skull and turned until a round piece of bone could be lifted out, exposing the cerebral membrane. Paré, the celebrated French surgeon of the sixteenth century, added a drill bit, chisel, pry bar, and pincers, and was quick to undertake trepanation for every injury to the skull and every concussion, his object being to remove blood, pus, and splinters or to eliminate symptoms of pressure upon the brain. He was also the first to report accurately on the results of such operations, which for us are scarcely conceivable without anesthesia. A number of his patients survived, as had some of the Stone Age patients whose remains Broca had studied. Indeed, there were persons like the Prince of Orange who were trepanned seventeen times and more. On the other hand, the losses from surgical infection, meningitis, and septicemia far exceeded even the deaths from

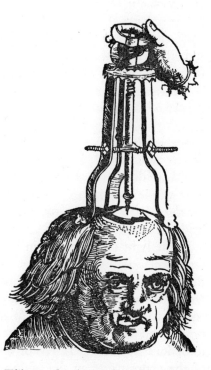

This crude sixteenth-century instrument was used, like a corkscrew, to lift out patches of bone previously sawed through.

peritonitis which followed early attempts at abdominal surgery. As time went on, these deaths became so much the ghastly rule that during the first half of the nineteenth century every single trepanned patient died of pyemia, and leading surgeons all over the world were forced to condemn all attempts at trepanation in the most forceful terms. But disastrous as the operation proved now that the sick were concentrated in filthy hospitals swarming with infectious materials, it was obvious that the devastating results were due not to the exposure of the brain in itself, but to infection of the extremely sensitive meninges. The hope loomed that in the future infection could be prevented by adequate antisepsis.

When nowadays I cast my mind back to those times, and to my many conversations with Broca, I sometimes shudder at the simplicity of our ideas, at the naïveté with which we approached what today remains the most difficult branch of surgery. But we were children of the period, burning with eagerness to achieve progress and filled with the kind of optimism that only too often springs from ignorance of real dangers. As we saw it, the problem of cerebral surgery was not so much the opening of the cranium and exposure of the brain; neither was it the removal of a tumor, but the locating of the tumor before operation. The trouble spot was concealed beneath the cranium. None of the diagnostic methods of the time could establish its position so clearly that the skull could be directly entered at the right spot. Pain was distributed over whole sections of the brainpan and could not serve as an indicator of the site of a tumor. Here was the gulf that had to be bridged.

In the light of this problem it is clear why the experiments and arguments of Fritsch, Hitzig, and Ferrier meant so much to Broca and me. If it were true that some small part of the brain were the fixed controlling organ of every muscle and every sense, and if it were also true that this functional center occupied a particular and unvarying place in the brain, then it should be possible to deduce from the paralysis or other affliction of the body the site of the abnormality in the brain, the location of, say, a tumor. It should then be possible to attack the disease by surgery aimed at the precise spot where excision was required.

Latterly, however, the school of thought which opposed Ferrier and the whole doctrine of functional centers had found a leader in Friedrich Goltz, that eminent scientist who was now residing under the same roof with me in the St. James Hotel. I had not as yet met Goltz personally. From photographs I gathered that he was a tubby, round-headed West Prussian of about fifty, the very image of the German philistine as this creature was then conceived —rightly or wrongly—in the non-German world. From all that I heard of him, he was a virtually fanatical physiologist. Even as a starveling student in Königsberg he had used his room as a laboratory, so avid was he to track down the mysteries of the brain and the nervous system. A pair of shears, forceps, a little thread, and a few frogs that he himself had caught were his whole equipment at this time.

For years Goltz had gone on working with his frogs, anesthetizing them and removing their brains to determine what this did to their vital faculties. From the results he had drawn up his theory of the functions of the brain and the spinal cord. He whom all his friends knew as the kindest of men had, in his passion for knowledge, severed the femurs of frogs until these were connected with the body only by a single main artery. He had "cooked" debrained frogs in water which he slowly heated to boiling and thereby learned that the frogs suffered no harm from slowly increasing stimuli, whereas sudden, shocklike contact with boiling water was fatal to them. In the mid-seventies he had demonstrated at a congress of physiologists meeting in Hanover that the vital processes of frogs were nothing but a chain of reflexes. He had deprived a large number of frogs of their brains. As long as he did not touch them, they squatted lethargically, incapable of any motion, even incapable of taking food. But when Goltz stimulated them at a particular spot, they reacted with twitching. If he touched another spot, they jumped, crawled, swam, or croaked. A skeptical fellow scientist challenged Goltz to make a debrained frog croak exactly five times, which trick he performed with the polished manner of an animal tamer in the circus.

Goltz had plainly been a pioneer in an entirely new field, namely the investigation of the sympathetic nervous system and of the automatic stimuli regulating the activity of the heart. He was therefore not a man to cling to tradition, as were most of the other physiologists who opposed Hitzig's and Ferrier's theses on the functional centers of the brain merely out of obstinacy and sluggishness. On the contrary, Goltz's opposition sprang from his convictions and was based on his own experiments. Since becoming professor of physiology in Strassburg he had been engaged on experiments with the brains of dogs. He had removed almost the entire cerebral cortex on both sides. Nevertheless, as he had demonstrated to a number of observers, these "debrained dogs ate, jumped, saw, and heard." The question he and all his followers addressed to Ferrier was: How could there be functional centers for all the organs of the body if these organs and the senses continued to function despite the lack of those parts of the cortex in which Ferrier claimed to have found his functional centers? Goltz's experiments had utterly shaken the theory which Broca and I viewed as the key to any attempt at intelligent brain surgery. Goltz had furnished the conservative majority of physiologists with reasons for standing firm, and had forced David Ferrier, the principal specialist on localization of functional centers in the brain, onto the defensive.

Such was the situation that evening when chance or fate brought me into close proximity with this formidable adversary. Such was the cause of the excitement which overcame me at the first sight of Goltz's name on the register, and which mounted when I first heard the whimpering of his dog.

Perhaps a quarter of an hour had passed in silence. Then I again heard a low, whimpering noise. This time the sound seemed closer than before. The last of my weariness fled. The animal which had made this sound must undoubtedly be one of Goltz's debrained dogs! But if Goltz had travelled all the way from Strassburg to London with the animal, he could have done so only because his hypothesis—that it was impossible to assign functional centers to the brain—must now be so securely established that he could flaunt his evidence before the assembled specialists of the world, and thereby smash Ferrier's doctrine to smithereens.

I took from my suitcase the congress program, which I had so far studied only for the surgical events and lectures.

I did not have to look far. After turning a few pages I came across the program of the "Section on Physiology," which was to meet in the hall of the Royal Institute on Albemarle Street. And there, scheduled for the first meeting of the section, on Thursday, August

4, at ten o'clock in the morning, was a lecture by Friedrich Goltz. Its title was listed: "Discussion of Localization of the Vital Functions in the Cerebral Cortex." So I had guessed rightly. Goltz's lecture, moreover, was to come before all the others. This was undoubtedly an indication of the importance the heads of the congress attributed to his paper. I went to the window and threw it open. The autumnal fog of London, yellowish, damp, and heavy, was already settling in. As I watched the movement of the slowly drifting swaths of mist, I realized the extent to which I had identified with Ferrier's school of thought—because of my eagerness to see diseases of the brain attacked by surgical measures. It was deeply disturbing to me that Ferrier's theory might now be on the point of receiving a deathblow. For what arguments could Ferrier offer in answer to a man who showed a debrained dog living, walking, howling, jumping, seeing, and hearing?

The fog poured in through the window, dampening my clothes. Shivering, I reached out to draw the casements together. But at that moment I again heard the soft whining of the dog, this time so close that it seemed to come from the room immediately adjoining my own. Immediately afterwards a rectangle of window sprang to light on the wall at right angles to mine, which formed one of the corners of the hotel's inner court. The curtains were not drawn, and I observed a man entering the room with a lamp. He placed the lamp on the table and stooped. I could see him raising the lid of a large box. Out thrust a dog's snout, uttering a half-whining, half-joyous cry. Under the man's caressing hand the dog fell silent. Plainly, the man was not Goltz. He must be the servant, I thought.

Now the dog's whole head and the fore part of its body appeared as the animal placed its forepaws on the rim of the box. In spite of the distance I saw distinctly what the clerk had described to me— the misshapen head with deep gouges which were surely the effect of radical surgery. This animal which seemed so lively must lack whole parts of its brainpan and brain.

The attendant lifted the dog from the box. Wagging its tail, the animal followed the man to a chair. There was no denying that it walked perfectly well, leaped in fact, and appeared to be not at all handicapped by the loss of part of its brain.

Suddenly I was no longer aware of the damp, cold fog. My full attention was concentrated upon the dog and the man, who continued to stroke it reassuringly. The dog settled down and curled up with its head turned toward the light. Now I could distinguish the cavities even more clearly. They were like deep, scarred craters. After a while the attendant stood up and went to the window, as though he had noticed me, or at any rate my own lighted window. I saw the dog jump up and follow him. Then he drew the curtains, cutting off the view.

Some while later a loud, joyous yelp startled me out of my dismal thoughts. I stood up again and went to the window without striking a light. The window of the room in which I had seen the dog was now wide open. I had a clear view of a corpulent, round-faced man with a walrus mustache, wearing a long black frock coat, sitting on the floor, while the dog, its tail wagging furiously, nuzzled against him. I recognized the man immediately from the pictures I had seen. This was Goltz, caressing in a curiously absorbed fashion the animal he himself had maimed.

"You had better close the window again." I could hear him quite plainly across the areaway. "You must never forget that this dog is no longer normal and may be extremely subject to colds. If anything should happen to it before Thursday, it would be simply dreadful. . . ."

"No need to worry, sir," the attendant replied. He was now approaching the window. "I am certain the air has done it good." As he spoke he closed the window. The curtains fell together at the center, and there was nothing for me to see but the fog as it sank in denser and ever more opaque swaths into the shaft of the courtyard.

I awoke very late the following morning, because I had tossed sleeplessly for so many hours. In the course of the night I had taken the decision to call on Goltz and look the facts in the face. But when I had a bellboy take my card to Goltz, the boy returned with word that the professor had already gone out, and left word, moreover, that he might not return to the hotel, as there were some friends he was likely to stay with.

It had grown so late meanwhile that it was high time for me to be leaving, myself, if I wished to attend the first session of the congress. I hastened downstairs. As I entered the lobby I noticed the same clerk at the desk to whom I had spoken last night. He was talking with a smartly dressed, middle-aged gentleman. I caught the last part of the conversation as I approached.

"You see the man is unfortunately a foreigner," the stranger was saying. "We are much obliged to you for your report and will keep close watch on the proceedings of the congress. But in Germany there is not yet a law against vivisection. As things stand we are powerless against a foreigner who brings with him a mistreated animal unless a British subject has participated in the cruelty. Where has the animal been taken?"

"To King's College," the clerk replied, lowering his voice. He thrust a scrap of paper across the desk. "To the laboratory of some professor named Yeo. I took care to find this out."

"We are much obliged to you for that, too," the stranger said. "We know the laboratory. Professor Yeo possesses a license for experimentation on animals, but we are convinced that he engages in experiments not covered by his license. Thank you once again."

The clerk murmured something to the effect that he was pleased to serve the good cause.

At that moment he caught sight of me. He broke off at once with a precipitate "Goodbye, sir."

As the stranger walked away, the clerk hailed me. "Is there anything I can do for you, sir?" he inquired with exaggerated friendliness. Had I slept well?

I asked him how the dog was. "What dog, Dr. Hartmann?" he said. "Oh, you mean Professor Goltz's. It isn't in the hotel any longer."

I left it at that.

On the way to St. James's Hall I ran into so many surgeons who were already old acquaintances from previous congresses that I was considerably delayed, and arrived rather late. The hall, when at last I reached it, presented an overwhelming sight. Thousands of medical men filled the well-decorated room from the platform to the wide doors, where ushers in splendid livery stood guard.

Thanks to the kindness of several prominent British doctors, I had a seat in one of the front rows. The Prince of Wales and his cousin, the German Crown Prince and later Emperor, Friedrich III, had just arrived. The German Crown Prince was regarded at this time as the very model of handsome young manhood, and had been extremely popular in England since his marriage to Victoria, eldest daughter of Queen Victoria. I had seen him once or twice before, but only from a distance. Here I found myself quite close to him, and his tall, lank, powerful frame, his full-bearded, manly, and at the same time rather gentle face, certainly struck me as extremely likable. At the time I could not guess how uncannily prophetic was his appearance at this medical congress. For close by him and me stood two doctors who seven years later were to play key parts in the tragedy of Friedrich's severe disease of the larynx, and to become the bitterest of rivals: Professor Gerhardt of Berlin and Morell Mackenzie, the most famous—and controversial—throat specialist in England.

The Prince of Wales delivered a welcoming address. He was followed by Jenner, president and absolute monarch of the Royal College of Physicians. Jenner spoke with that unsparing, rough-hewn candor which had earned him Queen Victoria's esteem as her personal physician. After him the chairman of the congress, James Paget, took the floor. His speech was a glowing tribute to the pioneering age of medicine, and a paean to the progress still to come. Then, abruptly and with an incisiveness and vehemence unusual for Paget, it became an attack upon the antivivisectionists, representatives of whom I had encountered for the first time in the St. James Hotel.

Paget stretched out a long, narrow hand. He pointed to Louis Pasteur, the discoverer of the microbes of putrefaction, who occupied a seat in the front row directly below the speaker's platform. Pasteur was an invalid now, having been stricken with paralysis on one side of his body. "There," Paget exclaimed, "sits a man who has contributed vastly to the progress of medical science." Pasteur's achievements, he continued, had been entirely dependent on experiments upon animals. Moreover, in vanquishing rabies and anthrax the scientist had benefited not only suffering humanity, but the animals also. Here was a glorious example of the kind of work which fanatical animal lovers in England were combating with such blind rancor that they threatened to stifle all progress. The members of this congress must, as a body, repel this threat to scientific freedom.

A storm of applause greeted the conclusion of this speech. It began with the English doctors, but quickly spread through the whole audience. I began to realize that antivivisectionists like the clerk at the St. James were a party to be reckoned with in England, and that in any contest between Goltz and Ferrier they would inevitably leap into the fray.

As the audience rose, I set out to look for Hughlings Jackson or Ferrier, whose lean frame in double-breasted coat was always easy to identify. Though frail of build, Ferrier looked, with his large, carefully combed mustache, like an officer in a British Guards or Colonial regiment.

The throng was such, however, that I was unable to locate either Jackson, Ferrier, or Goltz. Instead I ran across Joseph Lister, my old friend, whose struggle for the acceptance of antisepsis was still in progress, although by now the cause had nearly been won. I asked whether he had seen either Jackson or Ferrier. He had not. Then I told him about Goltz's dog and about the incident in the hotel lobby that morning. This made him look grave. His first thought, however, was concerned not with the dog and the question of cerebral localization, but with the conduct of the hotel clerk. Ferrier must be warned to watch his step, he said, in case Goltz's move should induce him to present evidence of his own in support of this theory of localization. He would have to be more circumspect than Goltz about demonstrating to the public with living animals. "Ferrier is not a foreigner, like Goltz. At the moment our adversaries make everything a crime. When the anti-vivisectionists began their agitation seven or eight years ago, and Her Majesty the Queen requested my opinion, I predicted the developments that are taking place today. The increased emphasis on physiological research has brought excesses in its train. But when people who take the cruelty of fox hunting and pheasant shooting for granted, who think nothing of fishing with hooks, and who spend huge sums for the promotion of vegetarianism while moving not a finger to save the tens of thousands dying of hunger in Ireland—when such people rise up to protect frogs against biologists and medical researchers, the gates are thrown wide open to the worst kind of fanaticism. Give a fanatic an inch and you'll soon find yourself fighting for your life. My warning was disregarded at the time, and now we have the result. In any case I shall tell Ferrier, if I see him, to look out."

I was beginning to feel more troubled than ever. It appeared likely that the impending contest on the functions of the brain might be given a strange turn by the power of the antivivisectionists. Ferrier, who was at their mercy, might well be hampered in the defense of his theory, whereas Goltz, as a German, would possess complete freedom of action.

I had never seriously discussed with Lister the question of the localization of cerebral functions. Hitherto his campaign for antisepsis had, I thought, occupied him completely, and it would have seemed unwarranted for me to bring up any other medical subject with him. I was aware, however, that he knew and upheld Ferrier's theories. "Do you think," I asked him now, "that Ferrier will be able to withstand Goltz's attack?"

Lister gazed at me out of his uncommonly bright eyes. "I don't know," he said, "but I hope so." And then he added something that stunned me. "Recently I tried to help a patient in desperate plight who was suffering from intolerable headaches and symptoms of paralysis. I suspected a growth in the brain, and trepanned at the site of the most intense pain. Unfortunately I did not come across the growth at that spot. I introduced my finger between the brain and the skull and felt about for a tumor, as far as I could reach. But without success. The patient died, and the autopsy revealed a cerebral abscess. My finger had missed the spot by only a fraction of an inch."

He sighed heavily—his Quaker conscience oppressed, as always, when a human life was lost in an unsuccessful operation. So engrossed was he with his own thoughts that he did not realize how profoundly his words had affected me. For what he was casually mentioning here I saw as nothing more nor less than the very first account of an actual attempt at cerebral surgery—the very experiment that Broca and I had urged in vain upon many surgeons far younger than Lister. Stammering a bit, as he sometimes was wont to do, Lister continued: "In the course of this operation I realized fully the tremendous importance Ferrier's theory of cerebral localization may have for all future attempts at cerebral surgery. If his theory can be established on a solid basis it will eliminate the kind of blind fumbling which was all that was left to me. On the other hand, if Goltz should be right . . ." He paused. "In any case, if I run into Ferrier I shall tell him. . . ."

He took his leave before I could ask about details of his brain operation and involve him in a conversation on this subject so dear to my heart. He had been invited to a lunch being given by the Prince of Wales in Willis Room, on King Street. We hastily arranged to meet again that afternoon, when Professor Virchow would deliver the second major address of the day.

Three and a half hours later, while the audience was gathering for Virchow's lecture, Lister approached me, accompanied by a young man, a wholesome-looking chap who would seem to be in his mid-thirties. The young man was introduced to me as Gerald Yeo, professor of physiology and chemistry at King's College and Ferrier's closest associate on research into the functional centers of the brain. I had talked with Ferrier before, but this was my first meeting with Yeo. It was evident from his tanned, healthy appearance that he did not breathe laboratory air alone, and Lister took occasion to inform me that Yeo spent his every free minute gardening, sailing, and fishing at Fowey, where he could indulge these hobbies. He spoke with a distinct Irish brogue.

"Ferrier has gone back to the laboratory," he informed me. Then he continued: "Dr. Lister has told me your story. The hotel clerk had his facts straight—the dog is now in a cage at King's College. Professor Goltz wrote us from Strassburg to ask us to accommodate the animal, but he arrived too late yesterday and so took it to the hotel for the night. Of course I do not know exactly what arguments Professor Goltz will advance against Professor Ferrier tomorrow morning, but I imagine my friend Ferrier is well armed. . . ."

"He is confident, then?" I asked, feeling a certain relief for the first time since I had heard of Goltz's presence in London.

He looked at me with a droll air of mystification. "I don't want to anticipate Professor Ferrier," he said. "But you can expect a few surprises, and they may be among the most important events at this congress. . . . As for the antivivisectionists—well, physiological research is no longer possible in this country without risk of prosecution. All of us live on the verge of being haled into the courts most of the time."

Our conversation broke off when we saw Virchow approaching the speaker's platform with his short, tripping steps. Here was the world-famous director of the Pathological Institute in Berlin, whose development of cellular pathology had banished older conceptions of tissue as the spawner of disease. The result had been to make pathological instead of clinical studies the heart of medical research. Virchow had performed thousands upon thousands of dissections, and built his doctrines upon a solid basis. He was not one to waste time on introductory flourishes.

"This congress," he declared, "is taking place in the midst of a wave of agitation. Persons who unscrupulously exploit the average man's love for animals are at work here in London to convince the populace that the British vivisection law of 1876 is inadequate. People who practice methods of hunting which far surpass in cruelty anything that is done in laboratories denounce the bill which provides that no one in England may experiment on living animals unless he is recognized as a serious scientist and holds a government license. It does not satisfy them that all scientific experimentation must be carried out under anesthesia and that animals must be killed at once after completion of the experiment. Whipped up by vegetarians who would like to forbid all killing of animals, and by homeopaths who hold that they require no knowledge whatsoever of the hidden functions of the human body, these agitators are no longer capable of listening to reason. Although they take it for granted that if they fall ill, medicine will heal their diseases and prolong their lives, they ignore the fact that they owe these blessings to one discovery among others which only vivisection made possible, namely William Harvey's discovery of the circulation of the blood."

Virchow's address received wild ovations. As the audience began filing from the hall, Yeo passed by again and had a few words with me. "Virchow has just outlined what the law of 1876 permits and what it forbids," he said. "It may be that Ferrier, in order to defend his theory of localization, will have to cite experiments which will expose him to charges of having violated that idiotic law. Rest assured, this possibility will not frighten him off."

He invited me to attend the reception at South Kensington that evening. The Prince of Wales, the German Crown Prince, and some five thousand guests would be present, he informed me. Probably Ferrier, also. I agreed to go, and returned to my hotel to dress.

Later, as I was struggling with my tie, there was a knock at the door. A well-dressed, bespectacled young man entered. He apologized for appearing at so inconvenient a time, and explained that he had been sent by the *Times* to interview foreign guests at the congress. He had also interviewed Professor Yeo, who had suggested that he come to me.

Suspecting nothing at first, I answered some general questions, and continued to dress. He appeared to be taking copious notes. After a while he asked how I liked the St. James, and how I had spent my first night in London. I remained unsuspecting until he suddenly mentioned, with a slightly spurious air of inconsequence, that several guests had complained about a dog's howling at night, and that I must have heard the noise also, since the animal had been in a room near mine. At that moment my suspicions were suddenly aroused.

I went up to the young man and glanced at his notebook. The pad contained nothing but a few meaningless squiggles. Disconcerted, he started to rise from his chair. I pressed my hands on his shoulders and held him down.

"You say you come from the *Times?*" I asked.

"Of course," he replied. "As I told you."

"Do you prefer to admit that you have nothing to do with the *Times,*" I said, "or to wait right here and be arrested as an impostor as soon as I send for a friend who is on the editorial board of the *Times?*"

The young man went visibly to pieces.

"Professor Yeo did not send you here," I said.

He shook his head. "Please let me go," he begged. "I merely wanted a statement that you had heard the dog howling miserably last night. A statement of this sort from a doctor would be particularly valuable. . . ."

"To whom?" I asked.

He remained silent, confounded.

"Well, you need not answer," I said. "Tell the antivivisectionists who sent you that in fighting their battles they would do better to practice the decency and morality they preach." And I showed him the door.

While his footsteps beat a retreat down the corridor, I donned my coat, took my hat, and went down to the lobby. Still stinging with indignation and filled with fresh anxiety that the struggle over theories of cerebral functioning would become embroiled with the vivisection issue, I took a cab to South Kensington.

Shivering somewhat in the raw London fog, I entered the building of the Royal Institute the following morning, and made straight for the auditorium of the physiological section which was to be the scene of the decisive struggle. Tickets of admission were being checked. This reassured me somewhat, for it seemed to ensure that the meeting would not be invaded by agitators or spies.

Shortly before ten o'clock Professor Goltz entered the hall. His broad chin was thrust forward beneath the dangling ends of his mustache. He appeared resolute and absolutely sure of his case. By and by, I spotted the slender figure of David Ferrier among the incoming throng. Ferrier was ten years Goltz's junior, and came forward with his characteristically quiet, retiring air.

Yeo took one of the seats reserved for the secretaries of the society. Close beside him sat the bearded chairman, Professor Michael Foster. Uneasily, I tried to read Yeo's expression. But he seemed as calm and unperturbed as he had been the day before.

Foster went up to the lectern and announced in tones of deep emotion that an hour of extraordinary importance to the whole of medical science had just struck. Professor Goltz of Strassburg hoped that he could at last present the final solution to the problem of cerebral localization, which for years had been the subject of so much controversy. Professor Ferrier would have the opportunity to reply to him. During the afternoon session at King's College both gentlemen would show experimental animals in support of their theses, and these animals would then be killed and dissected in the presence of the assembled members.

While the audience sat tensely, Goltz's heavy figure replaced that of Foster. There was absolute silence, although Goltz spoke in German, so that many of those present were unable to follow him. He spoke with cool precision in the best tradition of objective science, but it was easy to see that he too felt the drama of the occasion. He began with a retrospective summary of the conclusions and methods of work of Flourens, Fritsch, Hitzig, and Ferrier. Then, with vehement directness, he went over to the offensive. "A fruit," he declared, "can look extremely tempting and nevertheless be wormy at the core. It is not difficult to detect the wormy core in all the hypotheses of cerebral localization that have heretofore been presented. . . ."

Here it was, the blunt challenge to Hitzig, to Fritsch, to Ferrier, to all who believed that the brain possessed separate motor and sensory centers. I felt it as a challenge to myself. Goltz's voice thundered through the room. He was saying that he rejected the method of electrical stimulus with which Hitzig and Ferrier had located their so-called functional centers. "When as the result of a stimulus we observe a group of muscles twitching, say of the foot, we cannot say that the stimulus to a given nerve or system produced the reaction. Reactions of foot muscles can be produced by stimuli applied to the motor nerves, the spinal cord, the brain, or certain sensory nerves. Hence, the fact that stimulus of a section of the nervous system causes reactions in foot muscles does not necessarily lead to definite conclusions about the functional significance of the stimulated organ. I cannot know whether the origin of the stimulus was a motor or a sensory channel, or whether a central organ was directly stimulated. The problems are increased in experiments with the cerebrum because we do not even know the extent to which electric currents applied in depth to the brain are responsible for the results."

There was, he declared, only one reliable method of proving whether or not motor and sensory centers existed: removal of those parts of the brain which supposedly represented functional centers. If the part of the brain which according to Professor Ferrier governed the movements of a foot were removed from a living creature, the foot ought subsequently to be paralyzed. If the foot were not paralyzed, every thinking person must regard it as proof positive that the so-called center for that particular movement did not exist. If one removed the part of the cerebral cortex which according to Professor Ferrier's claims should govern hearing, deafness should ensue. If deafness did not ensue, the alleged center for hearing did not exist.

Fritsch and Hitzig, Professor Goltz continued, had already perceived the flaws of the method of stimulus and had attempted a few experiments with extirpation. But only a few experiments. As he would undertake to prove, such meager experimentation was wholly insufficient. Moreover, initial disturbances of the motor faculties or the senses after removal of parts of the cortex did not signify. If the experimental animals were kept alive for a considerable period of time, such disturbances or temporary paralyses disappeared completely or very largely. That alone proved that the old concept of the brain's functioning as a whole, so that any part of it could at all times take over for any other part, came closer to the truth than the theory of functional centers. He, Goltz, had for the first time developed the method of extirpation in a manner hitherto untried, and had kept numerous animals alive long enough to be able to draw valid conclusions. He would now outline the results of his work.

The already suspense-laden silence had deepened during the first part of his lecture. "In a large number of experiments," Goltz continued confidently, "I made it my task to excise the largest possible parts of the cerebral cortex and to keep the animal alive and under observation as long as possible. In order to avoid hemorrhage, I extirpated the brain matter by washing away whole areas with a jet of water at high pressure."

As soon as Goltz spoke of the jet of water, I began imagining the stir such a disclosure would create among the antivivisectionists. What an atrocity story they could make of this, even though the animals had been anesthetized. I shuddered at the thought of the outcry they would raise. But Goltz was proceeding so rapidly that I had no time for such considerations. Employing this simple "rinsing" method, Goltz went on, he had determined that dogs were only temporarily paralyzed, or disturbed in their sight, hearing, and sense of smell, by removal of large parts of the brain. They soon regained complete mobility and full sensory perception. These experiments refuted the theory of localization and proved that Flourens's old hypothesis had been the correct one all along. At most Flourens had overestimated the speed with which restitution of motor and sensory abilities took place. Flourens had, however, been mistaken in regard to a single point. He had assumed that a small remnant of brain would suffice to assume both the physical and mental functions of all the rest of the cerebrum. This was true of the physical but not of the mental functions. This error of Flourens's, however, in no way accrued to the support of the localization theory of Ferrier and his followers. They had confined themselves to studies of muscular and sensory functions and had failed to observe that every sizable operation upon both hemispheres of the brain led to more or less severe disturbances of mental ability. Ferrier alone had spoken of such disturbances. But he had also assigned a particular site to intelligence, namely the frontal lobe of the brain, and declared that mental disturbances followed only if this lobe were injured. Experiment proved, however, that every extensive injury to the brain produced mental derangement.

In order to establish these results, here briefly summarized, upon a firm scientific basis, Goltz continued, he had discarded the water-jet method and developed an entirely new procedure which enabled him to extirpate precisely determined parts of the brain. "I employed Whit's mechanical drill, which enables one to impart rapid rotation to small instruments. For the most part I used a kind of helical saw. By means of such an instrument it is comparatively easy to remove portions of the brain of any desired size. . . . In the cases of some dogs I undertook two, three, and four or more operations, and observed the degenerative symptoms with utmost care."

He described how he had trepanned the skulls of his dogs at various planes, removed the bone and the parts of the brain lying beneath, especially those areas which according to Ferrier constituted motor and sensory centers. Presumably he had done the same with the dog I had seen in the St. James in order to demonstrate that the removal of, say, Ferrier's pedal center did not result in inability to walk. "A dog," Goltz said, casting a look of rather infuriating superiority over the assemblage, "which was deprived of both frontal lobes of the cerebrum—one, that is, which according to Ferrier had lost its psychomotor centers—can move all its limbs, its lower jaw, tongue, tail, eyes, and ears. In short, it shows no evidence of muscular or sensory deficiencies."

Goltz opened a suitcase which lay on the lectern and took from it an obviously damaged skull of a dog, and a tiny preserved remnant of brain. "This dog," he declared, "whose skull and brain I have here, survived four major operations, and was not killed until a full year had passed after the last operation. The dog was completely idiotic, making no response to men or animals. All his sense perceptions were severely impaired. But he was neither deaf nor blind, had lost neither the sense of smell nor of taste. Not a muscle of his body was paralyzed, not a spot on his hide robbed of sensation. This animal's brain weighs only fourteen grams. The brain of a healthy dog of the same age, size, and breed weighs ninety grams. Clearly, nothing was left in this brain of Ferrier's motor or sensory centers."

Goltz hurled this last sentence into the audience with all the force of intense conviction, and there could be no doubt that it had had its effect upon the assemblage. His argument was too direct and effective to be ignored. His charges against Hitzig and Ferrier—namely, that they had failed to supplement their method of electrical stimuli by experimenting with extirpation, and had also not kept their subjects alive long enough for restoration of physical functions to take place—this criticism seemed difficult to refute. Chilled, I looked across at Yeo. But his expression remained as cool and untroubled as ever.

"To demonstrate the truth of my claims," Goltz continued in a still louder voice, "I have brought with me from Strassburg a dog from whose brain I have removed, in the course of five operations between November 15, 1880, and May 25, 1881, the cortex from both parietal and occipital lobes. . . . You will be able to recognize the enormous extent of cerebral extirpation by the peculiar deformation of the head. If you run your fingers along the edges of the large gaps in the bony structure you will realize even more clearly how extensive the operations were which the animal has survived. This dog is in many respects the most interesting case I have had in the course of my many studies, and it is therefore extremely fortunate that I am able to show you a sound, healthy animal." He would use this dog to show, he continued, that one did not paralyze any muscle by destruction of any segment of the cerebral cortex, or permanently stamp out any of the sensory functions. He undertook to prove beyond the shadow of a doubt that Ferrier's theory was, as he had stated, completely wrong.

With an expression of absolute self-assurance and consciousness of victory, Goltz gazed once more around the audience. Then he left the platform.

I can still recall how painful was the sense of defeat that swept through me. Quickly, I glanced around the hall. Everywhere I saw looks that revealed how deeply impressed the members of the audience were—enough of them were sufficiently conversant with German to follow every detail of Goltz's lecture. People began to clap, and the applause spread rapidly. For the third time I glanced at Yeo's face. But he, too, was applauding with gentlemanly courtesy. My eyes moved past him to Ferrier's high forehead, sparse hair, and wire-framed spectacles. He, too, was clapping but he was very pale. Now he slowly stood up and with careful, almost faltering step moved toward the platform. Either he felt that he had been defeated, or he was consciously endeavoring to restore this contest, which Goltz in the end had waged with such open aggressiveness and passion, to a plane of dignified, tranquil scientific discussion. Either he felt himself—in spite of Yeo's pledge to the contrary—forced by the pressure of the antivivisectionists to refrain from replying to Goltz's harsh and extreme experiments with similar experimentation of his own, or else his own findings were so conclusive that he could afford to participate in the applause for his opponent.

Clearing his throat, Ferrier began in a low voice: "I have listened with great interest to the facts and able arguments brought before us by Professor Goltz, on the question of the localization of functions in the cerebral hemispheres. If I cannot agree with him— and I must differ from him very widely—it is not because I dispute his facts. These, from Professor Goltz's character as a trustworthy observer, I should be prepared to accept without further verification. But I reject his conclusions."

I could not imagine how Ferrier intended to refute Goltz. But I felt a certain relief when he uttered the word "reject." Evidently he still possessed hidden ammunition, as Yeo had predicted.

Everything that Goltz had reported, Ferrier continued, was basically nothing new to him at all. This might possibly be surprising to some of his colleagues, but he himself had long since worked along the lines of extirpation—his methods, however, being fundamentally different from Goltz's. He had never made use of the imperfect water-jet method of removing brain matter, for the extent of the damage inflicted by this method could not be carefully determined. Nor had he employed Goltz's drilling procedure. For, contrary to Goltz's opinion, this did not permit really delicate work in the most delicate of all organs; rather, it resulted in relatively crude destruction. Since, moreover, it involved neglect of antiseptic precautions, the survival of the animals was purely a matter of good luck. After every experiment the danger of cerebral infection lurked. And each such infection, even if its course did not prove severe or fatal, influenced the results of the experiments. This was equally true of hemorrhages inside the brain. His friend Yeo had therefore conducted his experiments with animals with the latest and most valuable tools of surgery, antisepsis and the hemostatic scalpel. These alone had allowed him to introduce into the work the precision necessary for really conclusive results. He could remove parts of the brain with such exactitude that they lay precisely within the limits of the functional centers. After many years of work he was therefore in a position to inform this distinguished assemblage of the following facts. His experimental subjects survived; he did not run the risk, encountered in Goltz's experiments, of the subject's dying from infection or of compromising the precision of the experiment. Moreover, his animals lived longer than any of Goltz's subjects. This in itself, he judged, refuted a considerable portion of Professor Goltz's arguments.

My fascination mounted with each succeeding word—and not mine alone. The whole audience obviously was spellbound. From sentence to sentence Ferrier spoke more quietly and with greater assurance. His voice became firmer, clearer, and louder. He had, he continued, discovered in the course of time that it was impermissible to draw conclusions about higher animals, or even man, from the behavior of lower animals, or to deduce from these the nature of man's brain. The lower the animal, the less it was affected in its sensory or motor functions by the removal of even the entire brain. Removal of the brain in frogs and pigeons, for example, had almost no effect on their behavior. The effects grew more pronounced, however, the more highly developed an animal was. Professor Goltz's experiments had accordingly proved only one thing in regard to the motor and sensory functions: how large a part was played in the whole behavior of the dog by the lower parts of the brain. Now in the higher animals, the "higher" and "lower" portions of the brain lay side by side and the lower portions could, if need be, take over the functions of the specialized motor and sensory centers. This is what had taken place in Professor Goltz's experiments. Given the imprecision of his method of extirpation, remnants of the motor and sensory centers had undoubtedly remained, and these, in conjunction with the lower portions of the dog's brain, were able over a period of time to restore the functions severely impaired by extensive destruction of the functional centers. This, he believed, accounted for the effect Professor Goltz found so amazing, namely, the preservation or restoration of functions. However, it remained to be seen to what extent these functions were actually present in Professor Goltz's animals. The same argument applied to the alleged disturbances of the animals' intelligence. He himself had never observed such effects unless the frontal lobe were injured.

The ultimate end of cerebral research, however, was clearly to achieve an understanding of the functions of the most highly developed brain, that of man. Since no valid conclusions in regard to man could be drawn from experiments on dogs, which Goltz insisted on retaining as his subjects, he—Ferrier—had long ago undertaken to study the animal closest to man, whose brain was more highly developed than any except man's. He had therefore experimented on apes, and Yeo's surgical skills had enabled him to make extensive and precise observations.

Ferrier paused and cast a long, thoughtful look at his audience. Then he raised his voice once more. He had the honor, he declared, to invite the assemblage to visit Professor Yeo's laboratory at King's College during the afternoon. There he would show them two anthropoid apes from whose brains Professor Yeo had surgically removed certain centers. He was confident that in a few hours the audience would agree that not only had Professor Goltz's objections been met, but that above all the localization of functions in the brains of higher animals and of man had at last been definitely proved.

The end of the session found me so distracted, and so completely preoccupied with what would happen at the impending decisive confrontation, that I scarcely noticed what I ate during my lunch with Horatio Wood of Philadelphia and Professor Kronecker of Berlin. I took my leave of these gentlemen, and looked around for a cab in the hope that a quiet hour in my hotel room would settle my nerves and enable me to order my impressions of this morning session. As I opened the door of a cab which was just about to start off, I found myself to my surprise gazing into the colorless face of Charcot, the most famous French neurologist of the day. He looked baleful for a moment, then recognized me and snapped in his imperious voice: "Hello, Hartmann. Get in, if you insist on riding in this carriage, but for heaven's sake get in quickly. . . ."

His eyes lifted and stared over my shoulder at something on the street. I jumped into the carriage, which was already beginning to roll. Then I looked out of the window and perceived several ladies who had evidently been on Charcot's heels and were the reason for this sudden flight. Involuntarily, I thought of the hordes of hysterical women who besieged the waiting room of Charcot's Paris office on the Quai Malaquais. They came from all over the world and would wait for weeks in order to be admitted to the huge two-story library, copied from San Lorenzo in Florence, in which Charcot often delivered himself of a diagnosis after a single glance at the patient. Once he had made his diagnosis he no longer took any interest in the fate of his patients unless they chanced to come into his hands for autopsy; then he would methodically examine the brain and nerves of the cadaver to ascertain whether his judgment had been right or wrong.

Charcot turned toward me his forceful, rather Dantesque profile with the aquiline nose and vain, sensuous lips. Mockingly, he said: "I might have known that you would be here. What medical novelty are you tracking down now?"

His sarcasm did not trouble me. I had known him for years now, and was aware that outside his practice he could put off his pretense of being the infallible god of neurology. In his private quarters he was an altogether different person. He warmly loved his children and his curious collection of household pets. He adored Balzac and Beethoven. Cynicism was only one aspect of his personality.

"Have you been attending the section for physiology?" I asked.

He shook his head, and I recalled that he was not especially fond of physiologists or their experimentation upon animals. Skillful as he was at dissecting dead human beings and animals, and much as he approved physiology as a necessary basis for medicine, he seldom overcame his prejudices. He had only contempt for his female patients, and on the other hand cherished animals. Two monkeys dined with him daily at table in his home. No conversation about hunting was permitted in his presence. He despised the English from the bottom of his heart because here was a nation which was mad about hunting and nevertheless hypocritically raised the banner of antivivisectionism.

I gave Charcot an outline of the lectures I had just heard. His bull's shoulders twitched nervously. His pallid face reddened, and his eyes sparkled. I could see that his passion for knowledge of the brain and nervous system had been fanned to a blaze by my account.

"I'll take a look at this," he exclaimed brusquely. "When is the demonstration?"

"At three," I said.

"Good," he declared, more firmly. "I'll go along. I'll pick you up at your hotel at half past two."

Contrary to his habit, he was not punctual. By the time we arrived at King's College Goltz was already surrounded by a circle of eager spectators. At first glance I recognized among them Virchow's bespectacled owl's head. Like Charcot, Virchow had not been present at the morning session, but had been led here by the reports concerning it. His penetrating gaze was fixed upon the dog crouched at Goltz's feet.

Charcot thrust his way forward through the group. As they recognized the famous neurologist, other physicians readily made way for him, and behind his broad back I reached the front row.

Goltz's face was deeply flushed. "This dog," he was saying, "has travelled with me from Strassburg to London. As I indicated to you in my talk this morning, the animal has been deprived of by far the greater part of the cortical substance of both parietal lobes and both occipital lobes. A series of five operations were needed to produce this enormous cerebral extirpation, the last of these taking place on May 25 of this year. The deformation of the animal's head is quite obvious. You can easily thrust several fingers into the huge gaps in the bony structure."

Goltz went on to say that the dog would prove the claims he had made that morning. He made the animal run, jump out of its cage, and move its head. Then he picked up a whip and snapped it. "Go on, get out, go away!" he ordered, and drew attention to the cringing movement which indicated that the animal heard. He demonstrated that the dog could also see. He described his observation that the dog not only avoided large obstacles with facility, but would retreat from splashes of light on the floor caused by sun streaming in through the window. "Observing this," he continued, "I devised the following experiment. I had a kind of flag sewed, consisting of a brilliantly white, broad strip of linen framed by two black stripes. If this flag is laid on the floor, the dog avoids stepping on the white area. I have brought the flag with me, and will endeavor to repeat the experiment here."

The circle closed around Goltz as he spread out the cloth. The dog hesitated, then walked around the flag in a cautious arc. Goltz removed the cloth, and the dog at once stepped upon the place it had covered. "That the actions of this dog are determined by visual impressions," Goltz continued, "is furthermore proved by the changes in his behavior as soon as he is blindfolded. I have brought a hood which I shall draw over his head. Now not a ray of light can reach his eyes. You will see that the animal which a few moments ago easily avoided all obstacles will now repeatedly run into things. Observe how he tries to pull the hood off, using both forepaws."

Goltz then went on to demonstrate, using a pincers at various points in the dog's skin, that all parts of the surface of his skin and the mucous membranes as well were sensitive to pain. "At the institute we had a small, lively, extremely playful puppy," he declared. The bold little creature insisted on playing with the experimental subject, and had frequently bitten him. The dog now before us had in every case shown sensitivity to pain.

Goltz demonstrated the dog's sense of smell by asking Professor Donders of Holland to blow some smoke from his cigar into the animal's nose. The dog turned its head away. Goltz admitted, however, that its sense of smell was evidently not so keen as that of a sound dog.

At this point in his demonstration Goltz straightened up and glanced around with self-satisfaction. He proceeded to demonstrate that the dog had suffered loss of intelligence, and of nothing else, by placing the animal in a low, square pen which he had likewise brought from Strassburg. The dog could easily have jumped over the small wire fence. But although it was lured from outside, it ran around the inside of the fence and was unable to hit upon the idea of jumping over. It wagged its tail innocently when Goltz threatened it with his fist. A cat was brought from the college animal laboratory and held toward the dog. The dog showed no sign of hostility or fear, despite the cat's furious spitting; in fact, it attempted to lick the cat's paws.

Clumsily, breathing heavily, Goltz stood upright again. "In concluding this demonstration, gentlemen," he declared, "I hope that I have convinced you that none of this animal's sensory functions have been destroyed. It can see, hear, smell, feel. It does, however, display remarkable deviations from normal in its reactions to sense impressions. Its actions are so aimless, and at times so contrary to intelligent behavior, that we must deny it all capacity for reflection and pronounce it a canine imbecile." This, he continued, provided proof that the theory of localization was flatly wrong. Once more Goltz looked around the circle. As announced, he concluded, the dog would shortly be killed by chloroforming and the brain exposed for all to see that the cerebrum had been almost completely extirpated.

I was conscious of Charcot's sardonic gaze upon my face, as though he wished to say: Poor Ferrier is out of luck today, in spite of his claims; these Germans are thorough workers, and it does not seem possible that anyone could work more thoroughly than this German pedant here! With sinking heart I looked around for Ferrier and Yeo. I had seen them during the demonstration, but now they were no longer in sight. For a few seconds all was so still that we could plainly hear Goltz's panting as he locked the dog back in its cage. But then even this sound stopped.

Suddenly there was some-

Experimental dog in a portable cage such as Pasteur and later Goltz used.

thing in the air, an electric excitement as before a great scene at the theater. I heard Charcot suck his breath in between his teeth and exclaim, in a voice without a trace of cynicism: "It is a patient!"

A moment later I grasped what he had meant. My heart skipped a beat. A large monkey, led by an attendant, was crossing the room, walking erect. It walked—or rather, limped—like a cunning copy of those patients we had all seen so often, patients suffering from the consequences of a cerebral hemorrhage on one side, and paralyzed on the other side of their bodies. The monkey dragged one leg behind it, and its arm dangled helplessly.

"Why, it *is* a patient!" Once more Charcot's amazed voice rang through the room, filled with a genuine wonderment which I would scarcely have credited him with.

The monkey limped right into the midst of our group. Its restive, anxious gaze swept over our faces—it was the very look of a suffering human being. When it had reached the place at which Goltz had just finished demonstrating his dog, Ferrier appeared. He went up to the monkey and patted its head. Then he turned to us, jaunty, confident.

"Gentlemen," he said with quiet assurance, "you see before you a monkey upon which my colleague Professor Yeo operated in the careful manner I have described to you. The animal in question had the motor zone destroyed in its left hemisphere seven months ago. The area destroyed embraced the ascending frontal, and bases of the three frontal convolutions, and also the ascending parietal. We are not quite sure if the whole of the postero-parietal or paracentral lobule was destroyed, as these parts could not be completely exposed to view conveniently. But the result of this operation was complete motor hemiplegia of the right side, the limbs being perfectly powerless, with the exception of feeble power of flexion of the right thigh. The animal is in every other respect normal, except as to the movements of the right arm and leg. The condition of these bears the closest resemblance to hemiplegia in man resulting from cerebral hemorrhage. Otherwise the animal is perfectly healthy and shows not the slightest sign of other physical or mental deficiencies."

There was a moment of breathless silence. Ferrier held out a piece of food to the monkey. The animal snatched eagerly at it with its left hand, while its right arm dangled lifelessly. It ate with pleasure, darting looks all about it. So absorbed were we all in watching it that a second monkey was brought in almost unnoticed. When it was placed beside the first, it appeared to be a picture of perfect health. Ferrier took its left hand and fondled it. "As you know," he explained, "I have for years regarded the superior temporosphenoidal convolution in both hemispheres as the auditory center. In the monkey you see before you this convolution was destroyed ten weeks ago, once again by the precise technique that Professor Yeo has developed. You will see that this animal is in perfect possession of its sight and other sensory faculties, and of all its motor powers. But it has ceased to give any indications of hearing sounds."

Ferrier took from his pocket a cap pistol and held it close by the monkey's head. A fraction of a second later he fired. The report cracked through the room. The half-paralyzed monkey leaped aside in terror. It tried to flee with the aid of its sound arm and leg, and toppled to the floor, flailing two limbs grotesquely. The second monkey, however, stood motionless, although the muzzle of the pistol was still poised, smoking, directly back of its head. This monkey had heard nothing at all. There could be no doubt that it was completely deaf; it must have lost every vestige of the auditory sense.

Ferrier lowered the pistol. He waited until the attendant had picked up the frightened monkey.

"Gentlemen," he said, "these two animals, and Professor Goltz's dog, will be killed under chloroform. Those of you who care to examine the brains will be given every facility to do so. You will see that the parts removed by Professor Yeo correspond exactly to the functional centers I have indicated. If they do correspond— and I know that they do—this will serve as proof that every movement of a limb and every sense in a higher animal is produced by a specific part of the brain, in a manner which must still be the subject of extensive research. Henceforth there should be no doubt about this fact, which is of enormous importance to the treatment of diseases of the brain. And we shall all bend our full power upon localizing the as yet unknown motor or sensory centers of the brain, and discovering their mode of operation."

There was a long moment of silence after he was done. There was an expression of deepest surprise, of having been overwhelmed by irresistible evidence, on the faces of all of us. I myself would not have been capable of uttering a word.

The silence was broken by Yeo's deep, firm voice. By way of supplement to his colleague Ferrier's remarks, he said, he ventured to assert that Goltz's proofs for the alleged deficiency in intellectual power of his dog rested upon false reasoning. In all the instances in which Goltz assumed loss of intelligence to the point of imbecility, the evidence pointed rather to far greater sensory deficiencies, particularly of sight, hearing, and smell, and motor deficiencies, than Goltz recognized. Goltz should not forget how easily an animal adjusted its habits to the desires and even the suggestions of its master. Consequently, observation of its intellectual faculties could easily lead to wrong conclusions. The actual degree of deficiency in the dog's intellectual powers could be accounted for by destruction or lesions in the frontal lobe of the cerebrum, which Ferrier had long regarded as the seat of intelligence. For the rest, he was convinced that Goltz with his crude and nonaseptic method had not succeeded in destroying completely those parts of the brain he had hoped to destroy.* He was certain that autopsy of the animals would reveal that parts of the motor centers had escaped destruction in the brain of Goltz's dog, and that would sufficiently explain the dog's remaining muscular abilities.

Amidst a slightly ominous tension, Goltz attempted to give another explanation of the condition of his dog's brain. Michael Foster took command and quickly restored a scientific tone to the meeting. The final decision would come with anatomical investigation of the animals' brains, he said. He proposed that the animals be entrusted to Drs. Klein and Schaefer and Mr. Langley for examination. This committee would report its results by, at the latest, the end of the congress. He expected that its decision would be a historic one for medicine.

The motion was unanimously carried by the group, and the meeting closed. Charcot and I slowly descended the steps. *"Mon Dieu,"* Charcot murmured, "I should think this day will go down in history. It marks the beginning of a new era."

* Ferrier's views concerning the functions of the frontal lobe were confirmed decades later in the course of the development of surgical treatment of mental illness.

On Tuesday, August 9, shortly before the final session of the congress in St. James's Hall, the committee of physiologists announced the results of their careful investigation. Their statement constituted an unequivocal triumph for Ferrier, and an equally unequivocal confirmation of my hopes and dreams for the future of surgery.

The committee testified that the extirpated parts of the monkeys' brains not only corresponded to Ferrier's claims, but were localized precisely in those portions of the cerebrum which Ferrier had for years maintained represented the functional centers for the movements of arms and legs, and for the sense of hearing. In regard to Goltz, the committee reported that it had been unable to delimit precisely the destroyed portions of the dog's brain. As Yeo had predicted, some parts of the motor and sensory centers had been untouched and had therefore continued to function. These had sufficed, along with the lesser differentiation of function in the lower animals, to permit Goltz's dog to retain a considerable degree of motor and sensory functioning.

Enormously buoyed up by this decision, filled with a sense of victory, I attended the closing session of the congress. By chance I found myself sitting beside a young neurologist who worked at the National Hospital on Queen's Square, and hence was in close contact with Hughlings Jackson and Ferrier. While I waited for the proceedings to begin, he introduced himself as Hughes Bennett, and it turned out that I had known his father, John Bennett, an eminent professor of medicine at Edinburgh in the days when that city was the most dynamic medical center in Europe. John Bennett had introduced the microscope into physiological instruction in Edinburgh, and had held forth on the therapeutic importance of liver oil long before anything was commonly known of this.

Hughes Bennett had attended the demonstration of Ferrier's monkeys, and seemed even more gratified by the outcome than I. He spoke with high enthusiasm of the prospects for surgery now: the seat of cerebral diseases could now be diagnosed from the effects upon limbs and senses, and brain tumors could be removed surgically. Suddenly he said: "Do you know that my father died six years ago?"

"I remember reading of it," I replied.

"Not long before," he continued, "he underwent an operation for bladder stone performed by Dr. Cadge of Norwich. Whether it was the aftereffect of the operation which caused his death or his long-standing diabetes is not quite certain. At any rate, these were not the only causes. At the autopsy, Cadge and Professor Saunders found a cerebral tumor on the right side, about an inch above the ear, between the dura mater and the bone. It was the size of a hen's egg, and so well embedded that it could easily have been removed. That is the sort of thing one never forgets, and the thought that possibly my father could have been helped constantly preys on my mind."

Here, then, was someone as convinced as I myself that we were on the threshold of successful brain surgery. But we had no time to speak further of this, for at this point Michael Foster formally opened the concluding session, and put before the assemblage a resolution to the effect that "this congress expresses its conviction that experiments upon living animals have in the past proved of the greatest service to medicine, and are indispensable for its future progress." The applause that greeted this pronouncement was the loudest and longest of the whole congress. As the audience began to file out, Bennett was separated from me. Who could have said, from the few words that passed between us, that this young man would launch a whole science of brain surgery by initiating the first successful operation for cerebral tumor?

A few hours later a farewell fireworks display rose into the night sky above the Crystal Palace. The rockets splayed out to form portraits of Langenbeck, the foremost Berlin surgeon of his day, of the American Billings, and of the French neurologist Charcot, against the nocturnal firmament. The brilliant glow of these portraits seemed to me a symbol of that faith in the future of surgery which I felt more strongly than ever before.

Kocher

When I left London I would scarcely have imagined that another three years would pass before the first successful attempt at surgical removal of a brain tumor. With my usual impatience I thought that the recent revelations of the anatomical structure of the brain would induce one or another surgeon almost immediately to attempt operative removal of a cerebral growth. At the time I did not know that Lister's unsuccessful operation had not been the only one; that other surgeons had attempted to alleviate cerebral hemorrhages and cerebral abscesses, and had even met with some success. Had I been aware of this, I would have been spared many of those moments of despair and fatalism which overtook me during the next three years, until in 1884 the first great cerebral tumor operation was performed.

On the other hand, before this noteworthy event took place there occurred the solution of a surgical problem as old and as pressing as that of cerebral tumor. I am referring to disease of the thyroid gland, and above all to goiter. In the autumn of 1882 I was drawn by chance into the struggle for the operative cure of goiter. This involvement occupied my attention to the full, and resulted in one of the great and most exciting meetings of my life.

On October 15, 1882, I was invited to a reception at the New York home of William Cabot, one of the lumber kings of the State of Maine. Cabot, a genial gentleman of about fifty-five, was giving his annual housewarming party in his palatial Fifth Avenue house. All summer long he would be in Maine, where he owned vast holdings and directed still vaster operations, but every autumn he returned to New York to spend the winter season in the metropolis.

I found the entire house glittering with light. Some eighty guests were present. A flock of servants, in old-style English livery, were running to and fro with trays of ices and pastries. Two orchestras were playing on two different floors of the mansion. All this, I discovered, was but a preamble to the arrival of the master of the house, a widower whose family consisted only of a grown daughter named Esther.

At the bar I encountered Kendall Davies, reputed to be one of the sharpest of Wall Street lawyers. As he sipped his bourbon and soda, he growled in his rather cynical tone: "It's costing Cabot a pretty penny to put the girl on the marriage market."

I looked at him with blank incomprehension. "Oh," he said, "I guess you are new here. Hasn't it struck you that at least half the company are eligible young bachelors from the richest families in town? It looks as though Cabot has made up his mind to find her a husband by hook or crook this time. Before it's too late."

I had begun to think I understood the situation, but this last remark made me again look uncomprehending. "Well, you see," he continued, "Esther is quite a beauty, as her late mother was. But her beauty is something of a snare and delusion, and unfortunately far too many of the young men know . . ."

He was interrupted by a kind of fanfare from the orchestra, as Cabot and his daughter appeared on the landing. At the sight of the slender girl beside her tall, portly father, the general chatter ceased. After a moment the abrupt silence was broken by admiring exclamations. I felt, however, that very few of these were truly spontaneous; these "entrancings" and "ravishings" showered upon the host's daughter sounded like merely dutiful compliments.

And yet she might well have been called entrancing and ravishing. In retrospect that first glimpse of Esther Cabot still echoes within me. Her oval face was strikingly beautiful and her skin unusually fair, almost white. Her thick hair glistened in a shade between red and chestnut, and her eyes were amber-colored. But even as I stood there, looking up, lost in contemplation of this girl, I noticed something that did not fit into the picture of blooming loveliness. While almost all the ladies present wore décolleté gowns, Esther Cabot's expensive dress had not only a high neck, but terminated in an elegant, high and wide ermine collar which completely concealed her throat, in spite of the warmth of the house.

At first I was so much under the spell of her face that it did not occur to me to make any connection between these oddities and the lawyer's comments. When I was introduced, I had an opportunity to see Esther from close up. My impression of great beauty was confirmed. Above the high ermine collar her face seemed even whiter and more delicate than it had appeared from a distance. When I released her hand, I had the impression that Mr. Cabot had been regarding me with a keen, searching gaze. There was something melancholy about his deeply tanned face, and the broad smile with which he greeted each guest seemed forced. In the course of the evening I frequently glanced over at Esther. There was always someone dancing with her, or talking with her—but her escorts changed constantly. None of the younger men stayed with her any longer than convention demanded. I had the impression that every one of them shied away from anything that might suggest a more serious interest on his part. In view of her striking beauty this conduct seemed so strange that I began to ponder the meaning of Davies's remarks.

The party continued late. At eleven o'clock I was sitting with an acquaintance who like myself had spent the greater part of his life travelling. We had found a quiet corner in the "blue room." Two couples danced into our corner: one of them was Esther and a handsome young man. Esther's face was beaded with perspiration. That seemed natural enough, since she wore a fur collar. But she also had so terrified a look that I became alarmed. Suddenly she tore herself free from her partner's arms. With a gasping sound, face distorted, she rushed unsteadily past me toward a door, threw it open, and vanished. Her partner stood staring helplessly after her. I leaped to my feet. In a flash I had realized that she was suffering from a choking fit, and I followed her through the half-open door. The room I entered was unlit. But the whistling sound of panting respiration, and a faint breeze blowing into my face, made me aware that Esther must have opened a window and was standing by it, struggling to catch her breath. A second later I discerned her figure framed against the window, a moonlit oblong against the darkness of the room. The sash had been lifted and Esther was leaning out. Her whole body was writhing in convulsive movements, as though only in this way could she fight suffocation. I hastened toward her, and reached her just as the whistling respiration became easier. The climax of the attack was evidently past. A moment later the room behind me filled with light.

The girl turned her head and torso toward the interior of the room, although she still clung exhausted to the frame of the window, incapable of moving any further, deathly pale, her hair in disarray, an expression of utter despair upon her face. Yet all this was not what touched me to the quick. She had pulled off the fur collar and desperately clawed open the neck of her dress. The light fell upon her bared throat, and at once I understood why she had concealed it under that heavy ermine collar. For on both sides of her neck, under that face which was still beautiful even though marred by terror, there rose the hard, knotty, irregular swellings of advanced goiter. The attack I had just witnessed was the result of displacement of part of the goiter, caused by the exertion of dancing. Compression of the windpipe had led to one of those choking fits which were a constant threat to so many sufferers from goiter, and which frequently terminated in death.

Cabot's agitated voice startled me. Apparently someone had instantly informed him of the incident. He strode across the room. With a tenderness I would never have ascribed to this giant of a man, he drew the girl away from the window, stood shielding her from the draft, waited until the servant carrying the lamp had picked up the ermine scarf, wrapped it around her, and led her over to a sofa. He ordered the servant to go and close the door. I was left alone with the two of them.

Several minutes passed in silence. Finally Cabot slowly turned his now gray face toward me. "Well, Hartmann, now you know too," he said.

I asked whether his daughter had had such attacks often.

"Often," Cabot echoed wearily. "Of late they have been occurring at shorter intervals—suddenly, and usually without apparent cause."

It was on the tip of my tongue to tell him that every choking fit could be fatal, and that in the circumstances dances were scarcely indicated. But I suppressed this warning, which might, after all, be premature, and instead asked how long Miss Cabot had been suffering from the disease and what had been done about it.

He looked at me as though to say: Do you not know that nothing can be done about goiter? "The first visible signs," he replied instead, "began about five years ago. We tried various waters, and Dr. Winters gave Esther iodine frequently, and has even injected iodine into the goiter. Nothing has helped. Incidentally, Dr. Winters should be here shortly. He has been our doctor for years."

I knew Winters. He was one of those old New York physicians who seemed to have a special license to treat rich Fifth Avenue families. At the time Winters was around seventy, and like many specialists in internal medicine was a bitter opponent of surgery in general. He hated the surgeon's invasion of areas which had formerly "belonged" exclusively to internal medicine. More than once he had delivered himself of furious attacks upon progressive surgeons who were probing into the internal organs. His general attitude and his frigid personality were such that I was not particularly eager to meet him here, where I might seem to be intruding upon one of his patients. I therefore said that Cabot would no doubt prefer me to go now and leave him alone with his daughter.

Cabot looked at me with a heart-rending weariness as he cradled the girl's head; she lay rigid, as if fearing that any movement might bring on a new attack. Perhaps he read in my expression that I did not think much of Winters, and possibly my attitude fed doubts of his own. In any case he suddenly said: "I should very much like to consult you." Would I mind waiting in his study until Dr. Winters arrived? He would consider it a great favor.

I nodded. His request fell in with my own feelings. My chance insight into Esther's misfortune had filled me with involuntary sympathy for the girl and aroused the natural desire to help her. I knew only too well that internal medicine was relatively impotent to check the development of goiters. But I recalled having read only recently in German medical journals that attempts to remove goiter by surgery—in Vienna and Bern particularly—had led to some remarkable successes.

It was not hard for me to picture with fair exactness the development and the present state of Esther's disease. She was undoubtedly suffering from a progressive goitrous enlargement of the thyroid gland on both sides of the neck. In the United States this disease was incomparably rarer than in the alpine regions of Switzerland, Austria, and Germany. In the northern states of Maine, Vermont, New Hampshire, and Michigan, however, it was relatively more frequent, and in mountain valleys I had occasionally come across goiters such as were otherwise seen only in Switzerland or the Tirol. On the whole, however, this was a disease that was comparatively strange to me, as an American. Consequently, I had hitherto never paid any special attention to it.

Cabot must have been doing all in his power to conceal the existence of Esther's malady—but with small success, to judge by the remarks I had heard earlier in the evening. No doubt it pained him terribly to see the disease making a social outcast of his daughter. I wondered whether he had done more than consult Dr. Winters. Five years was time enough to have seen that Winters was quite helpless. In actual fact, internal medicine had no more effective treatment of goiter than doctors of a thousand years ago, who had learned by observation that eating roast sponges sometimes would reduce goitrous swellings. In 1820 the Swiss scientist Jean François Coindet had discovered that iodine was the effective component of sponges, and ever since then administration of iodine had been the principal treatment for goiter. It was rubbed in, taken by mouth, and injected into the goiters. Here and there the treatment had had some efficacy, and still did. But the number of failures was still larger, and injection directly into the thyroid gland had led to many deaths from puncturing of blood vessels and necrosis. Goiter therapy had scarcely got beyond the stage of vague experimentation. It had proved utterly pointless when goiters were developed so far that they compressed the windpipe. In the long run patients like Esther Cabot were threatened with certain suffocation. In those cases the only remedy was the emergency operation of tracheotomy and the creation of an artificial respiratory channel.

One of the principal stumbling blocks was that neither physicians nor physiologists knew what purpose the thyroid gland served in the human body. From the days of the ancient Romans until this year of 1882 no one had solved the riddle. The gland enfolded the windpipe; in its normal state it was small and consisted of two lobes and a connecting link, the isthmus. Most mysteriously, it possessed no duct like the liver or the salivary gland to carry away its secretions. Some physiologists held that it served solely to round out the female throat; others believed that it swelled in the evening, diminishing the volume of blood flowing to the brain by pressing upon the nerves in the throat, and thus engendering sleep. A third school considered it merely a support for the neck and reinforcement of the uvula. A fourth group considered it a blood-forming organ like the spleen; a fifth regarded it as one of the sexual glands; and a sixth, as a regulating organ for the entire circulation of blood in the brain. How could medicaments be found for the illness of an organ whose reason for being no one knew—just as no one could be sure that it was vital to life or not? In any case, the results of operations which had been undertaken in Europe—in so far as I was acquainted with these from casual glances at the literature— seemed to show that the thyroid gland could be dispensed with. Patients who had survived the operation itself continued to live without signs of other disturbances.

Pacing back and forth in Cabot's study, I realized for the first time how much I had neglected this aspect of surgical pioneering in favor of other fields, above all in favor of cerebral surgery, and how little definite information I had when confronted with a person whose sole chance for life possibly depended on surgery.

I was still pacing the room when the door opened and Cabot entered. He dropped into a chair with every sign of exhaustion. "Esther is in bed now," he said. "Winters thinks her condition may compel us to undertake a tracheotomy tomorrow; on the other hand, he says, she may go on this way for years. But what years for a girl like her. . . ." He sighed. "Winters proposes to try a new iodine cure. I suppose you are going to tell me that it is all senseless. But what won't we do that offers the least spark of hope?" He looked at me out of deep-sunken eyes. "Or do you have another suggestion? I cannot believe that this thing is beyond help. Perhaps somewhere in Europe . . . You once spoke to me about your travels. . . ."

I understood now what had impelled him to consult me.

"I know that doctors like Winters are not fond of surgeons— and refuse all consultations with them," I said. "But that should not sway you. Have you ever consulted a surgeon?"

"Do you think I would have left any stone unturned?" he exclaimed. "I took Esther to Dr. Bigelow in Boston. You know better than I that he is one of our foremost surgeons. But he told me that an operation for goiter is butchery which ends in bleeding to death. He agreed completely with Winters."

"Bigelow was one of my teachers," I replied. "He is a great man and a fine surgeon. But progress is passing him by, has already passed him in many respects. It is not his fault. This disease is extremely uncommon in this country, and surgeons have not been forced to make those hundreds of desperate experiments from which the one successful method emerges. On the other hand, there are parts of the world—Austria and Switzerland, for example— where the victims are so numerous that some action must be taken. Surgeons have undertaken operations of which we know nothing here. Even Bigelow has probably never heard of them."

Puffing, Cabot rose and went over to the window. "It isn't fair to stir up hope in me, Hartmann," he said. "I've had all too much of that."

"I can well understand you," I said. "And I must confess that I have not yet studied the recent literature on goiter in detail. Until this evening the problem was as remote to me as it is to Bigelow. But from what I have heard about work in Europe, Bigelow's view that surgical removal of goiter is butchery is no longer true. That is a textbook theory dating back to the days before antisepsis. I know that in Vienna and Bern, at least, a beginning has been made on surgical removal of goitrous tumors. From reports I have read their physiologists have made so close a study of the relevant blood vessels that the operation has become virtually bloodless."

"Do you have any faith in these accounts?" Cabot asked guardedly.

"Of course I have faith in them," I retorted. "Scientific medical reports are not quackery." With sudden resolve, I added: "I shall look through my library and assemble everything I have on recent developments in goiter operations in Europe. I can also write to the European surgeons, and as soon as I hear from them I'll call on you again and give you a complete report on what has been achieved in Europe."

Cabot stood with hands clasped behind his back and head bowed low. "I only wish I could believe you," he said at last. "How long will it be before you can tell me anything definite?"

"Getting replies to letters is a slow process," I answered. "But I will have a partial report by tomorrow morning."

I could see that he was beginning to feel a glimmer of hope, though he tried to armor himself against it in his fear of fresh disappointment and heartbreak. "I'll come by here tomorrow morning around eleven," I said. "If the reports I find sound the least convincing, we can cable to Bern or Vienna and so save the time that would be consumed on letters back and forth across the Atlantic."

My conversation with Cabot had so stimulated my eagerness to help Esther and to have some share in a novel development of surgery that I could not go to sleep, but straightway started my search through the medical reviews, of which I had extensive files.

At three o'clock in the morning I was still deep in my search hunting through the volumes of the *Wiener Medizinische Wochenschrift*, the *Archiv für klinische Chirurgie*, and the *Deutsche Zeitschrift für Chirurgie*, for publications on goiter surgery which I remembered having noticed during the past several years. The principal surgeons concerned, I remembered, were Professor Rose of Zürich, Theodor Billroth and his pupil Wölffler of Vienna, and Professor Theodor Kocher of Berlin, a young surgeon, not yet forty, whose name I had first seen mentioned with high praise in a letter by von Esmarch, the noted Kiel surgeon.

The history of attempts to remove goitrous tumors with the scalpel was actually as old as the disease itself. But that history had been one of endless disasters and mistakes which led eventually to the textbooks making it a dictum that every effort to operate on goiter was fatal butchery. The Roman physician Celsus had written an account of goiter. He distinguished a form in which nodules of varying sizes and hardness formed inside the thyroid gland, and another form in which the lobes of the gland as a whole swelled shapelessly. In the case of the first type Roman surgeons had attempted to cut down to the nodules and remove these from their cavities with their fingers. This had frequently caused tremendous hemorrhages which could not be stanched.

Two hundred years later Galen had reported a goiter operation on a child, in the course of which a deep-lying goitrous nodule had been forcibly "torn out." The child survived the loss of blood, but lost its ability to speak. Galen discovered that close behind the thyroid gland, near the windpipe, ran a nerve difficult to locate, the nervus recurrens, which influenced the activity of the vocal cords. If this nerve were injured, pulled, or even merely squeezed, speech was affected. In addition, then, to the danger of tremendous loss of blood, there was the peril to this sensitive nerve. Awakened to the twin contingencies, hemorrhage and loss of speech, surgeons took care not to touch the thyroid gland. It seemed better to let goitrous patients suffer through their malady until carried off by asphyxia, for operation meant almost certain death. A thousand years after Galen, Paracelsus continued to issue dramatic warnings against any attempt to incise goiters.

Still, efforts to find a treatment were made. In the thirteenth century Roland, a noted surgeon, burned holes with hot irons through large goiters and drew setons—threads of horsehair—through the holes in order to tie off parts of the growth and cause those parts to die. Other doctors strewed caustic lime into the goiters through tiny incisions in the throat in the hope that the malignant tissue would be destroyed. It was not until the end of the eighteenth century that a few French physicians—Desault, Dupuytren, and Roux—impelled by the hopeless condition of patients on the point of asphyxiation, experimented again with removing large goiters with the knife. Desault, however, stopped after successfully removing one lobe from his patient for fear of fatal hemorrhage. Roux's patient, who lost only "one and a half pounds of blood" even though some forty blood vessels were ligatured, died of surgical fever. It is almost impossible to conceive how much this poor man and so many like him suffered in days when neither anesthesia nor antisepsis was available. Even the tough surgeons of the day, who were hardened to pain, suffering, and death, were horrified. Less than thirty years before the night I sat up leafing through my files a German surgeon named Gurlt had spoken of "this butchery, a frivolous operation which the surgeon regards with horror." Until 1877—that is, until five years ago—there had been throughout the entire world some one hundred and fifty attempts to alleviate goiter by operation. The results were a tremendous sum of death and agony, of ghastly hemorrhages and loss of speech, pyemia and years on the sickbed for the few patients who survived.

According to the articles in the technical journals from Austria and Switzerland, however, there had been a sudden and fundamental change in this situation. The key factors were the discovery of antisepsis, which cancelled the danger of surgical infection lurking behind every operation in the past, and the invention of clamps for rapid closing of bleeding vessels. Equipped with these new weapons, surgeons in this as in so many other fields were emboldened to take arms once again against the curse that seemed to lie upon all goiter operations.

It was approaching four in the morning when I finished reading an address, delivered at the annual congress of German surgeons held in Berlin in 1877, by Edmund Rose, the forty-year-old Zürich surgeon. There could be no question that this speech was an epic one. Only one method existed for helping the countless numbers of goiter patients, Rose had declared. This was complete removal by operation of the diseased thyroid gland. Only total extirpation would avail, because the gland, once diseased, continued to grow malignantly, and any sizable parts of it which had not been removed constituted a new danger to the patient. Rose declared—for the first time, as far as I could judge—that the danger of massive hemorrhage could be overcome by the new methods of hemostasis; and that, with care, the recurrent laryngeal nerve could go untouched, thereby eliminating the danger to speech. Rose had demonstrated by several operations that complete removal of the two lobes of the thyroid, and later of the isthmus in front of the windpipe, was quite possible so long as the surgeon took the trouble to clamp and ligature every vessel that blocked his way, even the smallest. Such work, he said, was "like that in a spinning mill," and the surgeon must be prepared to "ligature some two hundred vessels and even more."

By sheer weight of experience Rose had countered the objection that it might be dangerous to remove the thyroid gland because no one knew whether or not its functions were vital to life. After successful operations all his patients had lived, and, their convalescence once over, they felt hale and hearty, freed of their terrible burden.

Rose's lecture had apparently first focused the attention of European surgeons on the possibility of extirpating goiter, and on previous work by two other surgeons who had experimented in this field. They were Theodor Billroth and Theodor Kocher. In 1862, while still in Zürich, Billroth had performed his first operation for goiter, and had continued along the same lines in Vienna. Kocher had begun goiter operations in 1872, when he was a young professor of surgery in Bern. Before beginning their work both men had once again explored with the greatest care the anatomical environment of the thyroid gland, with particular attention to the position of the major blood vessels to which this gland owed its unusually large supply of blood. They had then developed a new method of operation. Before actual removal of the goitrous tumor they located, ligatured, and severed all the major vessels. In the course of many years they had, indubitably, succeeded in rendering the operation more and more bloodless, and in greatly diminishing the number of ligatures required. Nevertheless, until the introduction of antisepsis they had naturally been plagued with surgical infection which negated most successes in this as in all other fields of surgery. From Billroth's or Wölffler's reports it was evident that the mortality in goiter operations had amounted to more than 36 per cent before 1876, whereas now, in 1882, it came to scarcely 10 per cent. The same results had been achieved by Kocher, who had performed some eighty goiter operations.

At six o'clock that morning, when I laid the last of the journals aside, I no longer doubted that Billroth and Kocher had developed an exact scientific method for the surgical treatment of goiter, and that their operational technique could be considered trustworthy. Where only a single lobe of the gland was diseased they had removed only this lobe. But where the entire thyroid gland was affected they had followed Rose in removing it completely. Their reports agreed that this extirpation—in spite of an initial skepticism on Billroth's part—had led to no deleterious aftereffects. Wölffler held that the thyroid gland had no function vital to life. Kocher concurred. As far as the success of the operation was concerned, both Kocher and Wölffler stated that after a few days of fever all the patients swiftly recovered. Mortality occurred where there had been faulty antisepsis, or where asphyxiation developed during the operation—chiefly because the patient or the patient's doctor had waited too long. Kocher summed it all up by stating that for the past several years operation had proved to be the "simplest and surest method of treatment for goiter."

I made a stack of the reviews containing pertinent material. I would take them to Cabot later in the morning, and translate for him if necessary. I was myself immensely impressed by the sober objectivity of Wölffler's and Kocher's reports and failed to understand how I could have given them so superficial a reading. I had already decided that I would accompany Cabot if he should determine to take Esther to Europe and apply for help to Billroth or Kocher.

Shortly after eleven o'clock my carriage stopped in front of Cabot's town house. No trace of last night's party was in evidence. The house seemed empty, lifeless, and joyless. The butler showed me into the study where I had talked with Cabot the night before.

When I entered, I found that Cabot was not alone. Sitting bolt upright in a black frock coat, hands propped upon the gold head of an ornate cane, was Dr. Winters. He studied me with cold hostility in his small eyes, while Cabot strode forward to shake hands. The big man looked nervous and indecisive.

He thanked me for being so punctual. Then he said with an odd side glance at Winters: "The question at issue is so grave that Dr. Winters, as our family physician, must help decide it. I have therefore asked him here. The attack of suffocation is over and Esther feels as well as can be expected. Dr. Winters now feels that any resolution to venture a new method of treatment—such as might have rashly been taken in the emergency situation of last night—must be carefully reconsidered."

There was no need for him to say more. Winters's grim expression told me all. The doctor was plainly determined to prevent any intrusions into his own domain. But this very hostility, and my own profound antipathy to him, strengthened my desire to see Esther off to Vienna or Bern for the effective help the European surgeons could offer her.

I marshalled my documents before Cabot. Winters followed my every movement with icy gray eyes. I summarized each article and explained all there was to explain. I did not conceal the dangers of hemorrhage and of injury to the vocal nerve which had revealed themselves in the very first goiter operations and had been overcome or minimized only in recent years. At last I gave a word-for-word translation of Kocher's statement that in the course of the past year operation had become the simplest and surest method of treatment for goiter. I could see that Cabot was following me with an attentiveness that sprang from the very depths of his woeful heart. I urged him to waste no more time, not to wait for further attacks of asphyxiation, which would reduce the prospects for successful operation. "Dr. Winters will scarcely deny," I said, "that in Esther's case internal medicine has come to the end of its resources. There is no drug that will prevent further growth of the goiter and ultimate compression of the trachea—that is, the windpipe."

I glanced at Winters and saw that his thin lips were firmly compressed. He stared back at me with icy, haughty distaste. In a louder voice I continued: "If you do not wish Esther to die of suffocation sooner or later, if you want to save her from what awaits her—an eventual emergency operation and the insertion of an artificial air duct through the throat which will allow her only a few more miserable years of life—then I urge you to take the only chance there is. . . ."

I sensed that Cabot was on the point of being converted. "Cable Professor Billroth in Vienna or Professor Kocher in Bern. Ask them when they can examine Esther. Have Esther examined in any case. Obtain the opinion of the two surgeons who probably know more about the thyroid gland and goiter than anyone else in the world today."

Cabot placed his big right hand on my arm. He said nothing. He gave Winters a tormented, uncertain look. "What is your opinion?" he asked.

Winters did not stir. Only his thin, withered hands twitched slightly on the glittering knob of his cane. Then he said: "I shall examine closely all of Dr. Hartmann's arguments. I read German and should like to study the documents myself." As he spoke, he avoided looking at me or addressing me directly. To Cabot, he said: "Perhaps you will ask Dr. Hartmann to leave his documents with me for a week."

In profound astonishment, I looked across at Cabot. Did he fail to realize that Winters had already passed judgment, that he had not the slightest intention of examining seriously the possibility of surgical treatment, and wanted only to gain time? I could not understand how a man like Cabot who commanded a vast army of workers, and was noted for his hard sense and enterprising spirit, could truckle so to the will of an aged physician. But Cabot said in a strained voice: "Will you do that, then?"

"Mr. Cabot," I said, "Esther is twenty-three years old. She herself ought to be asked, since her fate is at stake."

At this point Winters, who had sat as still as a wax figure, made his first gesture. He actually shook his head. "Esther is still a child," he ordained.

"Do you think so?" I queried. "Is that your opinion too, Mr. Cabot?"

Cabot's eyes still avoided mine. "Of course we will talk with her," he said irresolutely.

I sensed that there was some kind of mystery here, some hidden dependency which further complicated the situation.

"May I give Esther my wishes for a rapid recovery?" I said, hoping dimly to be allowed to talk with the girl myself.

"She is unfortunately not yet in a condition to receive visitors," Winters said. And Cabot again looked at me with that puzzling, incomprehensible irresolution, but said nothing.

"Mr. Cabot," I said, making a last desperate attempt, "I hope you will think the matter over with great care. There are sins of omission in this world that haunt us until the end of our lives."

"What do you mean by that?" he asked in anguish.

"You know what I mean," I said. Leaving my stack of journals on the table, I bade him goodbye.

I spent several uneasy days without hearing a word from Cabot. On the fifth day I cabled on my own initiative to Billroth and Kocher. I described Esther's condition as well as I could without having examined her, and asked whether Billroth or Kocher were prepared to perform an operation for removal of the goitrous thyroid gland, and whether they could promise that the operation had some prospect of success. A direct confirmation from them, I thought, might have some effect on Cabot.

The week Winters had requested passed, but I still received no message from Cabot or Esther. On the other hand, two days after my telegram Professor Kocher's reply arrived. It was perfectly clear and unequivocal. While of course he would have to make a personal examination first, he was quite willing to take the case. The operation had proved to be safe and successful, he declared.

The following morning my manservant woke me early with the news that a letter had just been delivered. Its bearer was a servant of Cabot's household, and the whole affair had a surreptitious cast. I glanced first at the signature below lines obviously written in great haste. The letter was from Esther. She wrote: "My father tells me that you spoke of a possible operation which might help me. Dr. Winters calls this possibility 'attempted murder.' He has convinced my father that it would be criminal to let me undergo it, and that my condition afterwards would be worse than before. But I do not believe him. I implore you—tell me that there is really a chance for me in Europe, and that I need not give up my last hope. Burt will bring me your answer."

Restive as he was, the messenger waited until I had written a few lines in reply. I copied out Theodor Kocher's cable and enclosed it with my answer. At the moment this was all I had to support my position. After the messenger had left I wrote a rather agitated note to Cabot, and asked him for an interview. I enclosed in this letter the original of Kocher's cable. My man took the letter directly to the Cabot house. But I waited in vain for an answer.

The following morning, however, two letters reached me. One was from Cabot, the other from Winters. Both had been written the previous day. "I know from your own stories," Cabot wrote, "that since your Harvard days you have believed fervently and impatiently in the future of surgery, and are convinced that someday the surgeons will be able to conquer all diseases. I can therefore understand that you want at all costs to put Esther into the care of a surgeon, although the fate of your own wife should have taught you how imperfect the surgeon's art still is. However, I do not understand why you concealed from me the greatest dangers of goiter operations in order to achieve your goal. Convinced though I am of the sincerity of your faith in surgeons, I find it hard to forgive such conduct. Dr. Winters will write you about the technical aspect of this matter. Today I am taking Esther to Florida. The mild air there will surely do her good and make breathing easier for her."

As I read the letter, my face flushed hot. I had not doubted that Winters would wage his battle against surgery with icy inflexibility, ruthlessness, and calculation. But I had not looked for a barefaced lie. For Cabot's letter seemed comprehensible to me only on the basis of some outright lie by Winters. I tore open the packet from Winters. It contained the reviews I had left with Cabot, and the following lines:

"To my extraordinary regret I have been compelled to advise Mr. Cabot against following your advice. Your German professors take the view that the thyroid gland is superfluous in man. I do not believe there is a single organ in the human body that is superfluous, even though years may pass after the reckless removal of an organ before the surgeons see what irrevocable damage they have done by their alacrity to use the knife. In your defense I should prefer to assume that you failed to notice several points in the reports of your much-praised Professor Billroth and his assistant, Dr. Wölffler. A considerable number of goiter operations were followed by cataleptic convulsions which either led immediately to death or to a particularly painful form of chronic convulsions which made the patients far sicker people than they had been before the operation. I scarcely think any more proof is needed that reckless removal of the thyroid gland is interference with nature which nature avenges in a fearful manner, and I have been forced to inform Mr. Cabot of the available facts. I am returning the various journals to you, and am much obliged for the opportunity to examine them."

I flung the letter to the table. For the first time I felt a thoroughgoing hatred of Winters. His deliberate blindness seemed criminal to me; his hypothesis of the indispensability of the thyroid gland narrow-minded and rigid. Once upon a time, after all, the gall bladder had been considered equally indispensable—a subject I shall deal with later. If in those days I had known of the forthcoming, equally embittered struggle between the surgeons and the practitioners of internal medicine over removal of the vermiform appendix—a struggle that cost so many lives—my condemnation of Winters would have been still harsher. I simply could not imagine what he was thinking of when he proposed sending Esther to "mild air," as though the quality of the air had anything to do with the merciless constriction of her windpipe by the growing goitrous tumor.

Once again I checked through all the reports and lectures by Rose, Billroth, Wölffler, and Kocher. I read every single word. At the end I did in fact come across several remarks by Wölffler con-

cerning postoperative symptoms—remarks I had previously failed
to notice. After the removal of goitrous thyroid glands and after
an apparently uneventful recovery, strange convulsions had appeared. Muscles had tightened until they were hard as boards, faces
contorted. The musculature of the thorax had become in two cases
so violently convulsed that asphyxiation followed. In the nonfatal
cases these convulsions had continued for years. They appeared
several times a day, and on each occasion lasted several minutes.
Most dangerous of all were the convulsions of the thorax because
they brought the patients to the brink of suffocation. With numbed,
cold hands, I put down the reports. Could some diabolic chance
have it that Dr. Winters was right after all?

Today, after so many years, I have long since come to regard
Winters and his hidebound conservatism in a milder light—today,
after so much has occurred to reveal the actual limits of surgery,
and after all those tragic events surrounding Kocher and goiter
surgery lie far behind me. But that day I regarded Winters only as
a blind, hate-filled enemy who would sooner sacrifice Esther than
yield an inch in his egotism and prejudice. Once more I checked
through the papers. The result was: Of some two hundred operations, Billroth had encountered convulsions—or "tetany" as he and
his associates called it—only in six cases. Did six cases mean that
loss of the thyroid gland resulted in severe illness, when there had
been no consequences in one hundred and ninety-four cases? How
many other causes besides complete or partial loss of the gland
might have produced tetany? I examined Kocher's reports. His
clinic reported no cases of tetany at all, at least in the journals I
had at hand. Billroth alone seemed to have observed a few such
cases. Unlike Kocher, Billroth had not yet responded to my cable.
I cabled again—this time requesting him to inform me on the
incidence, course, and danger of tetany. Inexplicably, he did not
reply this time either. Later I learned that Billroth was away. I
then appealed to Billroth's assistant of many years, Mikulicz. But
he also did not answer, for he was not in Vienna. After waiting
in vain, I sent a second cable to Kocher. A week went by before
I received a reply from his assistant, Roux. It was true, as I had
gathered, that Kocher had observed no such disturbing cases of
tetany as Billroth. But even in Billroth's experience, Roux pointed
out, so small a percentage of the patients had suffered from this

side-effect that it was not valid to conclude that loss of the thyroid gland was the cause. More probably the convulsions arose from injury to nerves, as in the earlier cases of loss of speech. In Kocher's clinic, at any rate, tetany had not been a factor of importance.

Meanwhile, several weeks had passed since Cabot's and Winters's communications. My initial feelings had cooled somewhat. But after I received the cable from Bern they flared up once more, and that same evening I sat down and wrote a letter to Winters in which I accused him of acting only out of stubbornness and egotism, and of deliberately risking Esther's life. I then sent my man to Fifth Avenue to ask for Cabot's address in Florida, only to have Cabot's secretary refuse to give it. At this I sent a letter to Cabot at his New York address, expressing my sense of outrage and my renewed conviction of what should be done for Esther. I concluded with the statement: "I thought you a man capable of making decisions. When you are confronted with the choice, as you are in Esther's case, between certain death and an operation which in about 10 per cent of the cases is likewise fatal or leads in a still smaller percentage of cases to what Billroth calls tetany, but which promises a 90 per cent chance for relief and recovery, it should not be difficult to make the decision."

After having done all this, I made an effort to set my mind at rest about the whole affair. But I could not. Again and again I heard that appeal for help which had rung so piteously from Esther's note to me. Again and again I felt a fury against Winters, and an urge to prove him wrong, to expose his stupidity and obstinacy.

More than three months passed. By the end of January, 1883, I was at last beginning to be less obsessed with the matter, when a special delivery letter came to me from Key West. It was from Cabot.

"If you still believe," Cabot wrote, "that Esther can be helped in Europe, please inform Professor Billroth or Professor Kocher of our impending arrival. I no longer have any other recourse. I have a good many explanations to make to you, but there is no time for them now. Perhaps you will understand part of the difficulty if I tell you that my deceased wife had the greatest confidence in Dr. Winters. At the time of her death she already knew that Esther was very ill, although it could not then be foreseen that the disease would develop to such an extent. At any rate, she made me take a kind of vow that I would always entrust Esther's health to the care of Dr. Winters as long as he lived. I have done this, although it frequently meant acting contrary to my own inclinations. I have received your letter, and beg you to forgive me for my last note. You are completely right. Esther's condition has steadily deteriorated, in spite of the favorable air. During the past weeks she has suffered four attacks of suffocation, one while she was fast asleep, and her breathing has a whistling sound, which seems to indicate that the goiter has continued growing. If in spite of all that has happened you are still prepared to take an interest in Esther's case, please make your own decision between Bern or Vienna. We plan to be in New York next week."

Since I had received no reply from Vienna by the last week in February, I decided we must go directly to Bern to consult Theodor Kocher.

Cabot, Esther, and I arrived in Bern on March 14. Our party also included a young New York physician, Dr. White, who in case of emergency could have performed a tracheotomy. Although Cabot had put an end to his curious dependency upon Winters, the emancipation was evidently not complete. White was one of Winters's assistants, and was obviously intended to play the role of observer.

On March 15, after a brief exchange of letters and messages, I arranged to meet Kocher on the afternoon of the sixteenth and discuss the case with him alone in his private office in Schlösslistrasse. Theodor Kocher practiced chiefly at this time in the antiquated, frightfully cramped old Island Hospital of Bern. By intimating that he might leave for a better post in Prague, Kocher had forced the cantonal authorities to start building a new hospital. But this building was not yet complete. Kocher therefore maintained a private office near his home.

My meeting with Kocher was set for five in the afternoon. Before I left the hotel, I stepped out on the large balcony to talk with Esther. The high fur collar which concealed her malady from strangers' eyes seemed quite in place in the crisp winter weather. But every one of her faintly whistling breaths betrayed her illness. Her face had grown thinner, and her eyes strikingly large.

Her lips, which only last autumn had been full and beautifully curved, now had a bluish cast. Symptoms of oxygen starvation were beginning to appear, and it seemed to me that a faint hoarseness lurked in her voice. This would mean that the goiter was pressing on the recurrent laryngeal nerve.

"I hope you will come back with good news," she said.

"Of course," I declared. "Soon we will have you all fixed up and as good as new."

She clasped my hand and smiled, while her eyes brimmed with tears.

At five o'clock I stepped for the first time into the spacious garden of the hotellike house which was later to be the center from which Kocher's fame spread over the entire world. The house was not yet what it was later to become: a vast sanatorium to which people came from the farthest ends of the earth, a luxury hotel for the weathiest and most illustrious of sufferers, who came with flocks of nurses or kinsfolk, who had also to be accommodated in its big rooms and seated in its lordly dining hall. As yet the rich and notable of the earth did not wait for weeks in Bern hotels for those terse messages from Schlösslistrasse: Professor Kocher will expect you for an examination at such and such a date. As yet they did not again wait for weeks after the examination for a room at the clinic to be free for them, and for admission to the modest little operating chamber where Kocher worked on Wednesdays and Saturdays.

Nevertheless, on that March 16 the waiting room held persons from at least four countries, among them a Turkish dignitary with several attendants. Most of the patients seemed to be suffering from thyroid tumors. This evidence that Kocher's reputation had already penetrated to the Near East further increased my confidence in him.

After a while I noticed that no one was called in, and that no one left the waiting room. Almost an hour passed. Nevertheless, the patients waited with astonishing resignation. When the hour hand of the clock passed six, I felt I could wait there no longer. I left the building and repaired to the Island Hospital. There was a young man standing near the gatehouse from whom I inquired whether Kocher were still in the building. "Yes," he said, look-

ing at me with an oddly absent and nervous expression. What
was it that I wished? When I explained that I had had an appointment with Kocher in his private office for five o'clock, he
recommended that I give him up for the day. Kocher was being
detained by special examinations, he declared, and there was no
prospect that he would be able to see any patients this evening.
He identified himself as Dr. Roux, Kocher's first assistant, apologized for being in a hurry, and said that he must return immediately to Kocher.

I hesitated for a moment, thinking that I could easily arrange
a new appointment for next day. But something restrained me.
It is difficult to say what it was; partly reluctance to return without having anything to report to Esther, Cabot, and Dr. White
—especially the last, who seemed to be waiting to pounce upon
any failures. Partly, too, I was struck by the peculiar uneasiness
of Roux's manner. And as a medical man I did not like to be put
off like any layman.

I therefore gave my name to Kocher's assistant, and reminded
him that I had come all the way from America with a goiter
patient suffering from frequent attacks of asphyxiation. The
patient was at the hotel, waiting in dreadful suspense for Kocher's
decision. I said I did not wish to return without settling the date
for her examination. Roux glanced at me with mounting nervousness. But then he asked me to follow him. He led me down several
corridors of the ancient hospital building. We turned a corner,
and I suddenly found myself confronting a number of persons
whose appearance stopped me in my tracks. I was catching my
first glimpse of the terrible drama which later shook the whole
world of medicine. And even today, when it is long a thing of
the past, I find it difficult to describe those people. There were
men, women, and children, tended and guarded by other men
and women in the peasant dress of the Bernese Oberland. The
faces of the women and children particularly were more or less
swollen, their features sallow and sickly. Among the group were
some figures such as I had last seen among the terrible denizens
of Charcot's Salpêtrière, where not only the insane, the mentally
crippled, and the morons were gathered, but also the cretins and
half-cretins of all Paris. Their eyes were dull and indifferent.
Their bodies, especially those of the children, seemed bloated,

stunted in growth, with thick, red, helpless hands. These were children deprived of all childlike delicacy and grace.

At first I was incapable of taking another step. I could not imagine the significance of these cretinous figures in a surgical clinic. Roux, too, had stopped. But almost immediately he moved between me and the group of shocking patients, quickly opened a door that led to a small laboratory, and asked me to wait here until he brought me some word from Kocher.

"Are these patients from a mental ward?" I asked before he could walk away.

Roux hesitated. "No," he replied at last, "this hospital has no such department."

"But those patients . . . ?" I persisted.

Again Roux hesitated. Then he said: "Perhaps Professor Kocher will answer your questions. I will go to him now, and find out from him whether there is any point in your waiting longer."

I was left alone in the room, which was certainly no waiting room, so that I could not help suspecting that Roux had closeted me here only in order to keep me from seeing more of the cretinous patients. However, I did not have much time to reflect upon the matter, for Roux returned very quickly. "Professor Kocher," he said, "sincerely regrets the circumstances which have prevented his being punctual. But he asks you to believe that these circumstances are extraordinarily important to us. He is ready to make another appointment tomorrow, so that you can discuss your patient's case with him. But if for some reason you cannot or prefer not to postpone your conversation with him, Professor Kocher suggests that you wait for him at his home. If that is your decision, he will send a note to Frau Kocher, who I am sure will make the wait as pleasant as possible for you."

Perhaps I would have called the matter off for the day had it not been for my glimpse of the cretins. This had strangely unnerved me. I told Roux I should prefer to wait at Kocher's house. Obviously he was not pleased by this decision. But American doctors and patients were still rare in Bern at that time, and were therefore deemed worthy of special consideration.

Following Roux out, I looked for the unfortunate creatures I had spied before. But they had vanished.

Fifteen minutes later I was sitting in Kocher's living room and conversing with his wife, who was then, I judged, about thirty. Marie Kocher came from a Bernese family of wholesale merchants who united in curious fashion a remarkable business talent with the strict religious outlook of the Moravian Brethren. This familiar background was reflected in Marie Kocher's personality, as were the French Huguenot origins of her mother. She was graceful, lively, animated, and for all her deep religious feeling highly responsive to the world and competent in mundane affairs —a competence that was to stand her in good stead when in future years she governed Kocher's vast household and relieved him of all business management.

When I met her for the first time that evening, however, I was still in the grip of my strange encounter in the corridor of the hospital, so that I had only a dim impression of this blonde young woman who poured me a glass of red wine. Had I known her previously, I would undoubtedly have observed how different she was tonight from the lively self I later met. Even so, I noticed a degree of constraint and depression, and became more aware of this when our conversation—after a long preliminary chat on America—turned to the purpose of my visit. At that point Marie Kocher suddenly became oddly taciturn. When after three quarters of an hour there was still no sign of Kocher, she remarked apologetically that her husband was usually most punctual. But in the past few weeks, and especially the past few days, she added, he had been engaged on a project which was almost too much for him, and which kept him occupied until all hours of the night.

My thoughts at once flew to those sinister figures at the hospital, and I asked her what this project might be. She replied that he would probably tell me about it himself. Then, with a moody, downcast look, she commented: "I am afraid you have not chosen a fortunate moment for your trip to Bern."

Until then I had felt only a vague uneasiness, whose basis I could scarcely define. Now all at once I felt profound uncertainty. Had something happened to shake Kocher's optimism, his confidence in the success of his operative technique for goiter? Once again the faces of those cretins loomed before me. I sensed —with an involuntary chill—that here was some key to the riddle of which Marie Kocher would not speak.

Our conversation became more forced, more punctuated by periods of silence, until at last voices in the vestibule announced the doctor's return home. His wife excused herself with visible relief. A few minutes later she led me into Kocher's study.

When I entered his room, I still had no idea of the kind of person I was about to meet. I knew nothing of this man I had come so far to see save for what glimmerings of character come through a scientific paper. Nor had I even seen a picture of him. Now I faced a rather small, slight man of barely forty, dressed in a plain dark suit. His steely blue eyes were of a kind which in some men are almost mesmeric in their fire—but these were clouded and almost drained of color with weariness. He extended his fine hand, then dropped back into a chair and for a moment closed his eyes. I sat down, and waited with baited breath for Dr. Kocher to speak.

At last he opened his eyes. He seemed to have rallied himself a little.

"You are older than I," he said abruptly, in a low voice. "Have you ever known the moment when God suddenly hurls us down from a peak of self-complacency and lets us recognize what small, bungling creatures we are?"

His outburst was so surprising that for the moment I was incapable of replying. In my world-wide journeys through all the large and small centers of medical science I had seldom heard talk of God. This question on Kocher's part, the question of a soul in agony, took me aback. I did not know as yet that Kocher also came of a family of Moravian Brethren, and that his mother had bequeathed to him her unshakable faith as an adjunct to the scientific precision which was his father's legacy. I was still unaware of those principles of life which Kocher had set forth in writing after receiving his doctorate: "The only certainties we possess are those God reveals to us. Before every work which is undertaken for the good of others, therefore, we should pray to be preserved from errors which may transform the intended good of our actions into harm." Nor was I aware of the guiding directives he had set for himself somewhat later, at the age of twenty-five. "Use every minute for work, and for work in which the heart can and does participate. Do not forget for a moment gratitude for the redemption and the promise Christ has brought into the world. . . ."

And: "Prayer can . . . compensate for our inadequate powers to combat death and fatal diseases. For Christ overcame death, and in individual cases He can aid us. . . ."

Had I then been acquainted with these aspects of Kocher's life and character, his sudden reference to God, and all that followed, would not have seemed so baffling. I would have grasped at once, rather than later, that here was a man passing through a crisis of conscience in which the very principles by which he lived were threatened.

Kocher seemed to expect me to speak. But his words had been unintelligible to me and I could say nothing to them. "When I cabled you several months ago," he continued, "I was prepared to treat Miss Cabot. In the meantime, however, things have happened which I must report to you before we exchange a word about your patient." He paused briefly. "You were at my hospital this evening. As chance would have it, in the corridor outside my examining room you came upon a number of unfortunates whom we would call, in our harsh terminology, cretins. All of them were once normal people like you and me. . . ."

He looked at me out of agonized eyes, and suddenly I felt the same agony in myself; I became aware of a tremendous burden of guilt weighing upon me. I imagined that I could hear Winters's voice quivering with malice as he took me to task for my hot-headedness.

Kocher continued: "There can be no question that we have mastered the goiter operation in the technical sense. We have learned to prevent hemorrhages. We have found ways to avoid disturbances of speech almost completely, by careful procedure. Billroth's tetany is a complication, but does not occur frequently enough to invalidate our work. But something else has happened." His voice grew louder. "It was rash to conclude from the experience of a few years that the thyroid gland is dispensable in man and can therefore be totally removed. In nine years I have performed total excision of the thyroid gland upon thirty-four patients. Thirty-one of them I sent home after satisfactory convalescence. But I neglected to observe these patients for a longer time after their dismissal, or to follow up their histories. Only chance prompted me to repair this omission. This chance induced me to call all my patients of the last nine or ten years to Bern for examination, or to ask them and their relatives to report to me in writing on their condition. The patients you saw this evening were the last of those who came to Bern. And the result of our examinations is more alarming and more crushing than anything I have ever experienced in all my previous work." Once more his voice rose. "I hope you are prepared to hear things which will dash your hopes." In the tone of a formal statement before some larger court, he announced: "Excision of the thyroid gland in my patients has destroyed that quality which gives human beings human dignity. I have taken people sick with goiter but mentally healthy and condemned them to the life of idiots. I have made many of them partial or complete cretins, and saved them for a life which is no life at all."

The history of medicine has given a full account of what this meant for the newborn science of thyroid gland surgery. The textbooks are scientific and precise. They describe the nature of the mistake, how it came to be made, what its consequences were, and how it was gradually amended. But they do not name the victims, and they do not reconstruct what Theodor Kocher felt at the moment he first recognized the terrible thing he had done in totally removing the thyroid gland.

For my part, I felt utterly shattered. Would I have to return to Cabot and Esther and tell them that the voyage across the ocean had been in vain, that there was no salvation, that Winters had been right all along, and that Kocher and I and all surgeons who attempted to operate on goiters were criminally wrong?

"Until September 2 of last year," Kocher continued, "I was completely certain that excision of the thyroid gland resulted in no serious aftereffects. Up to that time I had performed a total of seventy-seven operations on one or both lobes of the gland. I was not alone in my view. Wölffler, Billroth's assistant—Billroth is the only surgeon who has performed more excisions than I— had also concluded that the gland is dispensable.

"Today, however, I know that I received a first warning nine years ago. On January 8, 1874, I operated on an eleven-year-old girl. Her name was Maria Richsel. Maria was the older of two sisters, and a sweet, charming child. But she was disfigured by a goiter on both sides of the neck, consisting of completely round nodules the size of walnuts. The village physician, Dr. Fetscherin, had attempted iodine injections, but the goiter had developed rapidly. At that time I had already achieved my first successes in goiter operations. True, my first patient, a young man from Ochlenberg, had died of sepsis in May, 1872. But the following seven operations, performed under antisepsis, were consistently successful. The last among them had involved total excision in a sixteen-year-old girl whose breath was being strangled by the growth. This operation took place in December, 1873. Three weeks later the patient was discharged as cured. Hearing of these successes, Dr. Fetscherin sent Maria Richsel, accompanied by her mother and sister, to the hospital here. My first total excision had gone so well that I was prompted to repeat this operation on the eleven-year-old girl. After incising the skin, retracting the muscles of the neck, and ligaturing the superficial vessels, the operation was performed without the slightest trouble. Both lobes of the thyroid gland were removed. Afterwards the patient became slightly feverish, but by the fourth day her temperature had returned to normal. The child simply bloomed. Certainly this was one of the most dramatic successes I had had up to that time. By February 12 she was discharged and returned home.

"And then came the warning I have mentioned. Dr. Fetscherin, though I have never met him personally, must be one of those general practitioners out in the country who are closely in touch with their patients. Possibly he had had to fight a good deal of resistance on the part of the peasants up in the mountains before they consented to sending the child to a surgeon, and after her return he must have been quite proud that the patient's good health proved his judgment right. In any case, he took the trouble to keep me informed of Maria's progress. During the early weeks he wrote that the child was doing splendidly. But then the tenor of his reports changed. Maria, who before the operation had been gay and lively in spite of her illness, was changing in a peculiar manner. The condition of her throat remained good. But she had become sullen and lazy, was no longer interested in anything, and had literally to be driven to do any work at all. At the time, I was publishing a survey of my first thirteen cases of goiter, and noted, apropos of the Richsel case, that further developments would teach us whether there existed any connection between removal of the thyroid gland and the patient's changed mental attitude. I had therefore, as you can verify by checking the paper, given some thought to the matter. But then I heard nothing more of Maria Richsel—because, as I have recently learned, Dr. Fetscherin died and no one else took over this responsibility. Thus what Fetscherin had told me of the case remained a single observation, unconfirmed and incomplete. Only after the sixth-fourth operation did I receive another hint.

"In September of last year I attended the Hygienic Congress in Geneva and there met a colleague, Professor Reverdin, who had likewise been engaged in surgical treatment of goiter for some years. He had by then performed fourteen operations, most of them total excisions. Reverdin told me that he had noticed that some of his patients suffered after the operation from anemia and from mental and physical sluggishness. Moreover, he said, one patient had assumed the appearance of a cretin. In view of the far larger number of my own operations Reverdin wondered whether I had made similar observations. At first I said I had not, but then I recalled the Richsel case, and Dr. Fetscherin's communication. I therefore mentioned this to Reverdin.

"That was as far as we went then. There seemed every reason to assume that the observed complications were due to technical flaws, or to injuries to nerves in the course of the operation. After my return to Bern, however, the problem began to prey on my mind, and I resolved to track down Maria Richsel and discover what her condition was now, eight years later. I wrote to Dr. Fetscherin, and learned after a while that he was no more. I wrote to the patient's family, and received no reply. Finally I wrote to the district authorities. From them I learned that the Richsels and their children had moved to a still more remote mountain community. There I found them at last. By this time it was January of the present year. The roads up in the mountains were snowed in. Not until a month ago could the mother and her two daughters come down to the railroad station. In the middle of February they came to Bern and presented themselves at the hospital. Meanwhile I had operated for seventeen more goiters, performing two total excisions to alleviate dangerous compression of the trachea which would have been fatal if left unoperated. All these patients had recovered without complications.

"The mother was waiting in the same corridor in which you

encountered those unfortunate cretins this evening. She stood there in her finest peasant dress. Beside the mother stood a tall, well-grown girl, as tall as my eleven-year-old patient should have been by now. But she was not Maria; she was the younger sister. When I asked about the girl whom I had operated on, the mother pulled forward a small, thickset creature with clumsy, dangling arms, excessively broad head, and sparse hair. Her face was dull, her lips swollen; there were heavy white swellings around her eyes; and she had a lifeless, helpless, wandering look. This was my patient, now nineteen years old, who in the years since the death of Dr. Fetscherin had slowly but inexorably developed to this degree of cretinism without my being informed.

"This might still be an isolated case. But remembering what Reverdin had said, the case seemed so alarming that the very next day I had letters written to all the patients upon whom I had operated for goiter from 1872 to the beginning of this year. Every one of them was requested to come to Bern for examination, or at least to report in writing on his condition. A great deal of laborious searching, for people who had often changed their residences several times, was involved. Of ninety patients, some fifteen had died of various diseases during those nine years. Of the remaining seventy-five, seventeen have not yet responded. Five others had suffered from cancer of the thyroid gland. There remained fifty-three patients. On nineteen of these I have had reports in writing, either from relatives or from themselves. Thirty-four came for examination. The last group were the ones you saw this evening. In twenty of them we have observed various stages of cachexia and cretinism. The symptoms did not develop until weeks or months after the operations, and therefore escaped our attention. The first signs were tiredness, weakness in the limbs, and a growing sensation of coldness. Subsequently there developed intellectual sluggishness and a general slowness in speech and all other activities. Later the swollen condition of the face, eyelids, nose, and lips appeared. The skin became dry and the hair fell out. Severe anemia completed the clinical picture."

Here Kocher stopped, as if he could no longer bear to go on with the story.

"What conclusions do you draw from this?" I pressed. "Does this mean giving up goiter surgery?"

He did not answer my question directly. "I have announced

that I will report on these things to the congress of German surgeons in Berlin on April 4. There I shall present the results of my investigation. I shall call for a halt in total excisions of the thyroid gland. I am not certain whether my statistics are comprehensive enough to be accepted as a valid indicator. Perhaps others must go through the same tragic experience until the facts are recognized. That has happened before. In any case, I know what I must do."

He paused for a long moment. Then he said: "I shall experiment on animals to determine the functions of the thyroid gland and the reason for the complications consequent on its removal—a syndrome which for the present I have termed cachexia strumipriva. The moment we know the function it should certainly be possible to avoid the consequences. It may also be possible to find some way of reversing those trends once they have begun."

I guessed what was in his mind: the hope that he might someday be able to make good the harm he had done to so many patients in the belief that he was helping them. But all this was vaguely in the future. The immediate present was my urgent concern right now. Esther could not wait for future discoveries. The time at her disposal was far too short for that.

"But what about goiter surgery?" I insisted, returning to the question he had not answered. "Do you really intend to drop it? Is all the previous work to have been done in vain?"

"No," he replied. "The work will go on. I can tell you how I intend to act in the future. Examination of my patients revealed not only the existence of cachexia strumipriva. It has also shown that, with a single exception, only those patients were affected whose thyroid glands were goitrous on both sides and were therefore totally removed. Except for that one case, none of the patients who had had only part of the thyroid gland excised, suffered from cachexia strumipriva. This seems to prove that leaving part of the thyroid gland obviates cachexia, as though this one part were able to take over the still unknown functions of the excised parts of the gland."

This meant, then, that the cause was not yet altogether lost. Kocher had in effect pointed out a gleam of light in the darkened sky. But what was this light to my patient with her extensive goiter on both sides?

"Does this mean," I asked, between fatalism and a shred of desperate hope, "that patients with goiter on only one side can be saved, at least for a while, whereas the others must choose between cachexia and death?"

Kocher shrugged sadly. "I, for my part, shall never again undertake total excision of the thyroid gland, and when I go before my colleagues in Berlin I shall most earnestly warn them against such surgery. But I shall do my utmost to find some new attack. Perhaps it will be possible to remove one side of the gland completely and to excise just enough of the other to do away with the hindrance to respiration, while still leaving sufficient of the gland substance. We thereby run the risk of the remaining gland's eventually producing a new goiter, and further surgery's being necessary. Still, this may be our only expedient."

My tension had reached such a pitch that I could no longer sit quietly in my chair. I rose to my feet. "You know why I have come to you and how urgent the matter is. When do you think you will feel able to take the course you have outlined? How long will it be?"

Kocher did not reply at once. For seconds he sat facing me in painful silence. At last he said: "I quite understand you. What you are asking is too much for me at present. I cannot give you any such date." He paused once more. Then, to my enormous relief, he said: "Send Miss Cabot to me tomorrow afternoon at four o'clock. I shall examine her, and see what is to be done. More I cannot promise—not tonight."

My carriage rolled through the dimly illuminated, almost deserted streets. As it neared the hotel, the Berner Hof, I was still pondering the course to take. At length I decided to say nothing to Esther, and only tell her that she would be examined tomorrow. Perhaps Dr. Winters's diagnosis was just as wrong as my own opinion on the size and extent of the goitrous tumor. Perhaps Kocher would have a more favorable prognosis. Possibly operation on one side would be sufficient. Why arouse needless disappointment and fears in Esther before Kocher had spoken? Why burden Cabot with problems which were difficult to explain, difficult for a layman to understand? I decided to hold my peace with Cabot also. Perhaps my motive was an escape from responsibility. But I saw no other choice.

As I applied for my key at the desk, the clerk informed me that Mr. and Miss Cabot had asked repeatedly for me during the past two hours, and were now waiting for me in Miss Cabot's room. They requested me to come to them as soon as I returned.

As soon as I stepped into the room I saw Esther. Her constant struggle for breath had prompted her to sit, as usual, near a slightly opened window. She was wrapped in a blanket, and leaned against a number of cushions. This position apparently diminished the pressure of the tumor upon her windpipe, and made respiration somewhat easier for her. Nevertheless I heard the faint whistling sound of her breathing.

She raised her head at once, and her face brightened somewhat. "I was afraid you would not be back tonight," she said. I realized from her voice the tension she had been under all the while I was gone.

I made an effort to keep my own voice natural, even optimistic in tone. "Famous doctors like Professor Kocher have little time," I said. "I learned today that a good many patients wait not hours, but days, before they so much as hear from him. By comparison I did not have to wait long at all."

I had the impression that she believed me. Meanwhile, Cabot entered from the adjoining room. He, too, was perturbed, and gave me a searching look. Involuntarily, I avoided his eyes and went up close to Esther. "In fact you will have only a very short wait," I said. "Professor Kocher will examine you tomorrow. He would like you to come tomorrow afternoon at four o'clock."

Her relief visibly increased. "Thank you for all you have done," she said. "Is Professor Kocher continuing to have success? Does he think he can help me?"

"That," I said, wondering at the facility with which the phrase fell from my lips, "is something that Professor Kocher will tell you himself tomorrow. I must not anticipate him."

I hastened to leave the room before I became entangled in an outright lie. I was frozen through and exhausted, I said, and begged to be excused.

Cabot accompanied me to the door. To my surprise he stepped out into the corridor with me and closed the door behind him. Then he asked: "Is everything really all right?"

With a pang I realized that now there was no longer any shirking of the issue—either I told the truth or I blackened my conscience with a lie. In my cowardice I chose the lie. "Everything is quite all right," I said. But all my nerves were quivering as I said good night.

I was only a few steps from my room on the next floor when I ran across Dr. White, who was coming down the hallway. He looked at me with a peculiar coldness and hostility. "Oh, you are back," he said. "What was the outcome?"

"Professor Kocher will examine Esther tomorrow afternoon at four," I replied.

"And operate?"

There was such venom in the manner in which he asked that I was taken aback.

"I hope so," I said.

"Oh, by the way," he said in an ingratiating manner, "this afternoon I happened to have a talk with another American doctor who is in Bern at the moment. He told me a number of curious things. He has heard of cases in which Dr. Kocher's goiter operations led to imbecility, to pronounced forms of cretinism. I daresay Professor Kocher discussed this with you. Nevertheless . . ."

I thought for a moment that my heart would stop. Only with the greatest effort did I retain my composure. "I know nothing about this," I said, "and I would recommend sparing the patient any such rumors."

When I reached my room, I dropped exhausted on my bed. Suppose White spoke with Esther in spite of my injunction? Suppose he had already spoken to Cabot? Were Cabot's oddly probing looks and his last question based upon information he had received from White? For a long while I lay awake. Toward morning I managed to sleep for two hours, but I awoke again at seven. Then I decided to send a note to Kocher. I explained that I had not informed Cabot or Esther of the actual situation, thinking it best to await his examination and subsequent decision on the possibilities of operation. However, the doctor accompanying the Cabots had heard some rumors about the cases of cachexia, and I did not know whether or how long he would keep silent about them. I therefore asked Kocher to send me a letter by messenger immediately after his examination of Esther, reporting his decisions, so that I could at least anticipate White and not be caught at the crucial moment in a deception which would certainly shake the patient's confidence in the value of the operation.

I gave this letter to a bellboy, hoping that it would reach Kocher at home, before he left for his clinic. Then I spent a nervous half hour. At last the boy returned. Kocher had written on the back of my letter: "Accompany Miss Esther Cabot to the examination. You can then know my decision at once."

White, if he had not spoken yet, might avail himself of the hours between now and the afternoon to tell Cabot or Esther his sinister news. This thought sent me hurrying out of my room. I was reluctant to stay with Esther and Cabot all day, for it meant exposing myself to more questions about Kocher. But there was no other way.

The day proved to be as difficult as I had expected. Cabot's normal reticence, and the probing look in his eyes, increased my uncertainty. White's knowing expression and the quirk of cold mockery around the corners of his mouth forced me to be constantly on my guard. Esther alone remained simply and trustfully expectant. In fact her confidence appeared to grow stronger as the hour for the examination approached. It was, on the whole, a dispensation when she, Cabot, and myself entered the carriage at fifteen minutes to four to set off for Schlösslistrasse. To my surprise, Cabot decided that White was not to come along, but to await our return at the hotel.

A nurse received us and immediately led Esther into Kocher's examining room, while Cabot and I sat down in a small anteroom. Cabot was extraordinarily restive. Watching him, I concluded several times that he knew the whole story, or at least a part of it. But again and again I rejected this idea, as we always by preference reject the more terrible alternative.

Half an hour passed. Three quarters of an hour. The longer the waiting period became, the more my own uneasiness increased. If Kocher declined to operate, I could confess the truth and explain my various falsehoods by saying that I had not wanted to anticipate Kocher. But if Kocher decided to operate after all, I would really be in a quandary. I certainly could not continue to conceal the truth from Cabot. Even if I wanted to, White's clear intention of doing all in his power to forestall the operation would force me to explain to Cabot. Then I would not only have to con-

fess my deception, but would also have to persuade him to consent to the operation—in spite of the attendant risk that Kocher
might again be mistaken.

After a full hour had passed, the door opened and Esther appeared, her throat with all its disfiguring malformations still exposed. She appeared pale and exhausted, but happy. She went
quickly to her father, embraced him, and stammered out in a
hoarse voice: "The professor will operate! He will help me!"

My first feelings were of triumph and gladness. But hard upon
this came a consciousness of the struggle before me. The nurse
reappeared and called me in to see Kocher, thus sparing me the
necessity of facing Cabot at the moment. But I knew that this was
only a postponement.

Kocher was alone. He offered me a chair, and himself sat down
behind his desk. Thoughtfully, he picked up a wooden ear trumpet
(the predecessor of the modern stethoscope), and swung it back
and forth in his fine hands. Then he said: "Miss Cabot presents a
comparatively rare clinical picture. Her tumor is a mixture of a
follicular and a fibrous goiter, such as we rarely encounter in our
alpine country. The entire left lobe of the thyroid gland is considerably enlarged, so that even a casual examination would suggest
a massive colloidal goiter. The right lobe is infected by several
disconnected goitrous nodules."

"Then what are your conclusions?" I asked anxiously.

"If the patient's family consents, I shall attempt to excise the
entire enlarged left lobe. On the right side, it should be possible
to enucleate the nodules and spare the still healthy thyroid tissue.
This should leave sufficient glandular substance to prevent a total
elimination of the gland's functions." He laid the ear trumpet aside
and fixed his eyes upon mine. "However, I must inform you that
extraction of such nodules—a surgical art practiced even in the
days of ancient Rome and revived by the Italian surgeon Porta
about forty years ago—can lead to surprising hemorrhages, even
though the operation itself is technically simple. In this case the
large blood vessels cannot be ligatured in advance."

"When do you plan to operate?" I asked.

"Not until my return from the Berlin congress of surgeons—
about three weeks hence—unless acute danger of asphyxiation

should recur in the meantime." Kocher paused briefly. "I am placing my trust in the congress. I hope that others there will confirm my own hypothesis that preserving a part of the thyroid gland averts the development of cachexia. I would suggest, however, that Miss Cabot enter the clinic during the next few days, for preliminary treatment. She is young and still relatively strong. Nevertheless, after so prolonged a period of respiratory disturbances some medication to ease the strain on her heart would do no harm. Moreover, I should like to be in a position to operate at once if a dangerous attack of asphyxiation should ensue. A tracheotomy always imperils the success of the subsequent goiter operation because it opens the way for infectious materials to enter the operation zone from the trachea. With Miss Cabot in the clinic, I can operate at once at any time, except for the few days I shall be in Berlin. Moreover, she will be more apt to avoid colds in the clinic —and in her present condition a cold might well lead to a fatal edema. I have told Miss Cabot everything I thought she ought to know, and she seems prepared to put herself into my hands. I believe I have acted wisely in leaving you to tell her, as best you can, of the possibility of cachexia. At any rate, that is how I understood the note you sent to me this morning."

Kocher extended his hand. "I shall do the best I can in the present state of our knowledge. Incidentally, before I go to Berlin I intend to operate upon two patients who are already at the hospital, waiting for operation. This in spite of what I said last night. On reflection I think we must not give up the attempt to cure—even though we may spend sleepless nights."

As we left the clinic, Cabot said little. It was about half past five in the afternoon.

Esther had momentarily forgotten about her difficulty in breathing. She chattered away brightly about Kocher, about his kindness, the gentleness of his hands, his excellent English. Merely in the course of the examination Kocher had evidently inspired in the girl an unshakable faith. She pressed her father to take her to the clinic right away, tomorrow morning, and entrust her health entirely to Kocher. In her excitement she took no heed of her father's silence, which persisted throughout the ride. This struck me as more and more ominous.

After we reached the hotel and Esther had gone to her room, Cabot asked me to keep him company for a while, and to tell him about my conversation with Kocher. As he strode heavily down the hallway beside me, I grew more and more convinced that White had already spoken to him. And when we were alone in one of the smaller salons, and Cabot sat looking at me with deep sorrow in his eyes, this feeling became a virtual certainty.

"In New York a while back," he began, "you said to me that Esther was old enough to decide for herself and to make up her mind what should be done to save her life. I am certain you were right. It is Esther's life, and if she believes so fervently that Professor Kocher can save her, I have no right to stop her. In her dying hour she would never forgive me. She would tell me, by words or looks, that I was to blame for her death, for having blocked the only road to life. I dare not do that. But . . ." He avoided my eyes, as though he did not want to hurt me, or at least preferred not to see that he was hurting me. "But if I were to learn now that there was something which Professor Kocher has concealed from Esther, and which you are also concealing from us—something which to my mind is worse than a quick death—don't you feel that, as Esther's father, I must at least tell her, even though she probably would no longer listen to me and does not want to hear any more negative counsel? I don't think much of White, but I cannot believe he invented the story about the imbecilic patients in order to discredit Professor Kocher and you. Or am I mistaken?" Slowly he raised his head and looked questioningly at me, a look of mingled doubt and hopefulness. "Is the story White told me yesterday merely an ugly, spiteful rumor, or is it the truth? I could have gone to Professor Kocher and asked him directly. But I prefer to ask you."

My white lie, spoken in the despair of the moment and in an attempt to gain time, had clearly been preying on Cabot's mind since last night. I mustered all my self-control. "White told you a truth, but only a half-truth," I said.

Once more his eyes grew dark and troubled. "Then it is so," he said slowly. "It is so." He was silent a moment, and then continued: "After all that has happened I no longer doubt that you have Esther's best interests in mind. Therefore you must have a good reason for concealing this. But am I justified in concealing it from

Esther, now that I know and now that you tell me this thing is not false? Let us assume that she is cured—but only for a short time, and that then she will gradually lose her reason and develop into a sluggish, scarcely human creature. Do you not think that the indictment of me, which Esther herself may no longer be capable of making, but which I myself and all who know us would certainly make, would be a thousand times worse than the charge that I left my daughter to die of asphyxiation?"

Behind his words I felt the prayer that I decide for him, or at least guide him toward a decision.

"Mr. Cabot," I said, determined to win him over to faith in Kocher and at the same time to quell my own last doubts, "White told you only a half-truth. It is true that certain operations had the dreadful consequences White described to you. The unfortunate patients will never again be normal. But they taught Professor Kocher where his error lay. Their fate will save other patients from a similar tragedy. It will not happen again."

I tried to explain what had happened, and to outline Kocher's argument that retaining a part of the thyroid gland would prevent the development of cachexia strumipriva. I also discussed Kocher's plan for eliminating Esther's goiter without removing the entire thyroid gland. In conclusion I said, strengthening my own conviction even as I spoke: "All these tragic events are in the past now. Why should he burden Esther with them? She will need all her strength and all her faith in Kocher for the operation. Why undermine her confidence?"

The big man had covered his face with his hands. "Professor Kocher made a mistake," he said. "He now believes, if I understand you correctly, that he has found a better way. How do you know that he is not mistaken once more?"

As though I had not considered this question—the question and the impossibility of answering it. But even as I was groping for arguments, Cabot himself spared me the necessity for replying.

"I have grown modest," he said. "I would take it on faith if I could know that some other doctors agreed with Kocher on this matter. Can you name other doctors—at least one other?"

I was not prepared for this question. Who besides Kocher had passed through similar disappointments and torments of conscience, and come to the same conclusion? Then I recalled Kocher's reference to Reverdin. Had not Kocher said that Reverdin in Geneva had started him on his investigation? I did not know, of course, whether Reverdin had meanwhile come to take the same view as Kocher. But if there were anyone at all, it would certainly be he. Therefore I said boldly: "Professor Reverdin in Geneva." And with sudden resolve I added: "Why don't you ask him by telegraph? If he does not reply, or his reply is not satisfactory, I am prepared to go to Geneva with you and look him up."

Cabot hesitated. Then he said: "Very well, let us try it."

In Cabot's presence I wrote out the telegram.

I had just begun to dress for dinner when there was a knock at the door. Dr. White entered. His face was a pasty white.

"I have come to you before I undertake any further steps," he said. "I propose simply to tell you what I think of you. I have just learned from Miss Cabot that the operation is to be performed. Both Kocher and you are apparently happy to let Miss Cabot fling herself headlong into a horror you are perfectly aware of. I need scarcely tell you what responsible physicians would call men of your sort. Yesterday I told Mr. Cabot half of the story. I now find myself forced to speak more frankly to him, without any consideration for his feelings. I am not going to stand by and see Miss Cabot reduced to imbecility—even if I have to tell her the brutal truth and put an end to her delusive hopes."

The old hatred I had felt toward Winters surged up in me. But only for seconds. It subsided rapidly as I recalled the painful and instructive lessons I had received during the past few days.

"Dr. White," I said, "do what you feel you must do. Go to Mr. Cabot. You will find that he knows more about the matter than you. But do not go to Miss Cabot. Neither her father nor I would ever forgive you for that."

He stared at me in surprise and perplexity, and stalked out of the room.

There followed a second night during which I slept poorly. Every waking moment my mind dwelt on the problem of what we would hear from Reverdin. But the following day passed without any answer from Geneva. Next day, too, we waited in vain. Cabot was in a frenzy of impatience. Esther kept begging to be allowed to go to Kocher's clinic, and could not understand why her father was imposing this delay. Finally Kocher himself sent a note inquiring when Esther would be entering the clinic. At this point Cabot proposed that I go to Geneva myself next morning and obtain some word from Reverdin. He would take what Reverdin had to say as a mandate. He himself did not dare to leave his daughter. And so I went alone.

I reached Geneva that evening, and next morning attempted to get in touch with Jacques Louis Reverdin. At the Geneva Cantonal Hospital I learned that Reverdin was at his private clinic on the Rue de Courage. Reverdin was at this time well on his way to becoming Geneva's foremost surgeon. He came of an old French family from the Dauphiné which had fled to Geneva for religious reasons at the beginning of the eighteenth century. His maternal grandfather, François Mayor, had also been a doctor, and the discoverer of fetal heartbeat. His ancestors on his father's side, however, had practiced artistic rather than scientific professions. Whereas Theodor Kocher united scientific ambition with profound religious feeling, Reverdin combined scientific precision with the intuitive powers of the artist. He was about the same age as Kocher, and had studied medicine entirely in France, under Guérius and Guyons. With this background, French culture and French medicine were the formative elements in his thinking.

Ushered into Reverdin's office, I found myself in the presence of not one man but two. The older one, closer to forty than thirty, was a delicately built person with a sensitive scholar's face. He introduced himself as Jacques Louis Reverdin. The other, thickset, almost fat, with a round, lively, florid countenance, was Auguste Reverdin, his cousin and six years his junior. Both men conducted the clinic jointly, and, as I later discovered, had achieved a division of labor ideally suited to their varying natures. Jacques Louis, with his quiet, searching personality, concentrated primarily upon clinical examination and classification of syndromes; Auguste, with his great vitality, on the technique of operation. Both of them, but Jacques Louis in particular, listened with what amounted to an almost feverish interest to my account of Kocher's work, and questioned me keenly on the results of his checkups on his patients. They were extremely eager to learn what course he intended to follow.

I did not guess the reason for their excitement until Jacques Louis announced, with dignity but extreme emphasis, that Kocher's suppositions coincided with his own discoveries. He had, in fact, discovered this thing long ago. Moreover, as was evident from my account, Kocher practically confessed that the first suggestion had come from him. Auguste Reverdin then proceeded to read aloud the report of a meeting of the Geneva Medical Society held on September 13, 1882, in which his cousin had in fact indicated that of the eleven patients who had survived his fourteen goiter operations, all with one exception had subsequently developed anemia, and edemas of face and hands, while one showed pronounced signs of cretinism. Jacques Louis had suggested that these complications were probably attributable to injury to the sympaticus nerve during the operation, but that the possibility existed that the thyroid gland played a vital part in blood formation. Should this be so, its removal could bring about the above-mentioned illnesses. Finally, Reverdin had stated that the complications followed upon the total extirpation of the thyroid gland. For the one case free of side-effects was a case where he had excised only one lobe of the gland. Henceforth, he had decreed, only partial operations for goiter should be undertaken, and at least the enclosing capsule around the goiter should be spared.

Auguste Reverdin finished the reading, and looked up at me with a challenging air. Only then did I realize that I had in all innocence poured oil on a fire which might well flare up into a raging priority dispute. I now wished I had said less, and tried to fend off further questions on Kocher's plans. Moreover, I did not wish to be diverted from my principal aim, which was to have some formal confirmation of the probable safety of partial operation. Auguste Reverdin handed me an offprint of his communication to the Geneva Medical Society, and stated that since September of the past year he and his cousin had performed a large number of partial excisions, and that so far no signs of anemia or cretinism had appeared in any of the patients. Jacques Louis had something else to tell me. "In the course of our studies of the literature," he said, "we have learned that two British doctors, Gull and Ord in 1873 and 1878, described a hitherto unknown disease which corresponds precisely to the symptoms we have observed after total excision of the thyroid gland. Ord called this condition myxedema, and mentions that in one patient the thyroid gland was either completely atrophied or had never been present, owing to congenital defect. Ord, on the other hand, saw no connection between the disease and the absence of the thyroid gland. To us, however, the link is indisputable. We adhere to this rule: the substance of the thyroid gland must never again be entirely destroyed by the surgon."

By afternoon I was on my way back to Bern, relieved by what I had learned from the Reverdins, and carrying in my pocket proof which should remove the last obstacle. Arriving at the Berner Hof, I found Cabot tensely awaiting me; he had exhausted his last stratagems for postponing Esther's entry into the clinic. I reported to him in detail. When I was finished, he sat in deep thought for a while. Then he rose to his feet.

"I shall let Esther go ahead with it, then," he said. "She can enter Kocher's clinic tomorrow. I shall tell White he had better go back to New York. If in spite of all it turns out badly—I can fight no longer—there is nothing to be done. . . ." He looked at me. "And what about you?" he asked. "What are your plans?"

"After seeing you this far, you certainly do not expect me to leave you before the operation has been performed and the result known," I said.

On April 4 Theodor Kocher read a paper before the congress of the Deutsche Gesellschaft für Chirurgie, meeting in Berlin. In it he set forth the results of one hundred and four partial and complete excisions of goiters. At present, he averred, no one knew the reasons for the postoperative complications. They could only be deduced, and this he proceeded to do. Among the possibilities, he even suggested that complete ligaturing of all thyroid gland arteries in the course of total excision might lead to disturbances in the blood supply to the trachea, hence diminished oxygen intake producing the anemia which seemed to play a large part in the clinical picture of cachexia strumipriva. But such explanations, he continued, were simply a tissue of hypotheses. One fact was certain, however: that cachexia appeared only in cases of total excision. He therefore would urge that total removal of the thyroid gland be banished from the roll of permissible operations.

On the morning of April 12 Esther was taken into the clinic's operating room, then a very modestly equipped place. I was present, in addition to Kocher, Roux, a young assistant, and two nurses. Kocher, who during those years was still experimenting with a great variety of antiseptics, washed his hands for a long time in sublimate of mercury while Esther was being prepared for the operation. She had to be raised to a half-sitting posture because she feared that otherwise she might suffocate. The young assistant initiated anesthesia with chloroform, and then continued with ether. Esther threw one last glance at Kocher and me. She tried to smile, breathed willingly and without agitation, and sank into sleep.

Kocher stepped up to the operating table. I had the impression that his lean, sinewy body underwent a slight increase in concentration and tension, which made him seem smaller and thinner than he was. He commented as he proceeded: "The patient is calm, for which we must be grateful. One of the reasons for our preliminary treatment is the engendering of confidence on the patient's part. That facilitates anesthesia, which from the start has been a difficult problem in goiter surgery. The agitation so common at the beginning of anesthesia, and resultant pressure, can lead to blockages and the onset of asphyxiation. In older patients the condition of the heart and lungs is often so poor that anesthesia itself is dangerous. Incidentally, injury to the recurrens could be more easily avoided if it were possible to speak with the patient during the operation and thus determine immediately any disturbances of the vocal functions. But that is a dream for the future."

Esther breathed with a whistling sound, but quite evenly. The glandular swellings which disfigured her neck, some smooth, some knotty, had been pressed forward. The anatomical difference between the two sides of the neck was now plainly visible. Kocher made a vertical incision through the skin of the throat as far down as the annular cartilage, and then prolonged this incision by an angular cut over the left side of the goiter. The taut skin and the superficial fasciae parted of their own accord. Blood emerged from several veins, but the anterior jugular veins were promptly tied. The scalpel parted the muscles—the sterno hyoid, sterno thyroid, and omo hyoid. Swiftly, ligatures were tied around the small bleeding vessels in the muscles. A moment later the right side of the goiter lay exposed, swollen, wrapped in a capsule crisscrossed with thick veins. The tumor swelled with every breath; I had the alarming impression that it would burst any second. "This is the lobe I shall totally remove," Kocher said to me. His voice was clipped, precise now. "In contrast to former operations," he continued, "I am leaving the capsule untouched for the present. The principal object is to ligature all major blood vessels within reach. First I penetrate to the thyroid artery and vein at the upper pole of the tumor. For this purpose I use the probe. . . ." With a lightning motion Kocher picked up a long, shining instrument provided with three grooves. He cautiously introduced it over the surface of the goiter into the upper corner of the incision, behind which the upper pole of the tumor still lay hidden. The probe reached the thick, blood-filled arteries and veins. The ligatures were tied, and the scalpel separated the gland from the blood vessels.

Esther's breathing became louder, and the veins of the capsule swelled. I cast an uneasy glance at the assistant who was taking her pulse. But his expression remained calm. "There has always been a certain danger," Kocher said, "in the fact that the blood vessel system of the thyroid gland obeys no absolute rules, so far as my experience goes. In many glands a vein is found—the superior accessory thyroid—which runs diagonally along the outer edge; in others it does not exist. In any case I always look for it, to avoid unpleasant surprises."

Slowly loosening the tissue, Kocher moved from the upper pole of the lobe down along the right outer edge, and there stopped. Carefully, the probe slid downwards. "This time the vein is present," Kocher said, drawing the vessel forward and ligaturing. Then he moved his hand to the left, over the side of the lobe toward the trachea. His probing, infinitely cautious but wonderfully certain finger again slid down from the upper pole. "Now I am grasping the second diagonal vein," he said. "It will be tied and severed. Then I shall turn to the blood vessels of the lower pole of the lobe. In conditions of compressed trachea such as this I try to draw the lower pole forward at once and thus relieve the pressure on the trachea."

Kocher attempted to grasp the lower pole with his finger. When he did not succeed in this, he reached in with forceps and pulled. Barely a moment afterwards, Esther's breathing changed. It was amazing to see the rapidity with which this happened. The whistling noise suddenly was gone. The lungs sucked air forcefully. The anesthetist nodded to Kocher. But Kocher was already occupied with the large blood vessels which had been exposed by his drawing forth the lower lobe of the gland. For a moment I remembered descriptions of former goiter operations with their uncontrollable torrents of blood. Every new, thickly swollen vessel that emerged showed why all the old surgeons, who had proceeded without knowledge of these turgid veins and arteries, had been forced to capitulate in the face of unquenchable hemorrhages.

Repeatedly, Kocher tied vessels and severed them behind the ligatures. Then he declared: "There remains now only the connection with the inferior thyroid artery, which runs along the back of the lobe. In order to reach it the external capsule must now be opened and the tumor scraped out until this last artery is accessible."

At that moment Esther began to choke. The anesthetist lifted his hand from her pulse and turned his full attention to the mask. The choking sounds grew louder, passed over into a fit of coughing. Blood trickled into the wound. The tied vessels throbbed fearfully. I held my breath, fearing that the ligatures might give and flood the whole operating field with a tremendous hemorrhage. But then the fit of coughing ceased as suddenly as it had begun. "A plug of mucus released by the sudden relaxation of pressure upon the trachea," Kocher explained.

He had suspended his work for the duration of the coughing fit. Now he thrust several fingers of his right hand between the tumor and its capsule. Again he loosened and severed the tissues with the utmost care. Twice it happened that bits of the venous net were torn. These veins were instantly tied. Then, at last, the goitrous tumor popped out of the capsule, purple and swollen. Kocher rolled it out toward the center of the throat until the inferior thyroid artery appeared at the back of the cavity.

"Now I am working in the region through which the recurrent laryngeal nerve passes," Kocher announced. "The artery must be so completely isolated that there is no chance of including the nerve in the ligature."

Within a very few moments he had separated the artery from all the surrounding tissue. He tied and severed it. Then he drew the tumor further forward, and at the back of it, proceeding a millimeter at a time, he freed the remaining connections with the capsule until he reached the isthmus, the connecting link between the two lobes of the gland. "The isthmus too," Kocher explained, "must be completely isolated so that we can be certain here too that the recurrent laryngeal is not touched in the course of the subsequent severing of the isthmus."

Bit by bit he freed the isthmus from the surrounding tissue. Now numerous smaller vessels began spurting blood. One after the other they were closed by clamps, until a defensive ring of clamps protruded from the wound. Esther moaned several times. When Kocher finished exposing the isthmus, she gagged momentarily. Probably these maneuvers so close to the trachea stimulated the muscles of the passage. At one time her whole body heaved up and the anesthetist had to hold her head tightly.

At this point Kocher had begun cutting through the isthmus. His deft movements with scalpel and ligatures took a considerable time. At last he straightened up. In his hand he held the knotty, hard mass of the goiter from the left side. Immediately afterwards Esther lay quiet. Her respiration was firm and regular.

I peered into the cavity the scalpel had made. The trachea now lay exposed. Its lower end had been forced inward by the pressure of the tumor and remained dented even with the tumor gone. This had produced the respiratory difficulties, and removal of the pressure alone had sufficed to relieve her breathing. The first act of the operation was over—and had been successful.

Kocher straightened his stance for twenty or thirty seconds, as though he felt that he could afford this brief respite. Then he held out his hand for a new scalpel from the bowl of sublimate. He added a second cut to the vertical incision. This transformed the external incision into a Y whose left, upper end extended over the right lobe of the goiter.

"You now see the right lobe before you," Kocher explained. "Here you can see plainly one of the embedded nodules. Here, however, I shall limit myself to extracting the nodules. The vessels of the lobe will not be tied and severed, nor the gland pulled forward. I am cutting directly into the various nodules, ligaturing the superficial veins where needed."

Even as he was explaining his procedure he had laid bare the right lobe. He tied several surface veins and cut directly into the first nodule. Then he thrust his finger into the wound and worked it slowly around the nodule, which he loosened and at last brought forth. Like a pigeon's egg it emerged, blue and discolored, from the cavity. A small fountain of blood followed. Kocher pressed a tampon into the cavity. The bleeding slowed, stopped. His finger felt through the tissue of the gland for the next nodule. Then followed incision, loosening, peeling free. But this time the nodule clung. When he brought it forth at last it proved to be linked to a second nodule, and Kocher worked this one out also. Apparently it lay in the immediate vicinity of the trachea, for once again Esther began to gag fearfully. Kocher waited until the attack passed; then he cut deeply toward a fourth nodule. The incision began bleeding at once, and he was compelled to tie a large number of small, thin vessels. He proceeded to enucleate the nodules with the greatest care. It took a long time for him to loosen this fourth nodule, but at last it too emerged from the cavity, bringing with it several small subsidiary tumors. Just as the last of these appeared, spurts of blood shot out, drenching Kocher's hands and Esther's throat. My heart sank. The anesthetist stopped giving ether. I felt numbed with fear.

Kocher had reached swiftly for a sponge soaked in iodoform. He pressed it into the cavity. The bleeding slowed, but did not stop. Blood pulsed forth and ran down Esther's chest. Kocher followed with more and more sponges. Nevertheless his voice sounded firm and controlled as he said: "I have already mentioned that the great disadvantage of enucleation is the possibility of hemorrhage. To my knowledge such a hemorrhage once compelled Billroth to remove the entire gland in the end, solely in order to reach the bleeding artery. This course is not open to us, since that would be equivalent to total excision. . . ." He pressed more sponges into the wound, and still blood trickled out. I could already envision the end—the end of all our efforts, all our hopes, and the beginning of bitterness, futile recriminations. Still Kocher pressed in his tampons.

Abruptly the bleeding stopped, and Kocher straightened up. His ascetic face looked shrunken. He took several deep, deep breaths. Then he began cleaning the wound and bandaging.

The very first day after the operation I found, to my great relief, that Esther's voice had not been impaired. On the contrary, her previous hoarseness was gone, so that it seemed likely that the tumor had exerted a slight pressure upon the recurrent nerve. The next days, however, were marked by extraordinarily high fevers, but Kocher assured me that these regularly appeared during the first days after operation, even when there was not the slightest indication of infection of the wound. He was even then inclined to attribute this sudden rise in temperature to unknown changes in the body resulting from deprivation of a large part of the thyroid gland's activity. Just once Esther experienced a minor postoperative hemorrhage, but this was swiftly checked. During the second week the process of healing began at an almost fantastic pace, first on the completely excised side and then on the side where the enucleation had been performed. On the sixteenth day Esther left her bed for the first time. By the eighteenth the wounds were healed over. When I visited her that day I found her sitting before a large mirror which had been placed in the room at her request. Her hands were running again and again over the still flushed scars. The swellings which had disfigured her only a few short weeks ago were now gone. "I think I am going to be really human," she said. "I am going to begin to live. . . . I have never really lived yet."

In those days, when goiter surgery was a matter of life or death, not much consideration was given to the question of beauty, to making incisions which would leave the smallest scars. "A wide chain with a pendant will cover all this up," Esther went on in her newly awakened joy in living. "Don't you think so? It will conceal the scars completely, won't it?"

Watching her gladness, I felt a profound sense of happiness. "Yes," I said, "you will never have to wear your ermine again."

Two weeks later Esther left the clinic. She tripped gaily down the stairs toward Cabot, who was waiting beside me, her face utterly transformed, radiant with the conviction that life is good. At this moment she surely did not sense that the delight both Cabot and I felt was still clouded by anxiety. We were haunted by the thought that Kocher might just possibly be wrong, that Esther might in the end not be spared the horror of cachexia.

After a long vacation trip through Europe, Cabot returned to New York. On Kocher's advice he kept Esther away from the mountain country of Maine, which presumably was productive of goiter in the same mysterious way as some mountainous regions in Europe. Whenever I was in the States we saw a good deal of one another; otherwise we kept in touch by letter. When six months passed and Cabot still had no ominous symptoms to report, my anxiety diminished. Six months later Cabot wrote from Florida that Esther was in the best of health, and had become engaged. Although he thought highly of the young man in question, he said, he could not quite make up his mind to endorse an early marriage. At the same time he found it difficult to justify his wish for delay without telling Esther the truth.

Another year passed, however, without any sign of degenerative symptoms which could be remotely interpreted as leading to cachexia strumipriva. Esther herself informed me of her marriage, and shortly afterwards paid me a visit in New York, accompanied by her husband. Her father had just told her the doubts we had felt before the operation, and the anxieties we had suffered. She thanked me warmly for having concealed the worst possibilities from her. Probably, she said, she herself would never have had the courage to face up to the risk of imbecility. She radiated good health, and wore some strands of pearls so carefully measured and looped that not a trace could be seen of the malady which had overshadowed her girlhood.

By about this time the warning which Kocher had pronounced at the Berlin congress of surgeons in 1883 began at last to yield results. Goiter surgery as practiced by Billroth and Kocher became more widespread. It entered the repertory of many surgeons who had hitherto not dared to attempt goiter operations. However, this was not altogether a happy development, for with the multiplication of such operations, there was suddenly a multiplication of disasters, in particular disturbances of the functions of the vocal cords. This began to happen with a frequency which Billroth and Kocher had never experienced. Many surgeons did not yet possess Billroth's and Kocher's skill and experience. Consequently, they were apt to injure the recurrent nerve. I shuddered to learn, some time later, that in desperation many surgeons adopted the practice of operating without anesthesia, in order to hear their patients talk during the operation, so that they could maintain a constant check on the recurrent nerve. When word of this first came to my ears I thought that time was turning backwards several decades, to that age of barbarous surgery before the discovery of anesthesia. I was not reassured by the information that the thyroid gland itself was insensitive to pain. It seemed preferable to surgeons to hear the patients scream with pain than to have them awake from the anesthesia as mutes. It was a brutal solution, but having learned by experience that disturbances of the vocal organs virtually never occurred after such operations, they justified their means by the end. It became almost the rule to operate without anesthesia until the discovery of local anesthesia gave surgeons a tool which eliminated pain without diminishing the patient's consciousness.

Fifteen years after Kocher had performed his operation upon Esther, I found myself once again in his clinic. I had gone there with Esther, who had been in the habit of returning faithfully to Bern once a year for examination. When I was alone with Kocher, he told me that our patient had never shown any sign of recidivous goiter in the remaining portion of the gland. By then he had performed some six hundred partial thyroid excisions without a single case of cachexia. Leaving a portion of the gland had proved to be a completely reliable expedient in all except the virtually hopeless cases of cancer of the thyroid gland. Partial removal eliminated the goiter and its accompanying complaints, prevented cachexia, and largely eliminated recurrences. There could no longer be any doubt that this was the correct method for dealing with goiter by surgery.

Tumor

My meeting with Esther Cabot and my subsequent immersion in the problems of goiter took place a full year after the London congress of 1881, with its great promise for the development of brain surgery. Yet in that year I had not received so much as a single paper, or isolated report, of any surgical attempt to localize and operate for a cerebral tumor on the basis of the physiological knowledge which had so rapidly accumulated. When I left Bern in the spring of 1883 my mind turned once again toward that old preoccupation of mine. I could not guess that I would have to wait nearly two years more before witnessing the true beginnings of a surgical technique which is now taken for granted, although it remains a highly specialized branch of the surgeon's art.

I was visiting Charcot during the first half of September in the year 1884. I am not certain of this detail, but I believe that Charcot had already moved into his splendid house at the end of the Boulevard Saint-Germain. In any case, it was one of those famous Tuesday evenings when Charcot used to hold open house. On such occasions the ornate rooms filled with artists, politicians, doctors, and those multitudinous ladies who were not content with swarming into his office by day but sought out this cynic in the evenings as well, although he treated them "like dirt," as they sometimes complained.

The first stimulating hours of the evening were past. Charcot had brought forth his latest acquisitions, Italian sculptures depicting certain pathological conditions. Then there was a performance by a clown from one of those travelling circuses popular in Paris. Charcot, who was a devotee of clowns, had cast aside his icy dignity and laughed uproariously. A well-known pianist had played a Beethoven sonata. Alphonse Daudet had read one of his newest stories. In short, there had been a lively round of entertainment by the time the clock approached eleven. A few minutes later, at eleven o'clock sharp, Charcot routed all the ladies by pronouncing the magic phrase, "Now the clinic is being opened," from the smoking room. The phrase meant: "Leave us; the time has come for men's stories."

The ladies obeyed reluctantly, but they obeyed, for this "clinic hour" was a sacred institution on Charcot's Tuesday evenings.

Charcot himself started the ball rolling. His story this time concerned a high-ranking German government official who had come to him for help only a few days ago. The man related that he had been seized "to the point of nervous fever" by burning desire for the marble statue of a nude woman in his office. Charcot told the story with that mocking contempt which he felt toward all Germans. Thus, though he described the therapy he had recommended to the official, he concluded by saying that he doubted that these measures would do any good since the patient was after all a German official—a German official, *parbleu!*

After this story one of the guests focused the attention of the company upon a diffident young Japanese who until then had listened quietly from the shelter of a high-backed armchair. He introduced him as Prince Takada, a surgeon from Tokyo and lately from Glasgow, where he had been working with the holder of the chair of surgery at Glasgow University, William Macewen. Takada had a host of marvellous stories about Macewen to tell.

Macewen's name was thoroughly familiar to me, of course. He had been among the pupils of Joseph Lister while the latter was still at Glasgow, and I remembered Lister's once telling me that young Macewen had encouraged him when he was on the point of giving up his struggle for antisepsis in the face of widespread incomprehension. At a public lecture, in the presence of all the other students, twenty-year-old Macewen had stood up and declared that Lister's enemies were gnats who would be burned in the light he shed. Years ago I had seen Macewen at Lister's home— a huge fellow, but well proportioned, handsome as a classical statue, with a resonant, powerful voice—half Viking, half Apollo. At present, I calculated, he must be about thirty-six years old.

Accordingly, I was keen to hear Takada's story. The young Japanese was shy and needed much urging, in the end from Charcot himself. But then he told a series of anecdotes which suggested that Macewen, off in the provincial isolation of Glasgow, was an eccentric fit to rank with the great individualistic surgeons of my youth. Takada, who spoke amazingly good French, began by telling of a railroad journey Macewen had recently taken. He found himself in a compartment with a noisy drunk and two intimidated ladies. Macewen twice ordered the rowdy passenger to be quiet, but in vain. Finally he leaned forward, seized the drunken man's head, dislocated his jaw, and thus silenced him. Thereupon he gave the ladies a gentlemanly nod, calmly returned to his reading, and reset the man's jaw only when he reached his destination.

This amusing tale was quickly followed by another about an influential society lady of Glasgow who could have greatly furthered his career. This lady's unmarried daughter found herself in embarrassing circumstances, and the lady asked Macewen to certify that the girl was not going to have a baby, but suffered from a tumor. Macewen flatly refused. Months later the same lady took the opportunity, in the company of others, to inform him that his diagnosis had been wrong, and that a German surgeon had removed the tumor. Macewen replied loudly, in a manner no one could possibly misunderstand: "I am delighted to hear it. How is the little tumor doing?"

Once his initial shyness was overcome, Takada proved to have a virtually inexhaustible store of such anecdotes about Macewen. Still, I would have forgotten them all if our raconteur had not incidentally introduced a detail which suddenly stirred me to intense excitement. It seemed that Macewen had been called to see an unfortunate fourteen-year-old girl with symptoms of severe cerebral illness. He had taken the girl to Glasgow in time to operate, had trepanned, removed a swelling of the meninges, and the girl was now perfectly well.

After all that I have said in the first chapter, I need scarcely explain why this reference to a brain operation fascinated me. Impetuously I called out to Takada: "When was this?" He looked at me in some surprise, and replied: "Five years ago, in July, 1879."

I had jumped to my feet, and now went over to Takada. "And you say this was a trepanning operation, with the cerebrum exposed?"

I paid no heed to the effect created by my sudden excitement. Takada was looking rather anxious, as if he feared he were dealing with a madman.

"It was a swelling of the dura mater," he said uncertainly, "which exerted pressure on the anterior central gyrus and produced convulsive movements of the right half of the face and the right arm. Externally the girl had a visible swelling above the left eye."

"And the girl is still living, you say?"

"Why, of course." The Japanese could not understand the reason for my perturbation, and continued to look around for aid. But my seeming incredulity also provoked him into defending and amplifying his statements. "At first the girl's speech was slightly affected," he said, "but these disturbances have entirely vanished. I myself have had frequent opportunities to observe her. The girl is now nineteen, and came to call on Macewen just before my departure. She was perfectly well." And Takada added a casual comment which electrified me even more. "This was by no means Professor Macewen's first operation inside the cranium," he said. "He has performed several such operations. Certain quarters in Glasgow brand him an irresponsible and godless man on that account. But given his temperament, he is not a man to be stopped by such opinions."

Takada really had no idea of the momentousness of what he was so casually reporting. He had lived so completely under Macewen's spell that he saw nothing strange in the way the Scottish surgeon had defied the taboo against brain operations, not once, apparently, but several times.

Meanwhile all the other physicians present had risen and clustered about Takada and me. Charcot was no exception. The stories and anecdotes, the whole idea of the "clinic hour," seemed for the moment forgotten. "These are certainly bold statements," he said. "Why has Professor Macewen not written up these operations?"

Confronting the great Charcot, the young Japanese became even more unsettled. But he recovered quickly, and answered, with a nimble and arch wit: "Professor Macewen has indeed written them up. But I begin to fear that Professor Macewen's papers are read only in Glasgow."

"So it would seem," Charcot said. "They certainly have not reached Paris. Nor London either, for in that case I should have heard of them."

"I can only repeat," Takada said, "that Professor Macewen has reported on his cases. In addition to the case I mentioned he treated a second in 1879. This concerned a man with symptoms of paralysis which developed some time after a bad fall. On the basis of external signs, but also on the basis of Professor Ferrier's theory of localization, still controversial at that time, Professor Macewen diagnosed the source of the trouble in the brain. He trepanned the skull at the proper spot, removed a large blood clot under the dura mater, and achieved complete restoration. The recovered patient was presented at a meeting of the Glasgow Surgical Society. Last year—and I can personally attest to this—Professor Macewen diagnosed and successfully operated on three more cases of cerebral lesions. In two of these cases there were large blood clots, in the third a syphilitic granuloma which he opened. However, at the past meeting of the Glasgow Surgical Society Professor Macewen encountered nothing but hostility on the part of his colleagues. That may be one reason so little is known of his papers. There is another, highly instructive case a good deal earlier than these. If I may . . ."

"Go on, go on," Charcot urged him impatiently.

"It is a case he treated eight years ago, in 1876. Of course I was not yet in Glasgow, but everyone at Professor Macewen's clinic talks about this case. In 1876 Professor Macewen was shown a boy who had fallen and bruised his forehead lightly. Three weeks after the fall symptoms of paralysis appeared on the right side of the body. The boy also lost the capacity for speech—with the exception of the word 'no,' which he repeated constantly. Professor Macewen diagnosed a hemorrhage or abscess in the immediate vicinity of Broca's speech-center, and proposed to the boy's parents that the cranium be opened and the cause of the paralysis removed. The other doctors rose up in arms against Professor Macewen and prevailed on the parents to forbid the operation. The child died. Professor Macewen went to the parents once more, and proposed that the operation be carried out now, after death, just as he would have performed it on the living child. He pressed his point until at last they consented. When the brain was exposed, he found a large abscess exactly at the spot he had anticipated. The parents, I understand, have never forgiven themselves or the doctors. Professor Macewen, however, became convinced that many diseases of the brain are curable by surgery, especially the so-called incurable tumors. The fact that in his operations so far he has confined himself to blood clots and swellings of the meninges is due solely to the fact that no patient with cerebral tumor has been presented to him. He has firmly resolved to operate upon the first case of diagnosed cerebral tumor he encounters."

I could feel Charcot's icy, glittering gaze upon me. He knew quite well the thoughts that I was harboring.

"You cannot possibly reach the next boat sailing from Boulogne until tomorrow afternoon," he said to me. He turned to the Japanese prince, who looked his bewilderment. "You have brought our American friend news of extraordinary importance to him," he said. "To us, too, of course," he added. "I shall send for Professor Macewen's papers. But"—and he looked through the circle of doctors to the artists and men of politics who still had not grasped the reason for all the to-do—"let us recall our Tuesday evening rule which banishes medical problems from our conversation. The day is long enough for these matters. My friend Alphonse Daudet has some priceless anecdotes for us this evening. May I ask your attention—Alphonse Daudet. . . ."

The circle around Takada had dispersed at Charcot's mocking, semiformal little speech. The doctors returned to their chairs. I alone stayed where I was, prepared to ask further details of Takada as soon as opportunity offered.

Late that night I accompanied Takada to the modest hotel for students where he was staying. We sat talking there for a good hour longer. I explained to the young Japanese my special interest in cerebral surgery, and the further things he told me persuaded me beyond a doubt that I must go to see Macewen—just as Charcot had foretold. Takada gave me Macewen's address in Glasgow, but suggested that I find out first whether the professor was at home, since he had been on the point of leaving on a lengthy tour of consultations which would take him all through Scotland.

The following morning I wrote to Macewen at 73 Bath Street, Glasgow. I referred to my friendship with Lister, described the meeting with Takada, and asked when I might meet him in Glasgow. I had no suspicion that things would take a very different turn from what I had expected and that my meeting with Macewen would wait upon developments from quite another quarter.

On September 17—no answer had come from Glasgow yet—I was breakfasting with Paul Reclus, a surgeon who worked at the old Pitié Hospital in Paris, and concerning whose life, personality, and accomplishments I shall have much to say later on. I had met Reclus years ago when he was a young assistant to Paul Broca, had found him interesting and original, and had struck up close friendly relations with him long before he acquired international fame. Reclus, born in 1847 in Orthez, the son of a pastor, was one of fourteen children. He owed his medical education to Broca, who had been a friend of his father's, and used to like to tell a story of how this came about. The pastor was quite satisfied with his other sons, but distinctly worried about Paul's future. He went to see Broca with the boy, remarking: "But I really don't know what I am going to do with this one. As you see, he has a head like a pear, protruding ears, and a drooping lower lip. I expect him to be the cross of my old age." Whereupon Broca had patted the unprepossessing head of the "half-wit"—as Paul Reclus smilingly referred to himself—and announced that on the contrary he was going to be a man of note. He had advised Reclus to leave his son to him, Broca; he would make a surgeon out of him. Broca had proved quite right. Reclus became one of the foremost medical men of his age. As a practicing surgeon he was never much above average, however. In this he resembled his teacher, Broca, whose anthropological, anatomical, and physiological studies surpassed by far his achievements as a surgeon.

As was his habit, Reclus was skimming through the morning papers while I drank my coffee—he was so busy that he would never have seen them if he did not read them at breakfast. Suddenly he bent his head lower over some item or article. Then he looked up at me with an expression of profound amazement.

"Listen to this, please," he said in a low tone that did not conceal his excitement. "It's a news story from Heidelberg which seems to me tremendously important, if true." Reclus pointed out a brief item with the typical lengthy headlines of the day: "Will painless operations without unconsciousness be possible in the future? Viennese eye specialist claims to have discovered a pain-killing effect in the drug cocaine. Painless eye operations after use of a few drops of cocaine. Special report from the session of the Ophthalmological Society in Heidelberg."

The burden of those lines no longer seems unusual or the least bit sensational. Local anesthesia has long since found its place beside complete anesthesia with chloroform or ether, even in long and difficult operations. But at that time, on that morning of September 17, 1884, general anesthesia was still the only effective analgesic at surgeons' disposal. Only a year and a half had passed since Kocher had had criticisms to make of general anesthesia in goiter operations. Like every great discovery, anesthesia had in the course of decades revealed some of its disadvantages. Since its first application the technique of general anesthesia had been refined in many respects. But it was still far from its present-day state of development. Even the practice of drop-by-drop anesthesia had not yet been introduced into all operating rooms. In many large clinics young doctors were taught to anesthetize on the principal of administering chloroform until the patient turned "blue," and then allowing him a pause for recovery. Circulatory conditions and circulatory therapy were little known, and it was not unusual for the anesthetist, during an operation, to have to apply artificial respiration in order to revive a patient. Older patients and those with weak circulation often died suddenly under anesthesia. In the course of decades, therefore, surgeons had begun to long for an anesthetic which would make only the critical areas insensitive to pain, without imposing upon the patient's whole body the strain of general anesthesia.

Through numerous vain attempts, however, most surgeons had come to believe that this would remain a wish-dream. With my eternal optimism I had never subscribed to this view. I remembered the dramatic developments of my youth: the sudden, revolutionary discovery of the effects of chloroform and ether, and of the value of antisepsis. Both discoveries had solved problems which had appeared utterly insoluble for centuries. I saw no reason for local anesthesia to be an insoluble problem either. Nevertheless, I myself had observed so many mishaps that I scarcely continued to expect the miracle to take place in the near future.

In the light of this discouragement I need not describe the extraordinary elation produced in me by this news item. My eyes flew down the rather terse report. It appeared that a young assistant at the Vienna General Hospital, Carl Koller, had written a paper which was read to the assembled ophthalmologists by a Heidelberg colleague. Koller made the assertion that dripping cocaine into the human eye would render it completely insensitive to pain for long periods of time. He went on to report that even major eye operations had been carried out under this new type of local anesthesia. By way of test, several operations under cocaine had been performed in the presence of the assembled ophthalmologists at Heidelberg, so that there could scarcely be any doubt of the drug's effectiveness. The consequences of this discovery for surgery in general remained to be seen, the newspaper item concluded.

I looked up from the newspaper and met Reclus's eyes. Our faces both reflected the same feelings: stunned and at the same time delighted amazement. My reaction, of course, was a simple rejoicing over a new discovery; Reclus's had a slightly different cast, for he had long been conscious of the perils of general anesthesia, which had led to several deaths in the course of his practice. The news from Heidelberg must have seemed to him the glorious promise of a better future. How seriously he took it is indicated by the important part he later played in the further development of local anesthesia. As for me, my thoughts were deflected from Glasgow and Macewen. When by September 18 I had still received no word from the Glasgow surgeon, I decided to make use of the interval by taking a flying journey to Vienna.

The hectic story of this journey belongs to a later chapter, to the drama of local anesthesia. But I must describe its opening episode here because this was the first of two unusual circumstances which prevented me from going to Glasgow. On September 20 I arrived in Vienna. On October 15 a reply from Macewen reached me in that city. He apologized for his long silence, explained that he had been away, confirmed Takada's account, and cordially invited me to Glasgow to see the patients who had been the subjects of cerebral surgery. My studies on the background of Koller's discovery, however, had by then produced so much interesting material that I lingered in Vienna longer than I had intended to. On November 21 I started back to Paris, having written to Macewen to expect me in Glasgow on November 26. I reached Paris late at night on November 22. When I went to my hotel at half past two in the morning, the man at the desk handed me a telegram from London which had trailed me from Paris to Vienna and from Vienna back to Paris. I skimmed it without paying close attention, for it was already a week old. Then my eye caught the signature, Hughes Bennett, and I read it over more carefully: Remember our talk London congress. Have patient with definite cerebral tumor. Diagnosis on Ferrier's principles. Godlee will venture operation, Ferrier, Jackson present. Jackson suggested informing you."

I instantly recalled the last day of the London congress of 1882. Hughes Bennett, the neurologist of the National Hospital, had been sitting beside me there. We had spoken together and he had mentioned the cerebral tumor which had brought about his father's death and which, the autopsy had revealed, could easily have been removed. It seemed to me that I could hear Bennett's voice repeating the story, which had evidently haunted him. No doubt he had been waiting all this time for a suitable case, in order to make amends for what could have been done and had not been done for his father. And in all likelihood he knew nothing at all about Macewen!

I glanced once more at the date of the telegram. November 14. And it was now November 23. There was no indication of the day the operation was to be performed. Perhaps it was all over, and I had missed this unique chance to witness a historic operation upon a diagnosed cerebral tumor. If I went directly to Macewen, there was no certainty that I would see an operation; he had promised only to show me patients long since recovered.

I asked the concierge instantly to dispatch a telegram to Dr. Hughes Bennett, inquiring whether I would be on time if I arrived in London next day. I left instructions to be roused as soon as the reply came from London.

The hours of the night crawled by, each an eternity. Again and again I reminded myself that more than a week had gone by since the message was sent. Eight full days! By dawn I was on the point of abandoning hope. Then, shortly before seven, there was a knock at my door. A bellboy brought a telegram. It read: "Operation scheduled for November 25, National Hospital, Queen's Square, London. Hughes Bennett."

I still had two days' grace.

I reached England on November 24, after a difficult crossing, and arrived in London between four and five in the afternoon. It was raining, one of those thoroughgoing London downpours that seemed ready to go on forever. At my hotel, the Charing Cross, I found a message from Bennett. He was staying with Hughlings Jackson on Manchester Square, so that they could go over the details of the case once more; I could reach him there.

I had not seen Jackson since the London congress, and exchanged letters with him only occasionally. He had grown quite enormous in the meantime. Apparently he never took a step outside his apartment or the National Hospital. Bennett was bent over a table amid the fearful mess of Jackson's study. My chief impression was of mountains of papers and a sprinkling of skulls. Evidently no one had tidied the place since the death of Jackson's wife.

Bennett looked up from a drawing of the top of a human skull, with a few sketchy lines drawn diagonally and longitudinally across the dome. These last had been put in by Jackson. Bennett was so absorbed that he only looked up to greet me hastily, exchanged a few sentences with Jackson, and then turned to me again to explain the case.

"My patient," he said, "is a young man named Henderson. He is barely twenty-five, a farmer from Dumfries. He came to me on November 3, an apparently healthy, vigorous young man who could no longer use his left arm and whose left leg dragged behind him. He complained of headaches and twitching on the left side of his face, and in his left arm and left leg. The doctor in Dumfries could think of nothing better to do than place endless mustard plasters on the patient's head and neck, with the result that all the skin of the occiput is inflamed, sore, and covered with blisters."

Bennett picked up several closely written pages and handed them to me.

"Here is the description of the case in full," he said. "Perhaps you will care to read it over later. I'll confine myself to the most important aspects right now. Henderson had never been ill up to four years ago. At that time he first began suffering from headaches. They appeared with increasing frequency, but would vanish again. After about a year of this he became aware of a slight twitching in the left side of his face and the left half of his tongue. The twitching increased in intensity until it terminated in a convulsive attack affecting the left part of the neck, the left arm, and left leg, and at last the patient lost consciousness. Starting two years ago, these attacks came daily. Six months ago a distinct weakness in the left hand manifested itself for the first time. Another three months and this hand could no longer hold tools. Shortly afterwards Henderson began limping with his left leg. When he first visited me the headaches had reached an intensity which he called unbearable. My examination at the National Hospital yielded the following clinical picture: reduced mobility of the left half of the face; automatic deviation of the outstretched tongue to the left; complete paralysis of the fingers of the left hand and of the left wrist; partial paralysis of the elbow and shoulder joint; partial paralysis of the left leg; no visible changes in the head itself, but suspicious alterations of the base of the eye socket and inflammation of the right optic nerve. Since November the twitching motions of the entire left side of the body have appeared daily. They begin in the left thumb. This is followed at times by fearful vomiting and choking, even when the stomach is empty; such convulsions last hours, and prevent the intake of all nourishment. The headaches mount to the point of delirium, forcing the patient to scream wildly. Ice bags are useless; only large doses of morphine provide temporary alleviation. I soon saw that all this pointed to a cerebral tumor on the right side. The first problem was to locate it." He laid down a pencil with which he had been toying, and looked up at me.

"Do you recall that day three years ago," he said, "when we sat together; that day Ferrier proved his case?"

I nodded. "I could almost repeat every word he said."

"I too remember every word," Bennett continued. "It was plain from the start that our patient's cerebral cortex must be affected. The paralysis and the concomitant symptoms left little doubt of that. As I said, our problem was only the precise localization of the trouble. But we think that we have solved it with the aid of Ferrier's localization pattern."

He picked up the drawing of the head which he had been studying when I arrived. "This," he says, "shows the patient's cranium, natural size." The oval cranium was divided into six areas by one longitudinal and two horizontal strokes, making three equal areas on either side of the line. The right center area was again divided by a diagonal line. Below this line was a circle with an emphatic dark circumference.

"According to the present state of our knowledge," Bennett continued, "the motor centers for the left side of the lips and tongue lie in the lower segments of the ascending lateral and frontal convolutions. Somewhat higher are the centers for the left facial muscles. In the middle of the ascending lateral convolution are the centers for the left hand and its fingers. In the middle of the frontal convolutions are the centers for arm, elbow, and forearm, while the movements of the left leg are guided by the superior ascending frontal convolutions. Now in this patient we have found complete paralysis of the hand and fingers; on the other hand, the elbow, shoulder, face, tongue, and leg have experienced only motor disturbances, but by no means complete paralysis.

We therefore conclude that the seat of the tumor is in the region of the hand and finger centers, and that at present it is only exerting a slowly increasing irritation upon the other contiguous centers, those controlling the arm, leg, face, and tongue. The tumor must still not be very large because it is encircled on top by the as yet little affected centers for the leg, in front by the equally lightly affected centers for face and tongue, in back by the completely undamaged visual center, and below by the likewise unimpaired motor center for the pupil of the eye. The diameter of the area lying between these various centers is at most two inches. The tumor, therefore, cannot have a diameter of more than two inches, and we consequently feel justified in hoping that we can not only come at it precisely, but remove it without causing extensive damage." He placed his forefinger on the circle in Jackson's drawing. "The tumor must be right here, at this spot."

I stared rapt at the sheet of drawing paper.

"You do not know how long I have waited for this moment," I exclaimed at last. "The application of Ferrier's theories . . ."

Bennett smiled. "Oh yes, I know what it means to you," he said. "That is why I cabled you. Jackson has kept me informed of your doings." He glanced over at Jackson, who all this while had sat in brooding silence. Now the corners of his mouth twisted slightly, as they were wont to do whenever there was talk of the restless mode of life I pursued in tracking down the latest developments in surgery—twisted with a touch of sarcasm, but also with that kindly understanding which underlay the coolness of his manner. "We have not yet come through," he said in his matter-of-fact way. "Tomorrow you will find out whether you have analyzed it rightly, Bennett. Tomorrow you will be either a hero or a murderer. The antivivisectionists will not hesitate to call us all murderers."

"We will not give them the chance," Bennett said. "Because we are going to prove that we are right."

He turned to me again. "I am going to pay a visit to my patient now. Would you care to accompany me, and make Henderson's acquaintance before the operation?"

I nodded, and rose. Jackson saw us to the door. He took leave of us, saying that he would be at the hospital at ten in the morning.

We drove through a rainy dusk to the National Hospital on Queen's Square. The building seemed to me more dingy, more repugnant than I remembered it. It was far from our contemporary image of a famous hospital for nervous diseases. Brown-Séquard, one of the pioneers of craniological and neurological research, had founded the hospital some twenty-five years before, with a capacity of twenty-four beds. Now, somewhat enlarged, it still held barely eighty patients in fearfully crowded conditions—and yet it was the one hope of many persons throughout the world who believed that unless they could come here for treatment they were condemned to die. New buildings—the Albany Memorial Blocks —had long been planned and were currently being erected. With them completed, the National Hospital would have room for one hundred and eighty patients. But construction was proceeding slowly.

We passed through a dimly illuminated corridor smelling of carbolic acid, soap, and kitchen odors, and reached a staircase. As we climbed I had the impression that the stairs gave Bennett some trouble. For a moment I thought he was in pain. He pressed his left hand against his back, while he clung to the banister with his right. But perhaps this was only a chance gesture. An elderly nurse came forward to meet us on the landing.

"How is Henderson?" Bennett asked.

The nurse replied that he had been screaming with pain for two hours. At last he had been given morphine. This had driven away the pain, but left him as irritable as a person before a rabid or epileptic seizure.

We entered a ward in which stood only one bed; it had a dreary air of loneliness in the large room. A feeble light stood on the bedside table, just sufficient to show the patient's head. With a curiously slow movement of his young face, which seemed surprisingly fresh-skinned and hale, the patient turned to look at us. His left forearm dangled slackly over the side of the bed. The moment he recognized Bennett, however, he tried to sit up. His eyes had the staring look of the gravely ill.

Suddenly his sound right arm violently tore the blanket away from his body and hurled it to the floor, so that he lay half naked before us—a fine figure of a man, with the vigorous, muscular body of a hard worker. "Look at me," he cried, while he struggled with frantic effort to move his left forearm, hand, and leg—and succeeded in producing only a series of hapless, twitching movements. "Look at me! I'm healthy as a horse, and this damned little thing in my head is killing me. Can a walnut kill me?"

His voice was charged with maddened, helpless hatred for the tiny, diabolic thing in his brain, for the fate that had brought this paralysis upon him. He tensed the muscles of his sound right arm until they thickened, throbbing. Reaching for the stool that stood to the right of his bed, he raised it and smashed one of the stout wooden legs against the floor. Then he threw the battered stool halfway across the room and reached for his paralyzed left hand. He pulled it up and threw it, full of contempt and despair, against his own body and the wooden bedboard.

Abruptly as the fit of rebellion had come over him, it passed. He sank back, his face bathed in perspiration, and began to cry. Bennett stood looking down at him with sympathy but no surprise. Evidently he was familiar with these outbursts. He waited until Henderson grew calmer. Then he sat down on the edge of the bed, picked up the blanket, and drew it over the patient. Without a word, he tucked the paralyzed arm under it. "Henderson," he said slowly, "we have finally decided to go ahead. Tomorrow morning at ten o'clock Dr. Rickman Godlee, the famous surgeon, and I will try to cure you of your illness."

Henderson raised his sweat-glistening face. His right hand reached out to clutch Bennett's. "I tell you again, you can do anything you like," he stammered. "I'll thank you no matter what happens, I'll always thank you. . . ."

"All right," Bennett murmured, standing up. "Now you know why we took the other beds away and why the screen is there." He turned to me. "We have no operating room here in the National Hospital!"

He pointed to the wood-framed linen screen which shielded one corner of the room. "We intend to operate over there in the corner." He led me behind the screen and showed me an ancient, preposterously primitive wooden operating table and two smaller tables ranged with bowls, bottles of carbolic acid, and instruments. On the window sill stood the crude carbolic spraying machine, powered by steam, which Lister had developed to keep the entire operating field, including the surgeon's hands and instruments, under a constant, soaking mist of carbolic solution. "Godlee," Bennett said, speaking too low for the patient to hear, "has had equipment brought over from King's College, and has even had a few special instruments made; he thinks they may be useful for the special anatomical conditions inside the brain. He has prepared for the operation by dissection of cadavers. Of course no one can foresee what surprises we may encounter in a living man."

Since he himself had brought the conversation around to Godlee, I asked why he had chosen Godlee as the surgeon, as the hand, so to speak, which was to perform the operation he himself had conceived and planned out. Bennett looked at me out of the corners of his eyes. Then he said in a peculiar tone: "This is something we can discuss later."

He went over to his patient's bed once more to bid the man good night. Henderson clung to the doctor's hand, as though he feared to be left alone, feared the long silence of the night before the decisive hour, the forlornness of this empty ward. It was some time before Bennett could free his hand.

At last we were outside together. "I suppose you know Godlee pretty well?" Bennett asked me. I nodded. Godlee was Lister's nephew, and had grown up entirely in the shadow of his great uncle. He was about the same age as Bennett and was at this time working as assistant surgeon and anatomical demonstrator. Since he assisted at almost all of Lister's operations in King's College Hospital, I had very often had opportunity to observe him. He was a well-meaning, simple, direct person, a bit dry of manner, a good pupil of his uncle's, a capable technician, and an equally good and conscientious teacher of the Listerian method. But he lacked entirely any of the qualities that make the innovator. I found it hard to conceive of Godlee cast in the role of the first surgeon to remove a cerebral tumor.

"Well, then, I can imagine what you are thinking," Bennett continued. "The fact is, Godlee was hesitant about taking on such a task. It took me weeks to win him over. I cannot tell you how often I have cursed myself for not having become a surgeon and for needing a specialist's help. But as things stand so far, neurology is still a nonsurgical matter, and the National Hospital does not have a single surgeon aside from good old Dr. Adams, who has occasionally practiced orthopedic correction on a lame leg, but nothing more, and to this day does not know the meaning of antisepsis. Yet that is the chief thing here. It seems to me that more than in any other operation we need the highest degree of antisepsis that can be attained. The slightest infection of the meninges would spell our ruin. Now who among the younger surgeons in London today can offer more careful antisepsis than Lister's nephew?"

We started down the corridor. "What Godlee lacks I hope to bring to the operation," Bennett said. "I have driven him to the point of consenting, and I mean to drive him to take the last hurdles, if it should prove necessary. You will see tomorrow, in any case. For good or ill. Come, I'll drive you back to the Charing Cross now."

We started down the stairs. As we reached the bottom, a suppressed exclamation of pain escaped from Bennett. I recalled a similar manifestation on our first climbing the stairs, and after hesitating for a moment I asked if anything were the matter. "Oh," he murmured, "sometimes we can help others, but we rarely succeed in helping ourselves. I don't know what it is—some sort of persistent cold in the back." He recovered his composure quickly, and we stepped out into the darkness. The rain had let up somewhat, but the wind was howling as loudly as before. "At any rate, it isn't important right now," he said as we stepped into the carriage.*

The weather continued miserable next morning when I arrived at Queen's Square shortly before ten o'clock. I found the prevailing silence throughout the building distinctly depressing. It was as though every soul within those brick walls knew of the fateful act that was to begin a few minutes hence.

In the ward I looked first toward Henderson's bed. It was empty.

---

* Alexander Hughes Bennett died on November 1, 1901, barely fifty-three years of age, of a nervous disease which first manifested itself during those days of strain preceding the cerebral tumor operation. The principal symptoms were severe, painful attacks typical of tabes dorsalis. Other symptoms, however, suggest different possibilities. Bennett's complaint was never precisely diagnosed; not even his own knowledge of neurology, remarkable as it was for the period, sufficed in his case. He died after many years of pain, taking the unsolved mystery of his own illness to the grave with him.

Then I saw, half concealed by the screen, the group of doctors at the window: Bennett, Ferrier, Jackson, Godlee, a number of assistants whom I did not know, and several nurses. The others were waiting in their usual frock coats. Henderson lay on the table with eyes closed. He had been strapped tightly, and his head was shaved bare. The scalp looked smooth and extremely white, except for the conspicuous spots at the back of his head which had become inflamed and scabby from the effects of the mustard plasters. One of the assistants washed his scalp with pungent carbolic solution. Again and again he dipped the sponge into an enamel bowl filled with the solution. When he touched the sore places, the patient opened his eyes and groaned. The assistant vacillated for a moment, but then he spared the sore places and did not touch them with the carbolic.

I looked around at Bennett, and then fixed my gaze upon Godlee, who stood at Henderson's head. Outwardly, Godlee seemed as calm as ever. He stood quietly, looking rather broad and heavy, his somewhat coarse features unmoved. I imagined that I could read his thoughts. He who by nature was pledged to conservatism in doctrine and action was about to step across the frontier of an unknown country, urged onward by the stronger will of his colleague Bennett.

The second assistant had meanwhile begun to place carbolic-soaked cloths around the patient's head and face, until only the very top of the skull remained clear. Then he reached for the bottle of chloroform. A nurse moved the already steaming carbolic spray mechanism to the opposite side of Henderson's head. She opened the petcock which admitted the steam under pressure to the container of carbolic. Meanwhile Henderson breathed heavily of the chloroform, cried out, tried to heave himself up, and at last lost consciousness. The nurse at the spray instantly released the carbolic mist. A thin, pungent drizzle of carbolic hissed over the operating field. All was in readiness. It was up to Godlee now.

Godlee took the scalpel, dripping with carbolic, and cast a swift glance around. The scalpel moved down, and drew two long, intersecting incisions through the scalp into the bone. The incisions began bleeding at once.

The second assistant dabbed up the blood with sponges, and

clamped several spurting blood vessels. Then he raised the edges of the four flaps of skin between the incisions and folded them back. Godlee was breathing loudly. He scraped the periosteum away, the scalpel making a scratching, penetrating sound. At last the bone was exposed—a whitish gray, beaded with drops of carbolic which swiftly flowed into one another.

All of us moved a little closer. Bennett stayed close by Godlee's side. With visibly shaking hand he traced the "circle" upon the exposed bone.

Ferrier was leaning far forward. Jackson's ordinarily firm, controlled features betrayed his tremendous excitement. At that moment he certainly felt nothing of the coolness with which, in future years, he was to observe one brain operation after the other; nothing of that detachment toward the sufferings of fellow creatures which prompted him later, during a cerebral operation upon a young Scot, to make the famous comment that the surgeon had done his work well but had forgotten to place a sense of humor into the Scot's brain. All this, however, was far in the future, infinitely remote from the breathless decisiveness of this moment.

A nurse handed Godlee the trepan. Godlee placed the instrument on the bone. His hand seemed firm and sure now as he turned the wheel and the jagged blade began biting into the bone. The grinding sound of the trepan was for a while the only thing to be heard in the room. Splinters of bone, stained by blood, came up and out at every turn.

Godlee's head sank lower and lower. He seemed literally to be listening to the motion of the steel. He paused, measured the depth of penetration, began turning again. At last he stopped, loosened the trepan, raised it, and detached a small, circular piece of bone. He peered through the opening at the faintly pulsing dura mater. Then his hand took the scalpel and lowered it carefully into the opening. At that point some change seemed to come over him. With astonishing boldness he cut into the membrane. At once part of the surface of the brain bulged up through the incision. But it seemed normal, free of morbid signs, although there was a slight yellowish discoloration. The opening, however, was not large enough to permit any definite conclusions. Godlee took the trepan again. Overlapping the first opening, he now cut a second into the brainpan. The scalpel enlarged the incision through the dura mater. A larger portion of the cerebral cortex appeared. But it too betrayed no sign of morbid changes, no protrusion of a tumor or swelling of any sort.

Bennett's already pallid face whitened still more. All the emotion raging within him was revealed in his expression—anxiety, doubt, tormenting questions: Had his keenness and his deductive powers failed him? Fooled him?

Godlee, too, seemed to be overcome by momentary hesitation. His florid face glistened beneath the perspiration that streamed down his brow. But then he applied the trepan for the third time. Once more the blood-tinted bone chips flew. Godlee removed the third circle of bone from the skull. Then he took chisel and hammer, while the assistant, without further direction, held a copper spatula over the brain and membrane to protect them. Each blow of Godlee's chisel produced that low, and yet clear, sharp noise which is characteristic of chisel work on the skull. Splinter by splinter he removed pieces of bone. At last he had chiselled the three small trepan openings into a large triangle.

Every moment it had seemed as if the patient would surely awaken under the blows of hammer and chisel. But Henderson did not stir. Beyond an occasional moan, he made no sound. Godlee laid aside hammer and chisel and took up the scalpel once more. A surge of boldness seemed to have come over him. He exposed the brain to the full width of the triangle of bone he had removed. The exposed section proved to be part of a frontal and lateral convolution. A large, pulsating blood vessel ran across the portion nearest to the gap in the skull. But there was nothing else, not the slightest indication of a tumor. Nothing!

All of us stared spellbound at the window in the bone, beneath which there stirred before our eyes the living brain of a human being. Godlee seemed again uncertain. He exchanged a quick look with Bennett, a plea for advice. If all the diagnostic efforts had not been wrong, if this brain were not defying medical arrogance, then there could be only one explanation for the absence of any sign of a tumor. The tumor must be rooted very deep. Perhaps it had established itself beneath the visible cerebral cortex, in the white substance, and had penetrated from below into the cortex with its functional centers. Once more Godlee's eyes sought

Bennett's. His look expressed all the uncertainty, all the wild veering between heaven and hell, through which he must have passed at this moment. But then he inserted the scalpel through the hole in the cranium. Resolutely, he made an incision into the living, pulsating brain. The knife cut through the cerebral substance. My heart pounded. What would happen now? Would death ensue instantly, as thousands of doctors believed? But nothing happened. Henderson continued to breathe heavily but regularly.

Now there was a gap in the gray matter of the cortex, a gap of more than a quarter of an inch. Then, from the depths of this gap, something appeared, an unnatural, discolored, hard, alien thing—round, large as a pigeon's egg, encapsulated, and embedded in the sound substance of the cerebrum. Here was the source of the illness; here was the tumor, proof of the correctness of all Bennett's theories, plans, course of action.

I felt a surge of triumph, of pride, like that which I had experienced forty years before when the first patient in the world sank before my eyes into anesthetic sleep in Boston and endured Professor Warren's knife without uttering a cry of pain. But was not my triumph premature? This tumor still lay firmly embedded. It had not yet been demonstrated that it could be lifted out without injury to the most delicate and sensitive of all human tissues.

Godlee took a thin metal spatula and held it over the flame which was creating the steam for the spray. When the metal softened, he bent it into a spoonlike shape which conformed to what he could see of the shape of the tumor. He cooled the metal in carbolic solution, then thrust it with infinite care between the tumor and the cerebral substance. With careful, prying motions he tried to force it down. He made slow progress, but it was progress. After a while he introduced his forefinger into the cranial opening. He moved the finger along the side of the tumor and tried to lift it from its bed. I could see the tumor yielding, its visible portion rising. The groping, tugging finger enclosed it, seemed to grasp all of it and to pull it out entirely.

Suddenly there was a small, jerking motion. Godlee's hand held a semispherical thing. The tumor had torn in the middle. Only the top had come out. The deeper part had remained in the brain. And fractions of a second later the whole scene changed. Whereas hitherto there had been virtually no bleeding, a fine reddish trickling began, so fine at first that it was scarcely perceptible.

Godlee became plainly uneasy. He looked nervously among the instruments, finally took up a sharp Volkmann spoon, thrust it into the cavity, and tried to scrape out the base of the tumor. Now the cavity began filling rapidly with blood. It did not flow, it trickled, but trickled steadily from the tissues of the brain. Within a few seconds Godlee was engaged in a stubborn struggle with the blood. He asked for sponges, more sponges. Alternately he soaked up the blood with sponges and tried, the moment he had a clear view, to remove more of the tumor. Minute after minute passed. The patient spoke under anesthesia. His limbs twitched. But he was living.

None of us were aware that our clothes were drenched with perspiration, our faces dripping. I at any rate cannot recall having noticed this until later. I waited, almost choked by the terrible tension. Godlee was breathing heavily. The sponges cleaned the operating field only for seconds at a time. And still the deepest root of the tumor had not yet been reached, not yet been removed. But at last—a minute later—it looked as if healthy white medullary substance had been reached at the bottom of the cavity. A sponge once more removed the blood. The nurse who dipped sponge after sponge in the now blood-tinted carbolic solution had to work with both hands. The bleeding increased instead of diminishing. And everywhere there was only this maddening trickling which no clamp, no ligature, could stop. Godlee breathed gaspingly between colorless lips. I could guess what he felt and thought. The tumor was gone. What had seemed impossible had been done successfully. Was it now all to end in failure because he could not master this peculiar kind of hemorrhage?

I saw him glance once more over the instrument table. His gaze lingered on the galvanocautery. But he hesitated still. Would the brain endure such rough treatment? Meanwhile, the blood poured into the cavity. Once more a sponge. A cautious attempt at a tamponade. Pointless! All around the table there was utter silence. Godlee had the cautery heated, introduced it into the cavity left by the tumor. Hissing, it moved over the bleeding tissue. Here blood still trickled, then there. But at last it was over; the hemorrhage had been stopped.

Godlee straightened up, hands drenched with blood, utterly

exhausted, panting for breath. All of us listened to Henderson's breathing. The twitching motions in his limbs had increased. But still he lived, breathed. Godlee washed his hands in carbolic solution. Then he drew the severed edges of the dura mater together, placed a rubber drain in the cavity, sewed the membrane with several carbolic-cleansed silk threads. One of the assistants freed the periosteum from the clamps which had hitherto held it. Godlee pulled the edges together above the triangular hole in the skull and fastened them around the drain with silver wires. Then he laid carbolic-soaked gauze on the wound, removed the carbolic cloths all around the operating field, and bandaged the whole head.

For all of us who had witnessed this operation it was like the slow awakening from a long dream, from a world we had never seen before. No one said a word; exhaustion or emotion had reduced us all to silence. But we exchanged looks, looks full of meaning. This was reality. The tumor had been correctly diagnosed, had been found, had been surgically removed—and the patient was alive. This was the simple and yet incredible, tremendous truth. Henceforth cerebral tumors could be located and removed. They could be scraped out of the nutritive bed where they led their parasitic life, and the harsh remedy need not necessarily kill the patient. Bennett and Godlee had stepped over the frontier, had conquered new territory for surgery.

I left London five days later, on the morning of November 30, tormented by one of those frightful gallstone attacks which I had suffered for the first time many years before, in the early days of Lister's struggle for antisepsis, and which had been dogging me ever since. The attack this time, which struck like lightning out of a clear sky, was so severe that I felt I could no longer bear it, but was forced to seek out the only surgeon who had so far dared to remove calculous gall bladders: Carl Langenbuch in Berlin.

One day before my departure, in a little respite between two attacks, I managed to pay one more call upon Henderson at the National Hospital. That was on November 29. Henderson's condition was amazingly good. He had spent a good night, was mentally fresh and vigorous, and was enjoying the best of appetites. The convulsions and raging headaches which had made his life an agony had vanished completely. He could move his left leg freely.

However, the partial paralysis of the left arm had now become total paralysis. From this Bennett reasoned that removal of the tumor in the cortex had destroyed the still intact remnants of the motor center for the arm. But Henderson was more than willing to pay the price of complete loss of his arm for release from his previous torture. The edges of the wound had swollen slightly, and the inserted drain was discharging a secretion, but there seemed no indication of serious complications in the healing of the surgical wound. I intended to visit him once more next day, but was unable to do so. My own attacks had become so excruciating that I could hope to reach Berlin only with the aid of large doses of morphine.

As a result, I was not present during the subsequent weeks when Bennett and Godlee, like so many surgeons before them, waited day after day by the patient's bedside, alert for every positive and negative sign, swinging between confidence and despair, already certain of final victory and then doubting again, hoping and doubting, hoping and doubting. To the extent that my own illness allowed me time and strength to think about Henderson's fate during the next few weeks, I assumed that the young Scotsman would soon be leading a useful life once more. It was therefore a terrible surprise and blow to me when Jackson wrote on December 24 that Henderson had just died in the National Hospital.

At first I was plunged into deepest gloom. Had it then all been in vain? Had the taboo against a surgeon's entering the brain proved valid after all? Had Godlee's operation closed rather than opened the door to the development of cerebral surgery? Would it serve henceforth as a grim warning, the handwriting on the wall which would restrain even the most venturesome of surgeons from attempting the forbidden? Had all our sense of triumph been mere self-delusion?

Then, however, I read what else Jackson had to say. He wrote that the symptoms caused by Henderson's tumor had not reappeared up to the very end. Henderson had not again suffered from headaches or convulsions, and had been full of confidence. Death had ensued not as the direct consequence of the cerebral operation, but because of a surgical infection such as might have killed a patient after any operation. As I read I recalled the swelling on the edges of the wound and the pussy discharge I had noticed when I last visited Henderson. During the following weeks a serious infection, encephalocele (hernia of the brain), and finally meningitis had developed. The latter had been the cause of death. Jackson could not say precisely how the infection had come about. Perhaps the application of the many sponges used in the attempt to stop the hemorrhage had led to a breakdown of strict antisepsis. Jackson himself personally believed that the actual cause of death had been a minor but fateful accident. And he named it. As I read his comments, the stages of the operation rose before my eyes once more, and suddenly I knew that he was right. His sharp eye had observed what I, too, had subconsciously noted, but forgotten. I saw the assistant washing Henderson's scalp with carbolic solution and passing over the spots which were inflamed from previous treatment with mustard plasters. From these untreated, inflamed spots the infection had crept into the incision and killed Henderson. Chance, an accident, a diabolical whim of fate—but no more than that. No, certainly no more! It should serve as a spur to more careful work in the future, but not as a barrier to the further development of surgery of the brain.

A few months later, on May 12, 1885, Bennett and Godlee stood before the members of the Medical and Surgical Society in London. They reported, to an audience listening with keenest attention, on the operation and the lessons they had learned from it. Their principal lesson was: The removal of cerebral tumors is possible, but the technique must be carefully developed. At this time neither of these men suspected, any more than I did, how much more time that development would require, how many setbacks were still to come. But they could rightly believe that they had given the first effective impetus to a new branch of surgery.

William Macewen of Glasgow turned up at this same meeting. The silver-haired giant of a man had read the preliminary reports of the operation, which had been published in November and December, and had thought fit to announce his own previous surgical invasions of the human brain before this important group of medical men assembled in London. When Bennett had finished his talk, and Ferrier had stressed the epoch-making character of the operation, Macewen stepped to the platform and described the history of the operations of which I had already heard from

Takada in September, 1884. Since I was not present at this meeting, I can only relate what I afterwards heard about it. The response to Macewen's lecture can best be described as polite. He was regarded as an intruder from the provinces who had come to contest with Bennett and Godlee priority for the first brain operation. This impression gained ground when he made the statement that in all his cases not a single infection or meningitis had followed the operation. Bennett spoke up after Macewen finished. He thanked his colleague for his valuable contributions, but at the same time pointed out that there had been two crucial differences between his own and Godlee's work and the operations described by Macewen. In the first place, Macewen had never removed a tumor, but merely opened abscesses or relieved superficial blood clots and swellings of the meninges. Secondly, Macewen had plainly not based his diagnoses upon localization of the functional centers. In each instance he had taken his cue from externally visible changes in the patient's cranium.

Bennett was undoubtedly right about this. His and Godlee's operation was and remained the first deliberate operation for cerebral tumor. Nevertheless, the cool treatment accorded Macewen at that meeting was unjust; he undoubtedly deserved credit for being the earliest pioneer in surgery of the brain. How greatly he merited recognition in his own particular specialty of opening abscesses I later understood when I at last met him personally. At the congress of the British Medical Association in Glasgow, which I attended, he reported on a total of twenty-one operations upon cerebral abscesses, eighteen of which were unqualified successes. Seeing him in the flesh, however, I also understood that it was not only his living in a provincial city which had blocked timely and complete recognition of his achievements. The opposition to him was primarily due to his own personality, to the character traits Takada had made gentle jest of. Macewen was a handsome man who attracted attention everywhere by his appearance, his flashing eyes, and his wonderfully melodic voice. He was also a man of intelligence, courage, inventiveness, and brilliant technical ability. But he was above all a proud man who wore a mask of grim humor and sarcasm. He was boundlessly obstinate and unutterably independent. His own best pupils were in the habit of calling him "The Great I Am" and "Almighty God." All this somewhat explains his strange position. Few of his colleagues liked him, and that was chiefly why his just claim to having done pioneering work in the field of brain surgery was passed over. He remained an outsider to the end of his days. The glory of having opened the way to the development of cerebral surgery was conferred upon Bennett and Godlee.

Marion Sims — John S. Bobbs
Lawson Tait — Carl Langenbuch

Those pain-filled December days of the year 1884, when I left London and managed to keep going only by the injection of maximum doses of morphine, formed the climax of my own gall bladder disease. I could have traced its beginnings back some eighteen years. Because of it, I had come into fairly close contact with surgeons who were endeavoring to make afflictions of the gall bladder yield to the scalpel. As in the case of bladder stones decades before, my own illness made me the witness of another dramatic chapter in the development of surgery.

On the afternoon of January 8, 1867, I had arrived in Paris from England, still brimming with excitement over my meeting with Professor Lister in Glasgow, and his demonstration of the astonishing results of carbolic antisepsis. At eight o'clock that evening I was to have dinner in a small Paris restaurant with Dr. Marion Sims, the world-famous American gynecologist who was then practicing in Europe. I had no suspicion of the distressing surprise the evening had in store for me, nor of the part Sims was later to play in my life.

It was years since Sims had last seen his native land. Born in a remote, poverty-stricken farm in South Carolina, he had in the course of time become a country doctor. His territory was southern

Alabama, and there he had performed his first abdominal operations on slave women. His next step had been New York. The
first year of the Civil War found him in Europe rounding out his
medical education. In Paris he had introduced his method for
curing vaginal fistula, which created a sensation among Parisian
surgeons. In 1862 he returned to America. As a Southerner he
could not sympathize with the state of affairs in the North,
liquidated his possessions in New York, and in July, 1863, emigrated
to Europe with his family. Since then he had lived in France and
England. In either land his office was besieged by wealthy female
patients. The Empress Eugénie of France had been among his
patients; he had spent several weeks in Saint-Cloud treating her.
During all this time he had made no secret of his sympathy for the
Southern cause, and had contributed large sums of money to aid
the victims of Sherman's raiders. But the fact that I myself had
spent the greater part of the war working in hospitals on the side
of the Union had never affected the warm relationship between
Sims and myself. During the year 1862 in New York I had frequently been in a position to help his wonderful wife Therese and
their seven children. And now that I was back in Europe for the
first time in years, Sims was naturally eager to talk with me about
events back home, and above all about conditions since the end
of the Civil War.

Sims arrived shortly after eight. The moment he stepped out of
the shadow of the vestibule into the bright room of the restaurant,
many women turned their heads to look at him. He was fifty-
three at this time, but still a striking man, slim, erect, with thick,
chestnut-brown hair, full lips, magnetic dark-brown eyes, an
almost boyish liveliness in his movements, and a talent for dressing
with great elegance. No one would have guessed that he had come
into the world in a blockhouse on the edge of the wilderness and
that his father—farmer, village innkeeper, sheriff, organizer of
cockfights, fox hunter, and inveterate billiard player—had not
learned to write and do sums until he was twenty-three years
old. Sims was a man who corresponded to John Bell's ideal portrait of a surgeon: "The brain of an Apollo, the heart of a lion,
a clear eye, and a woman's touch."

Sims stepped toward me and shook both my hands. "Good
Lord, good Lord," he exclaimed, "you bring home back to me!"

He paid not the slightest attention to the curious stares of the other patrons, and had just repeated his heartfelt "Good Lord, good Lord!" when I suddenly experienced, without the slightest warning, a stabbing pain in my right shoulder which took my breath away. The pain was accompanied by an intense nausea. A second later I felt as though a fist were boring into my right side, just below the last rib on the right. This pressure changed into a dull, driving pain which swiftly spread first to the back and then into the abdomen. The pain became so intense that I let go of Sims's hands, leaned forward, and then doubled up, uttering a low moan.

As though through a mist I caught Sims's astonished, querying look and the expressions of others in the restaurant who quickly gathered around me. Instinctively I sensed that this was not the kind of pain that would go away at once, that I need bear for only a moment before it would fade. Perhaps I was aware that the pain would become more intense, and that shortly I would be unable to leave the restaurant by myself, that the pain would strike me down, and I would lie, apathetic toward all around me, waiting to be carried out to an ambulance. It was as though a tremendous crack had been driven down my right side from the pit of the stomach up to my shoulder. I staggered out through the door and paused in the narrow vestibule, supporting myself against the wall. There I stood, pressing my clenched fists against the right side of my abdomen, high up.

Someone pulled and pushed me forward. I no longer had command of my voice; I could hear myself groaning and screaming alternately. Dimly, I became aware of a carriage, and felt myself bundled into it. Every jolt during the ride caused a fresh and still more violent attack of pain. Questions were put to me, but I was incapable of grasping their meaning. The carriage stopped. Someone jumped out, returned after an eternity, and fumbled at my mouth. I felt the taste of some powder, swallowed and choked something down, and waited for relief. It was dark all around me. After another endless span of time the ferocity of the pain diminished. Slowly it gave way to a dull but far more tolerable sensation of pressure. For the first time I became aware of my surroundings again, and in the glow of a carriage lantern found myself looking into Sims's anxious brown eyes. I realized that I was lying, hunched to one side, on the rear seat of the carriage.

"Can you come into the house with me now?" I heard Sims ask. "We are in front of my house. I'd like to take you in."

With some effort I succeeded in sitting up. Like others of the surgical profession of those days, with its still limited repertory of operations, I was on not too familiar terms with the symptomatology of internal diseases. But this sudden attack of pain, whose worst stages I had just put behind me, carried one unequivocal meaning for me. It reminded me of my mother, who had died after years of unappeasable pain in the upper abdominal region. At the autopsy two large gallstones had been found in the abdominal cavity; these had finally broken through the wall of the gall bladder. The concepts of "gall fever" and "gallstone" forced their way into my mind like a sentence of slow torture.

Sims was repeating: "I'd like to take you into my house." I fought against a wave of giddiness, apologized for the trouble I was causing, and followed, clinging to his hand, into the ground floor of the already illuminated house. Sims had arranged a sofa for me, and helped me to stretch out on it. "Have you ever had an attack like this before?" he asked.

"No," I said, "this is the worst one." I sat up once more so that I could free my right side of the pressure of my clothing. With Sims's help I cautiously took off my coat and vest, opened my shirt and trousers, and lay back again. My right hand glided over the skin below the right lower rib. Near the liver the slightest touch was painful. Slight pressure above and to the right of my navel sufficed to produce a deep, piercing pain.

I resisted the idea of the diagnosis which was forced upon me. My whole soul rebelled. After all, I was barely forty years old. But how old had my mother been when her illness began? Memories came trooping to my mind, scenes I had almost forgotten. India in 1854. My stay in Khanpur! The terrible attack of bladder stone colic shortly after I first watched an Indian lithotomist at work. I recalled my despairing return to Europe in search of help, and at last relief, the rescue from pain, by the bloodless operation which Civiale had invented to put an end to the brutal practices of medieval lithotomy.

Did I, then, belong to the type of "stone formers" who, from some metabolic disturbance in their younger years, were prone to manufacture bladder, gall bladder, and kidney stones, and were condemned to spend their lives in an agonizing and often hopeless struggle with the malignant concretions?

"What do you think?" I asked, striving to preserve outward composure.

Sims sat down beside me on the edge of the sofa. "I have already sent for Dr. Trousseau," he said. "You must know him by name at least. He is the biggest man in Paris for internal medicine. Last year I worked with him in several consultations. He is a good friend of mine, and will surely come right over to examine you. I know very few cases in which he has failed as a diagnostician." He bent over me and laid his hand against my right side. I had so often heard of Sims's skillful hand. Now I felt it myself.

"I assume you have come to the same conclusion as I?" I said with sham firmness, while in truth I was desperately hoping that Sims might have diagnosed anything but gallstones.

He hesitated for a moment. Then he said, in an attempt to be humorous: "As you know, I am more at home with the other sex and on another floor of the house."

I felt that this joke was only an evasion. If any surgeon knew something about internal diseases, it was Marion Sims. He could not deceive me; I knew his history too well. His career had not only been more adventurous and varied than most physicians', but more fraught with suffering also. He himself had been visited by enough diseases to make him experienced and wise. After his poverty-stricken apprentice years with Professor McCallem in Philadelphia, an old surgeon of the Warren type, Sims had tried to settle down in Lancaster, South Carolina, as a general practitioner. He owned at that time nothing but a few old-fashioned instruments which he carried in his saddlebags. The death of his first two patients, children, had compelled him to move on. After a three-week trip in a pony cart he had begun anew at Mount Meigs, Alabama, among cotton planters and Negro slaves. There Sims bought— paying with a promissory note—the practice of a certain Dr. Childers. Childers, who had formerly practiced all over Georgia, from Augusta to Columbia, believed in rigorous phlebotomy, and by his bloodletting had speeded innumerable patients into the hereafter. He had just come to the conclusion that it might be wise to change the scene of his activities.

The sick people of the district took heart again when it became known that a new doctor was here. Sims became something of a hero to the local populace by going out to fight against the Creek Indians, who were harassing the Alabama settlers. The number of his patients increased. Consequently, as time went on he encountered virtually every disease prevalent in the South—and had certainly run into gall bladder troubles more than once. He practiced for four years until malaria—no one at the time knew that it was transmitted by mosquitoes—invaded Mount Meigs like a plague. Phlebotomy and purgation were the only known treatment, but the more these remedies were applied, the sooner the patients expired. The disease did not spare Sims either. While all around him white and colored people died by the hundreds, Sims himself was reduced to a skeleton. His life was saved only by the chance visit of an English apothecary from Montgomery who had some quinine with him—a drug extremely rare at the time. But as far as Mount Meigs was concerned Sims was thoroughly discredited. In 1840 he packed his ailing family and all his possessions into a small wagon and fled to Lowndes County. Here, he hoped, he could count on help from some of his relatives. But here, too, malaria raged; sickbeds stood in the open air in front of the plague-ridden houses, and Negroes fanned the feverish whites until they themselves collapsed. Sims continued his flight, on to Montgomery. Here he once more started a general practice among the few rich and the innumerable poor who lived in wait for the next cotton crop and were never free of debts and misery. His malaria became so bad that he spent nearly a year in bed, while his family led the dismal lives of debtors. At last, however, his health improved and he began to prosper. Once more he dealt with all the diseases for forty miles around the town of Montgomery, and he had seen all too many patients die of gall and liver diseases after years of agony—without being able to give them anything but a few drops of opium to alleviate their sufferings.

Five years after his removal to Montgomery he made the discovery to which he owed his fame as a surgeon. There, in the hot, godforsaken, malaria-ridden dreariness of the American South he had achieved, amid conditions of misery and poverty, what thousands of doctors throughout the world at this time had been unable to do. He had learned a surgical cure for vesicovaginal fistula, that terrible disfigurement of women so often caused by injuries during childbirth. As has frequently been the case in medicine, chance and destiny conjoined to produce this discovery.

In the summer of 1845—while I was studying medicine in Boston, that is—Sims had been called to a patient named Mervill, the wife of a notorious gambler and drunkard. Mrs. Mervill, a stout woman of more than two hundred pounds, had fallen from a horse and had suffered a displacement of the womb. In attempting to correct this displacement Sims had her assume the knee-elbow position, and discovered that in this position the genital passages opened wider than in any other, allowing room—and light—for hitherto impossible operations. On the way home from his visit to Mrs. Mervill, Sims bought a large tin spoon, and promptly went to see a Negro woman suffering from vesicovaginal fistula. The spoon helped him to widen still further his operation field—and since then this spoon, in modified form, had become famous the world over as Sims's speculum.

Emboldened by this discovery, Sims had begun to summon to him all available cases of vesicovaginal fistula. He spent his last penny providing beds in his house for a dozen sick Negro women. Lucy, Betsy, and Anarcha were the names of the first women who took their places on Sims's wooden operating table—this was still in the days before the discovery of anesthesia—that he might attempt to sew up their fistulas. Sims had often described to me the ensuing terrible years—years that seem unthinkable to us nowadays, as do so many other aspects of those merciless early days of surgery. He had carried out one hundred operations before he first succeeded in permanently closing and healing a fistula; thirty of these were on the unfortunate woman Anarcha alone. Again and again infection, suppuration, separation of the edges of the wound, undid his work and plunged him and his patients into despair. He went deeper than ever into debt from the expense of maintaining his patients for years. Other Alabama doctors regarded him as a pitiable fool. His only assistants were the Negro women themselves, who in spite of all the torture of the operations were determined to carry through the fight for their health. Each would assist in turn during operations upon the others. At last, in the summer of 1849, the miracle happened. Chance had led Sims to use silver wire to sew up the fistulas. He had no suspicion that silver is by nature hostile to pathogenic microorganisms. He did not know the reason, but he was vouchsafed his first cure.

But just at this time, with his first successful fistula operation behind him, he was attacked by a dysenteric disease which was endemic in Alabama and the entire Mississippi Valley. It troubled him for several years, and more than once brought him to the brink of death. With borrowed money he went to New York, hoping that the colder climate would bring him relief. The hope was vain. Then he journeyed for weeks by stagecoach and on horseback over rivers and swamps seeking out an itinerant preacher who allegedly possessed a medicinal spring whose waters cured diarrhea. For years he carried jugs of this water about with him until his analytic mind realized that it was not the water which helped, but the diet of salt pork which the preacher recommended. The high percentage of salt retained large quantities of fluid in the tissues and thereby diminished the liquid excretions. But until he learned this Sims had gone through an inferno lasting four years, and toward the end had been confined to his bed most of the time. Reduced to skin and bones, he had himself taken to New York again to try for the last time the curative effects of a colder climate. While in New York he discovered the effect of the salt pork, threw off the disease at last, and began anew as gynecologist specializing in operations on the genital passages. In this new career he had swiftly risen to his present eminence and prosperity. Certainly, however, there were few physicians who had amassed more experience of human suffering than he.

I had no opportunity to press him for his opinion, for his colored servant, whom he had brought with him from America, came in to announce the arrival of Dr. Trousseau.

Trousseau himself appeared in the doorway, a man of about sixty, tall but conspicuously lean and stoop-shouldered, with long hair brushed straight back, snow-white whiskers, and a face all sharp angles. He greeted Sims, was introduced to me, and proceeded without another word to make an examination. This was my first meeting with him, although of course I knew of his method of detecting diseases of the gall and liver by the presence of bile in the urine. I knew also that his great skill at diagnosis was founded upon the tremendous number of patients at his disposal in the fearfully overcrowded wards of the medieval Hôtel Dieu on the Île de la Cité. These diagnoses, to be sure, were rendered almost value-less by the ineffective methods of treatment available to physicians in those days. Trousseau—so I had heard repeatedly—resorted chiefly to bloodletting, doses of deadly nightshade, and diets of donkey's milk. On certain days his wards resembled abattoirs, so profusely did the blood flow from anemic, weirdly pale patients with barely strength to walk, patients whose cases of typhoid or cholera or tuberculosis were being treated by immoderate blood-lettings. For epilepsy Trousseau administered belladonna until the patient's sight was affected and blindness threatened. The donkey milk served as a tonic for an enormous variety of diseases, and Trousseau maintained herds of female donkeys which were led at regular hours to the houses of his well-to-do patients and there milked, so that the milk would be absolutely fresh and conse-quently possess the greatest curative properties. In the light of our present knowledge such things are grotesque, but they were char-acteristic of the times, when the foremost representatives of inter-nal medicine possessed amazing accuracy at diagnosis and were largely helpless in therapy.

Trousseau asked a few terse questions. At the same time he skill-fully palpated me. Instantly the pain in my right shoulder reap-peared. Immediately afterwards I felt the blow under my ribs, then the ache in my back, and finally the tearing sensation that trans-formed my entire right side into a single wrenching, intolerable pain. Involuntarily I cried out as Trousseau drove three fingers of his left hand deep into the pit of my stomach. He studied me with his strange, yellowish, unhealthy-looking eyes, unmoved by my pain, but listening closely to the sound of my cry as though it were of diagnostic value to him. He felt the lower edge of my liver, his thin hands displaying a surprising, brutal force. Then he abruptly straightened up, and with the tips of his fingers pulled down his cuffs.

For the moment I could not utter a word.

"I hear that you are a physician," Trousseau said. "Among col-leagues I am in favor of the unvarnished truth. I feel sure you agree with me on this." He did not wait for me to comment, but stood for just a moment with his strange eyes fixed reflectively upon my face. "There is no question about your case," he said. "It is difficult, ordinarily, to diagnose gallstones with any degree of definiteness. But yours is a special case. The gall bladder is greatly enlarged and protrudes from under the edge of the liver. It is unusually easy to palpate. You have at least one large, irregularly shaped gallstone which has been forming for a long time and is manifesting its presence for the first time today. The stone is large." He paused, and then continued with emphasis on each word: "It is in any case too large ever to pass through the bile duct, but large enough to block the duct."

There was no need for him to continue. I realized fully what this verdict meant. As in the innumerable cases of fellow sufferers, my gall bladder would strive to expel the stone. However, it would be unable to do this in the natural manner, as it might for small stones. The result would be repeated, violent attempts to attain the impossible goal; repeated attacks, growing in intensity, would torment me for weeks, for years. There would be blockages of the bile duct. Morphine would provide the only alleviation, and even that would not be completely effective. Inflammation of the gall bladder, suppuration, formation of an abscess, and finally rupture of the wall of the gall bladder would follow. The stone would then be carried out, along with quantities of infectious materials, into the abdominal cavity, producing peritonitis and death. Those were the prospects for me. The whole drama of severe gallstone disease, the course of which had not changed one iota in centuries, raced before my eyes. I realized that Trousseau was aware of my horror. But he remained cool and remote.

"I think further explanations are superfluous," he said. "There

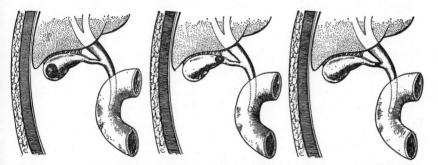

Stones: at the bottom of the gall bladder (left); *in the neck of the bladder* (center); *in the cystic duct* (right).

is one chance for you: to work the stone back into a position of repose, where it must have been lying for a long time. I shall prescribe a diet and belladonna for you. I also recommend a cure at Karlsbad to combat your evident inclination toward stone formation. Morphine during attacks, of course. I know cases in which a stone like yours has been kept subdued for very long periods of time."

I saw my whole world collapsing, my life of travelling from country to country, from continent to continent. It would be impossible, sheer madness, to continue such a life if every day were to be governed by concern over diet and rest, if I were always to carry within myself a foe who might assail me any time and anywhere, even in the most remote quarter of the globe. As if from far off, I heard Trousseau's cold voice: "You will have to fight for your life by your conduct of it. Medicine is powerless here, for no one can remove such a stone and no one ever will be able to. Occasionally, however, nature does not empty a gallstone abscess into the abdominal cavity, but outwardly, through the abdominal wall, and so discharges both the stone and the purulent matter."

In the haze that seemed to be floating before my eyes, I saw Trousseau pick up his bag. His gesture seemed to express the nadir of weariness. "The truth, then," he said, his voice as weary as his gesture, "leaves this possibility open to you. There are medical truths which allow us no prospects at all." His voice wavered for a moment, but then he continued: "I carry one such truth within myself." He stood above me, bolt upright, and his face seemed frozen with an icy pride. "I have cancer of the stomach, and my days are numbered. The only nourishment I can still take is milk. There is a clear contest between supply and consumption, and I have calculated the probable date of the end. I think I shall last until June 20 of next year. Your truth is not quite so pitiless. I shall send the prescription by messenger."

He made the hint of a bow. "Good night, messieurs," and he left before Sims, who sat stunned, could accompany him to the door.

I lay still, aghast. Trousseau's last disclosure had for a moment dispelled the dull, twisting pain and my personal fear.

"I always thought him an unusual man," I heard Sims saying.

"His wife has left him, his daughter is unhappily married, his son is a gambler and good-for-nothing. And in spite of all he marches proudly into death. I know him well, I meet with him frequently—and I suspected nothing. He only spoke of it because he wanted to impress you with the fact that you, in spite of all, still have a life before you." *

As I listened to Sims, I too felt a dim respect for such stoicism. But at the word "life" a bitterness surged up in me. "A life before me?" I exclaimed. "Haven't you seen what kind of life is open to people with this disease of mine? Haven't you seen hundreds of them—thousands, living on morphine and dying of slow starvation or peritonitis?"

Silently, Sims looked away, avoiding my eyes.

"I was never made for such a life, to live in fear from moment to moment," I mumbled. I tried to sit up. But Sims bent down and held me firmly, and the instantaneous return of the stabbing pain in my shoulder persuaded me to sink back voluntarily. But the renewal of the pain only intensified my despair. "So I am to wait and see whether nature in her infinite kindness provides me with an abscess which may burst out through the abdominal wall and remove the stone. . . . You are a great surgeon, Sims, a famous surgeon. You are not a dilettante and globe-trotter like myself. You've proved your ability and ingenuity. What would you answer if I begged you not to relinquish me to the slim chance of rescue on nature's part, but to use your scalpel to make a way for nature?"

Sims stared at me in horror. "You of all people should know that it is impossible; within a week after the operation you would die of peritonitis. I want to hear no more of this."

But my despair, my rebellion against the fate in store for me, instantly put me in mind of Joseph Lister, from whom I had just come. At this time Lister had tried his technique of carbolic anti-sepsis only on external wounds, chiefly compound fractures of bones; he had never used it in an operation on any body cavity. But would not the technique apply to such an operation, too?

* Trousseau did in fact die just eight days before the term he had set for himself. The first successful stomach operation—successful for a time at least—came thirteen years after Trousseau's death, when the Viennese surgeon Billroth undertook to operate for cancer of the pylorus.

"Would you venture to expose a gall bladder and remove a stone from it if there were a certain method of avoiding infection?" I pressed.

Sims looked dubiously at me. He, the revolutionary surgeon who in the interest of his great discovery had not quailed at inflicting suffering and pain a hundred times over, thought that I was going out of my mind.

"Would you make the attempt if the method existed?" I repeated.

He appeared to think that I spoke under the influence of the morphine. "If it consoles you, yes," he said in a soothing tone. "But—do you have such a method?"

"No," I said, "but Joseph Lister in Glasgow does have it. You have never heard of him. But you must meet him. Go to see him. Let him show you his surgical wounds!"

"Very well," Sims said, as skeptical as ever but wishing to calm me. "I shall do that if you for your part do what I prescribe. I am going to give you another dose of morphine, and then you must sleep, stay quiet, and remain here in this house until you are well enough to travel to Karlsbad without risk."

Today, when all the key events and interrelationships in the history of gall bladder surgery lie plainly before me, much of what happened that evening and during the subsequent months seems to me like a series of acts in a world-wide drama staged by destiny.

During those same May days of the year 1867 when after several months of confinement to my bed in Paris I was carried cautiously into a carriage and driven to the train in order to take my cure at Karlsbad, another carriage, an old-fashioned gig, was rolling along a bumpy, unpaved street in the American Midwest, several thousand miles away. Indianapolis, the capital of Indiana, was at this time a small town with few residences of any size or substance. The gig rattled loudly as it turned into Washington Street and came to a standstill in front of a frame house with a huge shingle which read: "John Stough Bobbs, M.D."

A tall man in a black suit helped a young woman out of the gig. He had to half carry her, for she could barely walk. The woman was at most twenty-eight or thirty. But her complexion had that pallid greenish hue typical of internal diseases, and her eyes were those of a person who year after year, day after day, was racked by intense pain. She held her right hand pressed against her right breast, while with her left hand she clung to her escort. He helped her over the threshold into a dusky waiting room, sat her in a tall chair in a corner, and strode straight into the doctor's adjoining consulting room. Gruffly, he said without preliminary: "Dr. Bobbs, I have brought my patient. Take a look at her."

The doctor rose from behind a desk covered with books. He was spare-bodied and of medium height, and was simply dressed in a linsey-woolsey coat. But the powerful brow, the even more powerful nose, the strong, prominent chin, and the shaggy goatee would never be forgotten by anyone who met him. John Stough Bobbs was at this time fifty-eight years old. He had been born in Green Village, Pennsylvania, on December 28, 1809, the son of parents of German descent. As a child he spoke nothing but Pennsylvania Dutch, and only learned to speak and write English later in his boyhood. At the age of sixteen he was apprenticed to a country doctor named Martin Luther, in Harrisburg, Pennsylvania, and as was usually the case with such apprenticeships was more engaged with caring for the horse and carriage and distilling whiskey for the doctor than with the study of medicine. Afterwards he had practiced as best he could in Middletown, gone to Indiana in 1835, and later returned to Pennsylvania to attend Jefferson Medical College in Philadelphia. Strangely enough, Sims was there at the same time, a fellow pupil under old McCallem. The young doctors had watched many an amputation, lithotomy, and lancing performed upon unanesthetized patients, with the surgeon constantly exhorting: "Courage, my sturdy boy, courage; we hurt to heal. It will soon be over; courage, my sturdy boy!" His studies over, Bobbs, with his old-fashioned surgical tools, a box of plasters, a few Latin books, and works of Voltaire, Hume, Gibbon, and Paine in his saddlebags, turned up in Indianapolis—to outward appearances a Philadelphia gentleman in tails and tall silk hat who addressed everyone as Sir or Madam, but actually a countryman as tough and hard as his future patients. He survived the cholera epidemic of 1854 which swept from Chicago through Michigan and carried away thousands, and as the years went on he won the reputation of cutting where no one else dared. He became professor of surgery at the newly established Medical College of Indianapolis, played a central part in the founding of the first medical society in that city, served at Laurel Hill under General Morris during the Civil War, learned to use chloroform, and owed his successes in lithotomy, amputation, and the extirpation of tumors—like McDowell and the other pioneers of those early days—to the tough constitutions of his patients and to the chance fact that in spite of ignorance of antisepsis he habitually washed his hands thoroughly before operations.

As was his custom, Bobbs donned his most solemn expression. Later, after his death, when I learned his story and travelled to Indianapolis, I found the consulting room just as he had left it. This was shortly before the house was torn down to make way for the State Life Insurance Building. I stood in the dark, old-fashioned room and imagined I could hear Bobbs's rasping voice saying to his colleague: "Well, bring her in. Have her undress and lie down on the couch."

From what other patients reported of the doctor's procedure it is easy to reconstruct that historic consultation. With his studied dignity and solemnity, Bobbs waited until the young woman, her face twisted with pain, lay exhausted on the old, leather-covered divan.

"Madam," he said, "I understand your name is Mary E. Wiggins?" Mary Wiggins, dying of shame at her nakedness, and attempting to shield her body with thin, worn, pin-pricked seamstress's hands, could not conceal the curious swelling on the right side of her pelvis. She nodded dumbly. "Well," Bobbs rasped, "tell me what is wrong with you."

The patient looked toward her doctor, Newcomer. Her look seemed to ask him to explain for her. But Bobbs moved between her and the doctor. "Madam," he said, "I want to hear the story from you yourself."

Faltering, faintingly, she explained. Bobbs listened, interrupting her only once or twice with a terse question.

Mary E. Wiggins had been working for years at her sewing machine, in her small house in a suburb of Indianapolis. Four years ago she had first felt a hard swelling, large as a hickory nut, on the right side of her body. This swelling had not been sensitive to pressure. But soon afterwards she began suffering from stomach-aches and abdominal cramps. Pain soon followed every meal, every drink, and grew worse from month to month. Sometimes the attacks lasted three or four hours at a time. As she lay writhing with pain on her bed or on the floor, she had often wished herself dead. The tumor had steadily enlarged from year to year. Finally it had become impossible for her to continue to do the sewing, on which her livelihood depended. During the whole of last winter she had been unable to walk a step. Only large quantities of opium would temporarily alleviate the pain. For months she had been living on tea and bread.

When she had finished her account, Bobbs looked at Dr. Newcomer. "Your diagnosis?" he asked.

Newcomer replied that he thought an ovarian tumor probable. That is why he had come. Ovarian tumors had been successfully removed by McDowell in Kentucky, and lately by Spencer Wells in London. Bobbs, he thought, would no doubt operate on such a tumor in the same fashion. Operation was obviously Mary Wiggins's last chance. She was prepared to take any risk.

Bobbs did not answer. He washed his hands, and silently proceeded to examine the patient. He found a large tumor in the right iliac region. Only the lower right edge of it could be precisely defined. To the left, above and below, no limit could be felt. The tumor could be moved from left to right, but each time he touched it Mary Wiggins uttered a gurgling cry. He examined her abdomen, moving the tumor with one hand, the uterus with the other. Mouth wide with agony, Mary Wiggins moaned. But Bobbs found no connection between the uterus and the tumor. The uterus did not seem enlarged. It did not protrude over the pelvic bone. Once more Bobbs tried to find the posterior boundary of the tumor. He was determined to discover what organ it rested on, what organ it was connected with. But his efforts were in vain.

Bobbs straightened up. After a few minutes of tense, gloomy silence, he stated that he could find no proof of the existence of an ovarian tumor.

Newcomer looked down at his faintly whimpering patient. "Are you sure?" he asked.

Bobbs washed and dried his ruddy hands, washed and dried them again and again. He did not reply directly to the question. No one was ever to learn what had made him doubt the presence of ovarian tumor, and what at the same time attracted him to the mysterious case of Mary Wiggins. In his own report he passed over the question. He lived on the margin of the so-called civilized world. Nevertheless from time to time the papers of famous surgeons reached him from Europe, from Paris, London, or Berlin. He knew that the removal of ovarian tumors had been ventured by few surgeons indeed up to this year of 1867. He knew also that Spencer Wells, so famous for his ovarian operations, undertook them only under strictly defined conditions. The tumor, ordinarily connected to the ovaries by a stem, had to be so large that it would well out of the abdominal wound after the first few incisions. The stem had to be severed outside the abdominal cavity and be clamped to the outside until the wound healed. But what was the condition of this poor woman who lay on the couch before him? Everything seemed to contraindicate an ovarian tumor. Probably this was an unknown, possibly malignant growth, which no surgeon had ever yet ventured to attack. On the other hand, if this were an ovarian tumor, it by no means had attained the size Spencer Wells stipulated before he would consent to operate.

"Dr. Bobbs," Newcomer declared, "Spencer Wells has erred in diagnosis more than once because he is too cautious. He has refused operations and then discovered in autopsy that there had been an operable ovarian tumor."

Bobbs thrust out his chin, and the color of his face changed.

"Are you questioning my courage?" he growled.

"I am speaking of Wells," Newcomer said, "and of Mary, who has come to you to beg you to help her or ease her from a life that is no longer worth living."

"Release from life is God's business, not the physician's," Bobbs retorted.

Later, when it was all over, Newcomer admitted that he had been aware of Bobbs's sensitivity to aspersions on his courage, and had deliberately challenged him to force his hand.

Bobbs stood silent for a long while. Then he turned to the patient once more. "Madam," he declared, "you want me to cut you open, even if you die under the knife?" The patient nodded with that desperate resolution which comes only after protracted suffering.

"And you are prepared to repeat your consent in the presence of witnesses, and to accept the possibility that if there is no ovarian tumor, the operation will have to be suspended?"

The patient nodded again. Bobbs was now squarely up against a question of conscience, as was every surgeon of his day when he contemplated a step into the vast unexplored regions of the body. He faced a crisis of the soul that scarcely any contemporary physician can grasp.

Bobbs decided that he wanted to wait another two weeks. He would then examine the patient once more. If the second examination produced nothing new, above all no additional reasons for not operating, he would go ahead.

What he said was both evasion and acceptance of an obligation. Mary Wiggins, however, heard only the acceptance, and this gave her the strength to endure for another two weeks. Newcomer took her back to her humble little house. On June 14 he returned with her to Washington Street. Bobbs made the following notes concerning this crucial consultation: "The examination yielded nothing new. It strengthened my previous opinion that the tumor had no connection with the organs of the lower abdomen. But nothing definite could be ascertained concerning its character or its connection with other organs. The patient was informed that the ovarian character of the tumor was extremely doubtful. . . . She nevertheless insisted so strongly upon removal of the tumor that I finally declared my readiness to make the attempt."

Bobbs had the patient taken on the morning of June 15 to a third-floor room above Vinton and Kiefer's drugstore, on the corner of Meridian and Pearl Streets. He was in the habit of renting this room for operating purposes. Newly operated-on patients remained there until they recovered or died. A nurse remained in attendance. When Bobbs himself trudged up the steep flight of stairs to the room, he found awaiting him, in addition to the patient, the greater part of the Indianapolis medical profession. Besides F. S. Newcomer there were Doctors R. N. Todd, George W. Mears, John P. Avery, D. H. Oliver, John Comingor, and a student named John Cameron, a nephew of his wife's. They had all been invited to be present. Bobbs wanted plenty of witnesses to see that he was acting to the best of his knowledge and ability.

The operating room was nothing but a bare, extremely simple place with a wooden table, a bed, and a chamber pot.

Bobbs laid aside his coat and bound about him a towel which had been hanging from a hook by the door. While the nurse pushed two chairs toward the operating table, and placed on them two bowls of water, Bobbs arranged his instruments on a third chair which was covered with a cloth.

"Have the gentlemen present noted that Miss Wiggins desires the operation no matter what its consequences?" he asked.

"They have," Newcomer replied, chloroform mask in hand.

"Very well," Bobbs said. "Then pour on the stuff."

He waited until the patient, after several painful fits of coughing, sank into unconsciousness. Then he took one of his scalpels and without further ado made an incision between navel and pubic bone. He worked with the swiftness of those surgeons who had grown up in the preanesthetic age, when every second spared would save the patient pain.

The abdominal wall gaped open at once. It scarcely bled. The mesentery had adhered to the wall. With lighting speed Bobbs thrust a finger into the incision. He loosened the mesentery all around. Immediately afterwards a firm protrusion appeared, taut under the mesentery. With two fingers of each hand Bobbs made a rent in the mesentery. The index finger of his right hand grasped the tumor. He loosened it, and its interior attachments. A bulbous object, of a glistening, whitish color, was forced upward. Bobbs tried to seize it with his hand. But the incision in the abdominal wall was still too small.

Once again he took up his scalpel, enlarged the incision, and drew out the head of the tumor. Then he entered the wound with his hand, groping for that pedicle on which an ovarian tumor should be located. He found no such formation. His pessimism, then, had not been unjustified. The tumor adhered, firmly attached, somewhere in the middle of the abdominal cavity. It was, as far as could be seen, some four inches long by about two inches wide. Its walls appeared thin, translucent, and filled almost to bursting with an equally translucent fluid.

Bobbs pressed the tumor in his left hand. Inside the fluid he felt a firm body, then two, then three. He hesitated. His fingers felt here and there. Again he hesitated, wholly perplexed by this riddle. And then his scalpel sliced through the wall of the tumor.

With a whistling noise fluid spurted out of the opened sac. Along with the jet of fluid some hard bodies flew out. The slap of them could be heard on the wooden floor, followed by another impact and then a pitter-pattering like a shower of hailstones.

Bobbs stood stock-still, the now limp sac in his left hand, the knife in his right. His eyes and the eyes of all the others present in the room stared at the floor. They saw a number of brittle, yellowish, pebbly objects, glistening with moisture, about the size of ordinary buckshot. Bobbs shook off his numbness. His index finger probed inside the tumor.

A moment later there lay in his hand a number of stones and tiny pebbles, all having that same ugly sheen as the ones scattered on the floor, ranging from a mustard seed to a hazelnut in size. The things Bobbs held, the things that lay glittering on the floor, were plainly gallstones. The tumor he had opened could be nothing more nor less than a gall bladder inflamed and enlarged by an accumulation of stones that had gathered for many years.

The whole thing was so fantastic that Bobbs looked for more evidence. More and more stones were scraped out by his finger. The sac seemed to be divided into two parts. In its rear was a cavity which seemed to have a partition wall of its own. Within it, Bobbs's finger detected a stone the size of a rifle bullet. But he could not manage to grip it. Finally he pulled the tumor downward, at which the lower right lobe of the liver appeared, with the sac firmly attached to it.

There could no longer be any doubt. Mary Wiggins had suffered from gallstones, and Bobbs had performed an operation of which he had never heard and never read. But there was no time for him to stand amazed. Nor was there time for him to total up and be alarmed at all the new contingencies that faced him. What was he going to do with the now empty sac? Impossible simply to return it to the abdominal cavity! Its secretions of gall would flow into the cavity, cause peritonitis, and lead to certain death. Equally impossible to sever the sac, since it was obviously identical with the gall bladder. Was not a person without a gall bladder condemned to certain death? Nor could the incision in the gall bladder be simply sewed up. What stitches would be firm and close enough to retain the flow of gall? And what would happen with the threads? According to all of Bobbs's knowledge, the stitches would suppurate in the abdominal cavity and likewise produce peritonitis.

Bobbs had only a few seconds in which to make a decision. According to his notions, which were the notions of the day, every additional moment allowed poisonous air to penetrate into the abdominal cavity and thus increased the peril of peritonitis. He therefore acted almost by instinct rather than long reflection. He stitched up the incision in the gall bladder, and placed this incision so close to the incision in the abdominal wall that it would have to heal right there. In a flash it occurred to him that in this way he not only avoided the perils of stitches deep in the abdominal cavity: if the complaint recurred, he would simply have to open the scars in the abdominal wall. Since there was one stone he had been unable to remove, it was reasonable to leave the way open for a future operation.

He stitched up the abdominal incision, covered it with plasters, and stood erect, taking deep breaths. Newcomer and the nurse carried Mary Wiggins to bed and gave her thirty drops of opium when she came out of the anesthesia.

Then began the wait for fate's or nature's verdict. Bobbs had been through this period of suspense so often in his career as a surgeon that most of the time it scarcely bothered him. But this time he fretted. Several times a day he trudged up the steep flight of stairs to Mary Wiggins's room to examine the operative wound. He changed the dressings frequently, each time expecting to discover the first traces of malignant suppuration and fatal peritonitis. But nothing of the sort developed.

By June 22 the larger part of the incision had healed. Purulent matter oozed out from only one spot. This alarming suppuration lasted for only a few days, however. By July 7 the patient was able to sit up in bed. A week later she went downstairs for the first time, and in another week she was allowed to go home. In all this time she had not suffered a single attack of her former pain. She resumed her work as a dressmaker, remarried, and as Mrs. Burnsworth lived for many years. On occasion she suffered a slight complaint which she attributed to the stone that had not been removed. She survived Bobbs, who died on May 1, 1870. She survived all but two of the doctors who had been present at the operation.

There are no certain indications whether John Stough Bobbs died in the clear awareness of having performed the first gallstone operation in medical history. Later, when I learned of this operation, which was quite unknown in the outside world, I went to the Middle West to see whether I could find traces of Bobbs's solitary feat. No one who knew him could tell me what he had thought about it. Perhaps he had suspected, perhaps hoped, that it would prove important. But probably he did not know how unique his operation was, any more than I knew of it as I sat waiting in Karlsbad for the famous waters to take effect—during those same June days of the year 1867. And while I waited I suffered agonies of mind at the thought that no radical, surgical remedy for gallstones existed.

Had I known during that summer in Karlsbad that more than fifteen years would go by before the problem of gallstone surgery approached a solution, who can say whether even my constitutional optimism would not have flagged?

As far as I know, surgical solution of the gallstone problem began in 1879. It was initiated by Lawson Tait of Birmingham, undoubtedly one of the most eccentric, stubborn, and unusual men ever to wield a scalpel. When I first met Tait, twelve years had passed since that day in Paris when the stones in my gall bladder first caused me pain. During those years I had died many deaths. I had endured the greatest agonies that human beings can suffer. More than once I had been on the brink of morphine addiction, and in the end had steeled myself to the constant nearness of death. I never travelled without supplies of morphine, and rarely made a trip without at least being reminded of my illness. Nevertheless, I had garnered a host of new experiences. My trouble subsided for a time, and I passed through a period of apparent health which lasted several years. It was after an unforgettable voyage to the South Seas that Lawson Tait first entered my life.

On a day in late autumn of the year 1879 I arrived in Paris. One of the first persons I visited was Marion Sims. In the interval Sims had tried going back to the States, and opening an office in New York. He had forgotten much of the unpleasantness and evils of the Civil War years, and had even come around to a grudging approval of Lincoln's defense of the Union. Nevertheless, he had never felt entirely at his ease in New York. In 1872 he was appointed surgeon in the Women's Hospital in New York. His presence there promptly attracted patients and observers from all over the world.

In 1874, however, he resigned in a huff when the hospital administration tried to restrain him—on the basis of an old ordinance—from admitting more than fifteen spectators (doctors and medical students) to his gynecological operations. In the administration's view, any greater number constituted an offense to female modesty. To Sims, this incident was the breaking point, and he had returned to his old mode of life—that is, to spending most of his time in Europe, in either Paris or Rome. His fame and the number of his patients had by no means diminished. He struck me, however, as looking rather worn. Two years before in New York he had suffered a severe bout of pneumonia which had left its traces upon his tough physique, tried by so many diseases.

"Well," he exclaimed, when his old Negro servant had led me to him, "how vividly I remember the day you lay stretched out on my couch here in Paris, and Trousseau diagnosed your trouble. Remember your desperation—how nothing would do but I must cut out your stones and save your life. You've always been a great one for pushing medical progress before the time was ripe. Never wanted to wait." His eyes roved over my face. "You need not tell me that you have been through several infernos. But you're alive, and you certainly look better than I do."

He smiled, and turned the talk to political matters for a while. But by and by he returned to his reminiscences. "Remember, you were obsessed by a single thought: to see the development of gallstone surgery before your own stones were the death of you. That was how you put it. Now I understand that you have just come back from the South Seas? Then you have probably been out of touch with scientific developments. Or are you already aware that what you so longed for has come to pass?"

He was right; I had been out of touch, and had heard nothing lately of any experiments in the field of gallstone surgery. Watching the little twinkle on Sims's face, a suspicion dawned on me. "Was it you . . . ?" He shook his head. "No," he said. But then he added: "I only had a try at it."

"So you did!" There rose vividly before my eyes that scene in Sims's house, more than a decade past, when I had implored him to study Lister's antiseptic technique and turn his surgical skill to the removal of gallstones. Had my desperate appeals touched his heart after all? "So you did!" I repeated.

Sims did not answer directly. "If I know you," he said, "you have been studying everything ever written about gallstones and the possibilities of removing them surgically."

I nodded.

"Well," said Sims, "I have done likewise. At least your persuasion led me that far. Surgery has, after all, profited more than once by such historical studies."

"Then you have come upon something that passed me by in that hopeless story," I replied.

It was no exaggeration to speak of the story as hopeless. I had come across an endless series of useless theoretical recommendations, and no account of practice whatsoever. I could have recited the whole thing by heart, case by case, phase by phase. It began with an offhand comment on the part of Alexander of Tralles, physician of the sixth century A.D., that in diseased livers the air became inflamed and transformed into stone. Some thousand years later there was a brief acount by Benivieni concerning the discovery of stones in the gall bladder of a woman "who died in abdominal pain." Then, in 1570, came the report of a dissection performed by a Dr. Fernandus Fall, who had discovered in the body of a dead woman a perforated gall bladder, a large stone in the abdominal cavity, and signs of fatal peritonitis. Finally, in 1655, a French physician named Glisson described his own gall colics, "from which there is no release except by death."

Another short account, written about 1630 by Zambeccari, an Italian anatomist, described the opening and sewing up of the gall bladder of a living dog. The dog was killed after two months, and the incision in the gall bladder was found to have adhered to the abdominal wall. During the two remaining months of the dog's life there had been no signs of any disturbance of the gall bladder's functions or of the flow of gall into the intestines. In 1667 Dr. Stalpert von der Wiel discovered a purulent abscess on the upper abdomen of a patient who had been suffering frightful agonies for years. He opened the abscess, and found to his surprise that the discharge from it contained gall and stony concretions which had been forced out along with the fluid contents. It is difficult to say whether the doctor himself realized that he was confronting a rare maneuver on the part of nature. After years of vain efforts to discharge the stones into the intestines, the body had finally forced them out through the abdominal wall. In any case, if Stalpert von der Wiel did realize this, he drew no conclusions from the fact. It did not occur to him that nature was literally showing the surgeon the approach to the gall bladder.

Later in the seventeenth century, however, Petit, the most noted Parisian surgeon of the day, again studied the type of abscesses Stalpert had described. Petit did draw conclusions. He proposed that the surgeon not wait until the abscess had matured, after years of torment. He believed that the formation of the abscess began with adhesion of the inflamed, calculous gall bladder to the abdominal wall. Once this adhesion took place, he concluded, an incision could be made directly into the gall bladder without simultaneously opening up the abdominal cavity and producing peritonitis. Therefore he suggested that at the first sign of reddening skin on the abdomen the surgeon lance the newly forming abscess and draw the stones from the gall bladder with forceps. Of course a gall fistula would remain. But, he wrote, "what would this be compared to the preceding torment? How many persons have died because the disease was not recognized, or because no surgeon could be found who dared to liberate the patient from his illness by operation!"

What noble words! But there was no indication that Petit ever followed his own prescription. And if so, whom would his operation have helped, aside from those few persons in whose unusually robust bodies nature herself had already begun the process of self-healing? Petit's suggestion remained nothing more than a proposal to accelerate a rare natural event.

New proposals by other surgeons followed. In 1744 a Berlin doctor named Bloch theorized that the adhesion between the abdominal wall and the diseased gall bladder could be artificially stimulated. He recommended the application of powerful irritants to the skin in the region of the gall bladder, until adhesion occurred. Thereupon, Bloch declared, incision and removal of the gallstones should be possible. He did not, however, say a word about any practical attempt of this sort. In 1798 Dr. Richter proposed that the swollen gall bladder be pierced with a pointed tube, through the abdominal wall, the stones rinsed out, and the tube left in the body until the hole in the gall bladder adhered to the hole in the abdominal wall and all danger of peritoneal infection was past.

But this too remained a mere idea which no one attempted to apply.

Sixty years of helpless silence followed. At last, in 1859, new proposals were launched. Their authors were Dr. Thudichum, a German-born Englishman, and Dr. Carré, a Frenchman. Both physicians recommended incision of the abdominal wall, drawing the gall bladder up into the incision with lightning speed, and sewing it there. There would then follow a wait of several days to give the gall bladder a chance to adhere. Finally the stones would be extracted, and the sealing of the incision left to the body's natural healing process. But as far as I knew this, too, had remained in the realm of theory—empty words, with none of that courage behind them mandatory for success in surgery. Fear of peritonitis and the shrinking from society's condemnation of boldness had apparently stifled all action, even where death had in any case already laid its hands upon the patient. Lister's discovery of antisepsis had produced no change in the situation. . . .

I heard Sims saying: "You are familiar with the suggestion Thudichum made twenty years ago. . . . You must certainly know it."

I nodded. "Good," Sims said. "I have tried it—just a year and a half ago. Tried it on a young American here in Paris. She was twenty-five years old, an intelligent, beautiful woman, the mother of one child. Since 1877 she had been suffering from increasingly violent pain in the right upper abdomen. When I saw her for the first time she was extremely jaundiced. Her skin had almost the hue of mahogany. She was no longer able to eat, constantly threw up, screamed with pain. All internal medicaments were ineffective. Her husband had consulted half a dozen doctors, including Péan, in vain. I need not tell you that I was reminded of your history when I saw the poor woman. I found a movable, fluctuating tumor which seemed to be connected with the liver. I immediately suspected a calculous, inflamed, greatly enlarged gall bladder. And I thought of everything I had learned since your first attack. I thought of Thudichum and Carré, and of Lister, whose antiseptic procedure you urged upon me at the time. I had since tried it frequently and with success in abdominal operations. If I carried out Thudichum's suggestion under antiseptic conditions, I thought, it should be possible to draw the gall bladder up to the abdominal walls without too great danger. Under the protection of carbolic spray it should also be possible, without first sewing and then waiting for adhesion, to incise the gall bladder at once, remove the stones, and then sew the bladder to the abdominal incision. Either the wound would heal and I would then have the attached gall bladder easily within reach under the abdominal wall if new concretions formed, or else a fistula would remain. That, of course, would have to be constantly treated and kept bandaged, but it would also facilitate later removal of new stones in the gall bladder."

Sims fell silent for a moment. I did not break in, but restrained my eager questions. Ignorant as I was then of Bobbs's success, I thought Sims was about to tell me of a triumph for which I had waited in vain for more than a decade. I was simply incapable of speech just then.

"Nevertheless, I did not decide at once to take this step," Sims continued. "There is no use in blinking the truth of the matter. I realized that I too was by no means free of our deep-seated fear of the world which is so ready to denounce us whenever we venture anything new, and fail. Since the tumor could be felt so easily, I first sought a stratagem which might keep me from taking the crucial step. I punctured the tumor through the abdominal wall. From the trocar flowed thirty-two ounces of dark-brown bile. The diagnosis was evidently correct. The patient felt almost instantaneous relief. For two days she was without pain, but then all the symptoms reappeared, worse than before. Her completely jaundiced body was subjected to a fearful itch which allowed her no rest by day or night. For as long as she had strength, she crouched on elbows and knees, so that her body would not touch the bed. But the abdominal colic prevented her from keeping this position for very long. Altogether, she was a truly horrible and piteous sight."

Sims looked at me, and guessed what was going on in my mind. "I know that you have endured a great deal. But luckily you have never reached that stage, or you would not be sitting here. It was so frightful, and so hopeless, that I decided to venture the operation I had conceived. Dr. Hauden, Dr. Bremond, and Dr. Pratt assisted me at the patient's house. We worked strictly according to Lister's principles, with carbolic spray. It was an unusually long time, almost half an hour, before the anesthetic took effect. But then everything went surprisingly well. We encountered a huge, swollen tumor under the lower rim of the liver. In order to discover whether this was in truth the enlarged gall bladder, I had to penetrate deeply into the abdomen with my hands, which would have been fatal but for my confidence in the antiseptic measures. We drew part of the gall bladder to the edges of the abdominal incision. I opened the bladder and found, as soon as a fresh quantity of blocked fluid was discharged, more than half a dozen gallstones, some of which had completely blocked the bile duct. These I removed. The operation required, up to the sewing of the gall bladder opening into the upper corner of the abdominal incision, the closing of the rest of the incision, and the dressing, a total of one hour and sixteen minutes. During the following days the patient felt enormously relieved. I was already thinking the operation a success. Then she died, eight days and ten hours after the operation, of a massive internal hemorrhage.

"Forgive me," Sims went on, "if I say little more about this affair. To me it was a frightful shock. Nevertheless I am convinced that the operation could be developed, and that it ought to be successful. I gave it the name 'cholecystotomy' at the time, and I had made up my mind to try it again on a patient suffering the same disease, but this time not on one who had reached such a stage of hopelessness and exhaustion of the vital forces." He looked at me with an expression of resignation. Then he said: "Someone has beat me to it."

"Who?" I asked.

"Lawson Tait. Of Birmingham. I'm sure you have heard his name. He is at present the greatest and most successful rival of Spencer Wells in the operation on ovarian tumors, and has performed several hundred successful operations, with a mortality of only 13 per cent. It is curious, is it not, that gynecologists have been the first to attempt gall bladder surgery? But who else among surgeons have undertaken abdominal operations on such a scale? At any rate, just two months ago—on August 23—Tait in his private hospital in Birmingham operated on a woman of forty, following my method. He removed two large gallstones, sewed the gall bladder to the incision, and has achieved complete cure, except for a fistula. I come by this knowledge from Tait himself, who wrote informing me that he had adopted my procedure. He has not yet reported publicly on the operation, but intends to do so in London on November 11."

Sims bowed his head, and his expression of disappointment grew more pronounced. "I suggest that you go to see Tait," he said. "I'll give you a letter to him." He smiled. "If you can bear up for a few years more, even the largest collection of gallstones will not be able to put you in your grave. I have begun to feel old and tired out lately. But Tait is thirty-four years old, half my age. In time he will develop the cholecystotomy into as neat an operation as the ovariotomy, and you will have no compunctions about entrusting your health and life to him."

A week later I set out for Birmingham. For twelve years I had lived in utter dependency upon the vagaries of a few stones, and with the consciousness that nothing could help me. Now a man existed whose skill could save me if the disease should bring me into peril of death. Merely knowing this seemed to give me a second life.

In London I called on Lister. For the past two years he had been holding the post of professor at King's College, where he had wider opportunities for teaching antisepsis—which, while it made great strides elsewhere in the world, was still strongly opposed in England. I mentioned that I was on my way to see Tait. Lister stiffened and appeared a bit morose. "I have heard about his operation," he said. "But I suggest that you do not mention my name when you visit him. Tait is a sworn foe of antisepsis. Like Spencer Wells, he had considerable success with operations on ovarian tumors before my discovery, and some time ago reported a series of fifty cases with only 13 per cent fatalities, as against 25 per cent in Wells's operations. He is supposed to have tried out carbolic spray in the meanwhile. But like so many others he has no doubt used the technique superficially and incorrectly. Now he dismisses my work as sheer nonsense. His speeches and articles are sharp, not to say vicious, in tone."

Lister was unaware, of course, what damage this piece of information did to my hopes. So Tait, whom I had been exalting as one of the pioneers of a great future for surgery, worked without antisepsis—at this late date, in the year 1879. It was simply inconceivable that he should nevertheless be meeting with success in his cholecystotomies.

With feelings of mounting uncertainty, I arrived in Birmingham. Tait was something of a local celebrity here. Even the porter knew that he operated at Spark Hill Hospital and, when I wondered where his home and private hospital were located, was able to reply, "Crescent 7, sir."

I sent a boy to Tait with Sims's letter of recommendation. The messenger was gone several hours before he was back at the hotel with a reply, evidently written by a secretary. It read simply: "Tomorrow morning at eleven o'clock." Not a word more.

Tait's house, which also contained his private hospital, was a rather dreary, unattractive, boxlike building, resembling hundreds of others in Birmingham. At the door stood a waiting victoria drawn by two gray horses. I ascended a worn, uninviting stoop and entered a room occupied by a secretary, a youngish man who was at the moment taking dictation. The words he was transcribing came from the adjoining room, through a speaking tube let into the wall. A booming, rather choleric voice crackled through the tube:

"Write the fellow that I'll be damned before I'll do as he asks."

"Very well, Mr. Tait," the secretary said. "I shall write that Mr. Lawson Tait regrets that he is not in a position to grant your request."

The voice from the speaking tube roared with fury: "I did not say that!"

"Certainly, certainly," the secretary murmured, "but it amounts to the same thing and sounds better."

"The devil take you!" the voice retorted. "We'll discuss this later. I am busy."

"Mr. Tait," the red-haired secretary called, glancing at my card, "Dr. Hartmann from New York has just arrived." There was no answer. The secretary shrugged. "Mr. Tait is about to operate," he said hurriedly. "Come with me, sir; otherwise I will not have a chance to introduce you to him before the afternoon visiting hour."

He led me down a dim corridor. Somewhere a door was slammed and a powerful but nevertheless pleasant voice growled: "Where in hell is that nurse, Mary?" And a woman's voice replied in language which quite took my breath away: "I don't know where the bloody girl has gone!"

At this moment we stepped into a somewhat lighter corridor. I saw a young nurse, and facing her a middle-sized man with broad shoulders and coarse frame, wearing a large rubber apron. The stocky body was topped by a massive round head and thick, flowing hair. The man's hairy arms were bare.

The eyes in Tait's florid face glowed with wrath. They reminded me of the look in Simpson's eyes, especially during those later days in Dublin when he had declared war on Lister. Tait's glance shifted rapidly from the nurse to me. His thin but finely shaped lips under the huge nose seemed about to part in another curse when the secretary moved swiftly between us and identified me. I heard the name Sims. Then the surgeon's eyes flashed again in my direction.

"Well," he grumbled, but there was a distinct change in tone, an almost tangible effort at courtesy, "if you want to see something, come along. We can talk later."

He wheeled around and tramped down the corridor, followed by the nurse and an assistant. The nurse opened a door which led into a bare operating room. On a wooden table covered only with a waterproof cloth lay a woman. Alongside stood another table with various bowls of cold and steaming hot water, a great deal of soap, and many towels which looked extremely clean. Instruments and sponges were arranged on a towel. But that was all.

Lister had been right. There were no bowls of carbolic acid, no instruments in carbolic acid, no cloths dipped in carbolic acid for covering the operating field, no spray—none of the many implements of antisepsis which Lister had introduced into surgery and which had resulted in so beneficent a revolution.

Tait washed the woman's abdomen with soap and water. The assistant administered chloroform. Tait opened the abdomen with a strikingly short incision. A few further incisions, and those fat, coarse-looking, but extremely skillful fingers reached deep into the pelvic cavity. Apparently Tait was freeing growths by feel alone. Sponges stilled the small hemorrhages. A blood vessel spurted. Tait's head whirled around. He thrust the handle of the scalpel between his teeth and with both hands ligatured the vessel. At the moment that he turned I saw the expression on his face, a peculiar expression of wild gaiety. He seemed to be taking a fierce pleasure in what he was doing.

The vessel tied, he drew the handle of the scalpel from between his teeth. A few swift incisions followed, and then the scalpel was tucked back between those predatory teeth again. Once more he ligatured vessels, once more used the scalpel. The severed adnexa were dropped into a refuse pail. A few more ligatures. Then the stitching of the abdominal wall, performed with a wizard's speed and without any help. His assistant had to administer the chloroform; beyond that he did nothing. Finally the dressing—and the whole operation had taken less than eight minutes. Tait washed his hands in hot water. He hung his apron on a nail in the wall and threw a penetrating look at me. "So you have come from Dr. Sims to see about my cholecystotomy?" he asked. Before I could reply he was out the door, signalling me to follow him. We entered a dimly lit ward in which lay many women. Even more distinctly than in the operating room there wafted to my nostrils what Lister had called the "stench of the slaughterhouse," that peculiar odor which in all hospitals run on antiseptic principles had long since yielded to the smell of carbolic acid. Surprisingly enough, however, I did not detect that reek of pus and decay which was so common in the old, preantiseptic hospitals. Nevertheless the air seemed to me repellent.

"Smell the natural air?" Tait growled. "None of that chemical stench with which a certain gentleman in London has befouled hospital wards. We have no fear of those imaginary creatures he calls germs. Plenty of good English water and good English soap will send them packing better than all his chemicals. I am a practical man and don't give a damn for all these philosophical arguments. Good common sense is what counts."

Several of the women moaned. They were evidently in pain. Pausing at the last bed, Tait threw a quick look at me. The horror that had passed briefly over my face did not escape him. "In my hospital we do without medicines that keep down pain," he said. "Those are only good for people who are going to die."

Was he utterly emotionless, a cold technician, like Péan in Paris? Had he himself never suffered pain? Had he, the first surgeon in Europe successfully to remove gallstones, no conception of the agony that such stones could cause? Had he mercilessly allowed the gallstone patients whom he had restored to a bearable life to suffer intolerably beforehand, simply out of some strange fanaticism? Had he carried out his cholecystotomy with the same furious haste that I had just witnessed?

"Well, come along," Tait said in another effort at politeness, "you must have lunch with me. Then I'll show you the gallstone patient. She is in top-notch condition. Unfortunately, I do not have another case that I can operate on before you."

Once more he did not wait for my reply, but stepped through a door which led into his private apartment. There he slipped into a black satin jacket which emphasized his solidity and corpulence. Two cats rubbed against his legs and purred. He bent down and stroked them. Then he took a bottle of whiskey and filled two large glasses. I took only a few sips, but he promptly downed his, and refilled it twice. "Sims," he said with a touch of grim humor, "wrote me about your stones. Whiskey will do them no harm—and if it does, I'll cut them out of you."

He led me through a second room which was stuffed with Chinese and Japanese curiosities. On a small table stood an open box containing pearls and precious ivory combs. "Gifts from a doctor's wife in Burma," he growled in passing. "With an ovarian tumor as large as a melon, she had herself carried on the backs of bearers several hundred miles through jungle to reach the ship, so that she could come to me." Beside the Oriental things I noticed a number of fine examples of ecclesiastical art, bejewelled crucifixes and miniatures. At that time I did not know that Tait was quite a connoisseur of such art, for all that he had early become an enthusiastic follower of the doctrines of Darwin and Huxley, had made himself a forthright foe of the Church, and during his university years in Edinburgh had been branded as a rebel. This was why he had never won the title of doctor, and had remained Mr. Tait.

We were alone in the dining room except for a servant who silently carried in large quantities of food and wine which Tait consumed with enormous appetite. He explained to me that Mrs. Tait was away, and that I would have to take potluck—and scarcely heeded whether or not I ate. Now and then he fed one of the blue Persian cats who had settled down beside his chair. When he had finished the meal with an enormous piece of cheese, and washed it down with two more glasses of wine, he looked up again for the first time, lit a fat cigar, and lurched to his feet.

"Time to get back to work," he said. "I shall show you my

Sir David Ferrier (1843–1928), whose experiments on apes showed the functions of the body to be controlled by specific brain centers.

Professor Friedrich Goltz (1834–1902). At the London Medical Congress of 1881 he expressed the sharpest criticism of Ferrier's theories.

*Sir James Paget (1814–99),
chairman of the 1881 London
Medical Congress.*

*Hordes of stray dogs, rounded up by the London police, were killed in gas
chambers, while the antivivisectionists fanatically fought experimentation on
animals.*

Theodor Kocher (1841–1917), out-standing pioneer of modern goiter surgery.

The Richsel sisters eight years after a goiter operation on Maria, the older (left). In mental and physical development she lagged far behind her younger sister.

William Macewen (*1848–1924*), the first surgeon to succeed in lancing cerebral abscesses and operating on cerebral hemorrhages.

Rickman Godlee (*1849–1925*), who undertook the first surgical extirpation of a cerebral tumor.

Brain from which a tumor has been removed. The hollow left by the excision is visible in the foreground.

Jean Martin Charcot (*1825–93*), outstanding French neurologist of his time.

Marion Sims (1813–83), who performed the first deliberate operation for gallstones.

John Stough Bobbs (1809–70), Indianapolis surgeon, who unwittingly performed the first gall bladder operation.

Friedrich von Esmarch (1823–1908) in his black operating gown.

Lawson Tait (1845–99), the "Bull of Birmingham," British surgeon noted for his extreme obstinacy.

Carl Langenbuch (1846–1901), founder of modern gall bladder surgery.

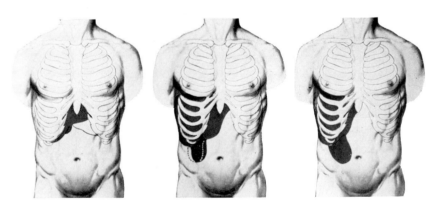

Healthy liver and gall bladder (left); gall bladders distorted by stones (center) and inflammation (right).

The Lazarus Hospital, North Berlin, where Langenbuch performed the first surgical removal of a calculous gall bladder, thus taking the decisive step toward modern surgery of this organ.

Sir Victor Horsley (1857–1916), the first to succeed in the removal of a tumor of the spinal cord.

Richard Gowers (1845–1915), who diagnosed the tumor on which Horsley operated.

John Hughlings Jackson (1835–1911), noted British neurologist and advocate of neurosurgery.

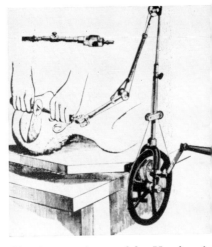

Circular saw, invented by Horsley, for cutting into the skull bone.

Sir Felix Semon, who took a major role in the tragedy of Emperor Friedrich III.

patient now. Come along. My regular visiting hour begins at twelve-thirty; there will be dozens waiting by now. I need only a minute for every examination, and only half a minute to tell each patient what is wrong. But even that consumes time."

He tossed his satin house coat onto a chair and put on a heavy tweed overcoat. Outside, the carriage and two gray horses were still standing, and we rode for about five minutes through streets I did not know, and stopped in front of a large house. Inside, a few moments later, a woman of about forty came to meet us. She appeared to be perfectly well. Tait introduced me hastily as an American friend and surgeon. "How do you feel?" he boomed.

"Oh, very well," the woman replied.

"Any trouble at all?"

"Only the fistula, which drains a great deal. But that is nothing compared to what I used to suffer." She looked at Tait with the blissful gaze of a patient who has been saved by a miracle. Tait asked her to take us to some private room and uncover the incision. As she complied, with a somewhat timid glance at me, he explained brusquely: "This patient came to me suffering severe cramps on the right side. I found a pendulous growth above the right kidney. There were only three possibilities: floating kidney, tumor of the pancreas, or gallstones with swelling of the gall bladder. On August 23 I made an incision four inches long through the abdominal wall, discovered the gallstones at once, drained with a needle ten ounces of blocked bile, opened the bladder, and found several large stones. One stone had to be broken up inside the gall bladder before it could be removed. The edges of the gall bladder were sewed to the upper corner of the abdominal incision. The patient was on her feet again after four weeks. As you can see, she no longer has any pain." With a quick jerk he removed an adhesive plaster which was holding in place a layer of gauze. I saw before me the healed scar of the incision, and a small, reddened opening at the upper end of the scar. From it dripped a few drops of bile. "A wonderful fistula," Tait said. "Some bile is running out of it. But for the most part it follows its natural path. The gall bladder has returned to its normal size, and if ever another stone should appear, we will break it up through the fistula."

He placed a new dressing on the fistula. "And the opening will really never heal up?" the woman asked.

"Of course not," Tait said. "Good day."

He scarcely gave me time to say my own goodbye, and kept the horses at a gallop back to Crescent 7. Eight or ten carriages had lined up there in the meantime.

"The same treadmill every day," he grumbled. "I must take my leave of you now. In London you can soon hear my detailed report on the operation—on November 11 at the meeting of the Royal Medical and Surgical Society. From what I know of those fine gentlemen, they will show little enthusiasm. But that does not trouble me. Perhaps I shall run across another gallstone case in the meanwhile. As I have said, if your condition should grow critical it will be a pleasure to me to remove the stones. But you must excuse me now!"

Ponderously, he tramped up the worn steps to his office and vanished behind the dingy gray door.

I left Birmingham that same evening. I cannot say that I had been deprived of the hopes with which I had come to Tait. It was still a comfort to know that a surgeon existed who would be able to operate upon me in the hour of dire need. But this comfort was rendered somewhat ambiguous by the impression Tait had made upon me. Now I could only pray that the extremity would not come which would give me up to Tait's mercies, that it would not come at all or, if it did, at least not until there were other surgeons who could perform the same operation. There was no denying to myself that this first meeting with Tait had been a shock. There was his stubborn rejection of antisepsis, which made me regard his successes as a mysterious succession of coincidences. How could I know whether his luck would hold in my case? There was his brutal harshness toward human suffering. And there was something else which I could not immediately formulate. It was something I had felt from the moment I saw the dripping fistula in the abdomen of Tait's first gallstone patient.

As long as all my thoughts had centered on the possibility of surgical removal of my gallstones, I had never asked the price I might have to pay. But now, the moment the possibility became a reality, that subjective change took place which can always be observed in people who are freed from the extremity of danger and immediately begin to forget the modesty which distress has taught them, and to raise their demands. I asked myself whether an operation which condemned one to a lifelong open fistula deserved the name of a cure. Why need the gall bladder be sewed to the abdominal wall? Why create a fistula which would never heal? True, there were grave dangers to sewing up an incised gall bladder and replacing it in the abdominal cavity. One could never be certain that the stitches would stop the efflux of bile and infectious matter. Moreover, it was certainly an advantage to have the bladder fixed to the abdominal wall so that it could be opened again with relative ease if a new accumulation of gallstones should develop. But was the gall bladder anything more than a storage chamber for bile which was then passed into the duodenum? Was it indispensable? Could not the bile flow directly from the liver through the hepatic duct and the common bile duct into the intestine? Could not the entire gall bladder be severed from the liver and removed, together with its stones? When I speak of these problems, it may seem as if I were laying claim to the ideas which later governed the course of gall bladder surgery. But these were only the questions I brooded on during the railroad journey from Birmingham to London.

The moment the train stopped in London and I leaned out the window to call a porter, the dreadful thing happened which I had been spared for some years past. The attack was very like the one I had experienced in Paris that evening with Marion Sims. The first flash of the pain struck into my right shoulder, then clawed my abdomen below my ribs on the right side. I gasped out two words: "Not Tait!"

In great distress I managed to reach the Westminster Palace Hotel, where I had reserved a suite. My pain was maddening and could only be allayed by heavy doses of morphine and belladonna, and an endless succession of hot compresses. I tried to get in touch with Lister, but could not reach him. Instead Sir James Paget came to see me, accompanied by an assistant who remained by my bedside all night. He diagnosed blockage of the bile duct by stones caught in the passage. My whole body assumed a yellowish hue. I was shaken by violent fits of vomiting. At the lower edge of my liver a swelling formed which increased in size from hour to hour.

The case histories of Sims's and Tait's patients preyed on my mind. At dawn I was also assailed by that burning itch which Sims had told me of.

The hotel's physician, Dr. Guild, was also called in, and as I lay half conscious and in frightful pain, he had two hotel servants come to help him administer a form of first aid which he had once employed on an Irish workman. After preparatory treatment of hot compresses and doses of belladonna, to enlarge the bile duct, he hung me upside down by the feet and rocked me back and forth, with the idea of causing the stone to fall back into the gall bladder. Under this treatment I finally lost consciousness. But the grotesque, wholly unorthodox experiment actually worked. Twenty-four hours later I woke up to discover that the pain was almost entirely gone. However, I needed another month of complete bed rest before I was on my feet again, and two more weeks of convalescence.

This was not the only miracle. At the end of the sixth week I received answers to the letters which I had sent out to various physicians of my acquaintance during my convalescence. Most of them offered mere consolations and proposed old-fashioned treatments. But one of the letters was from Professor Friedrich von Esmarch, whom I had met several years before in Kiel. Esmarch, at this time about fifty-six, had won fame by his method for temporarily reducing the supply of blood to the extremities by tying them with elastic rubber tapes. This was done in the interest of "bloodless" operations—or rather, operations with small loss of blood. He wrote at length and in terms which I found most enlightening.

"You may take heart," he wrote, "at the news that surgery of the gall bladder, following the procedure of Sims and Tait, has now reached the stage of rapid development. In Bern, Kocher is occupied with it. In your native land, Keen. König in Germany also proposes to attack the problem. And probably the most important progress will come from the young men. One of my assistants, Carl Langenbuch (who six years ago, at the age of twenty-seven, was appointed director of the well-known Lazarus Hospital in Berlin), was discussing this very problem with me a few days ago; why, he asked me, should we not remove the diseased gall bladder entirely? Experiments on animals appear to have proved that the gall bladder is by no means essential to life. This is also suggested by the fact that numerous persons are born without a gall bladder and nevertheless reach advanced ages. Langenbuch has the rare good fortune of heading both the surgical department and the department of internal medicine in his hospital. In the latter department he has had the opportunity of observing many cases of gallstones which in the ordinary course of events do not find their way to the surgeon's consulting room, since in our present state of knowledge they are not submissive to surgery. Langenbuch has come to the conclusion, in which he is supported by a number of Berlin specialists in internal medicine, that the gall bladder is not merely the storehouse for the stones, but that in cases of chronic inflammation is itself engendering most of the stones. He therefore holds that it is pointless to cut out the stones in the manner of Sims and Tait—quite aside from the fact that this method usually leaves a fistula in the abdominal wall. For a lasting cure, he argues, it is necessary to remove the entire gall bladder, which should not be difficult, given good antisepsis. As you may or may not know, Langenbuch had a hard boyhood; he was left an orphan and for many years supported himself and pursued his studies by working as an organist. He is a very sober-minded person who does nothing without careful consideration. He has already begun experimenting on cadavers to determine the technique of the operation he has in mind, and will in all probability reach his goal within the foreseeable future. It is only a matter of time, and not a very long time, at that. As for medication of any sort, I have little faith that any can produce lasting results."

Esmarch's letter, then, contained a miraculous confirmation of the idea which had come to my mind during my railroad journey from Birmingham to London.

Two weeks thereafter, the attack and its aftereffects past, I wrote to Carl Langenbuch, describing to him my odyssey in search of help and my own thoughts on the subject, and expressing the hope that he would continue to work along the path Esmarch had outlined. Langenbuch replied early in January, 1880. He had already heard of me from Esmarch, and wished me to know that he had fairly well settled the technique for removal of the gall bladder. He was convinced that this was what was necessary. The most difficult aspect of the operation was ligature of the cystic duct before the gall bladder could be severed. He was proceeding with great circumspection, fully aware of the responsibility he was assuming. If I came to Germany he would be delighted to show me his experiments and the progress he had made.

Early that spring I went to Berlin. I was no sooner there than I set out to find Langenbuch. His address took me to a huge four- or five-story house on Schiffbauersdamm. It was a Saturday evening. Standing before his door, I was no little surprised to hear a harmonium being played with wonderful skill and feeling. Then I recalled Esmarch's reference to Langenbuch's work as an organist, and I bided my time until the music stopped.

At my knocking, Langenbuch himself opened the door; I saw before me a slender man of at most thirty-five, of shy and retiring manner. His eyes, however, showed an unusual degree of kindness. He spoke little at first, but became livelier and more talkative when he drove out with me to his hospital on Bernauerstrasse, in the northern part of Berlin. This hospital had been established in 1865 by Pastor Boegehold in the middle of a working-class district of incredible poverty and squalor. With this as headquarters, Langenbuch had already acquired a great medical reputation. He had come to it in 1873, at a period of crisis for the hospital. Its original director, Pastor Boegehold, who had poured all his strength into this charitable enterprise and had even seen it expanded to one hundred and forty beds, had passed away. The endowments and contributions which his zeal had secured came to an end. Medically, the majority of the patients were in critical or moribund condition. The nurses, sisters of a Protestant nursing order, had fought an uphill battle. At this time Langenbuch was assistant to Wilms, the surgeon of the famous Bethany Hospital of the Sisters of Charity. Wilms had invited the young man to go for a drive with him, had taken him to the Lazarus Hospital, and there announced to the stunned Langenbuch: "Well, this is your hospital." The fact that Langenbuch took on the assignment without demur was an indication of the remarkable determination concealed behind his shyness.

Langenbuch had first created a sensation a few years before I came to see him, when he attempted to cure illnesses of the spinal cord by dilation of nerves. Numerous prosperous patients began to come to the Lazarus Hospital—an altogether novel note in this slum hospital. The method had in the long run not proved its worth. But it had raised Langenbuch from obscurity. Now, the day of my visit, he led me into a rather low, poorly illuminated cellar room which served as morgue and dissecting chamber for the hospital. He told me that he was using cadavers to find the simplest way to remove the entire gall bladder.

There followed a fantastic, unforgettable half hour. Langenbuch tied an apron around his waist and demonstrated, on the dead body of a young woman, the method he had developed for removing the bladder in fairly quick time and without endangering the patient. He made a diagonal incision into the abdominal wall, about on the line of the anterior edge of the liver. With a longitudinal incision along the rectus abdominis he extended this in the form of a *T*. A moment later the protruding dome of the gall bladder appeared under the lower surface of the liver. With the aid of sponges Langenbuch pushed the large and small intestines down behind the unopened part of the abdominal wall, drew up the right lobe of the liver, under which the major portion of the gall bladder lay, and thrust into my hand a hook with which I was to hold the lobe in this position. With quick strokes he severed several ligaments and exposed the bladder and the excretory duct which connected it with the hepatic duct and the common bile duct. He drew a silk ligature around the excretory duct, tied it, again took up scissors and scalpel, and cautiously freed the gall bladder from the pocket in which it was attached to the underside of the liver. He slit the covering of peritoneum and severed several connecting tissues. No blood vessels were in the way, and so there was no necessity for ligaturing vessels. Langenbuch worked without haste, with a careful and delicate touch. It was as though his technique mirrored part of his nature. He avoided any injury to the region around the liver, and soon had the gall bladder in his hand. A last stroke of the scalpel parted it from the already ligatured bile duct. Quietly, he held it out to me.

"You see," he said, "this is the thing that torments you. Don't you agree that it can easily be removed? The extirpation cannot be difficult, even if we are dealing, not with a healthy gall bladder, like this one, but with swellings, adhesions, and inflammations. In the case of gravely swollen bladders it will probably be useful to drain them with a trocar before severing. All the rest should present no great obstacle."

158 THE TRIUMPH OF SURGERY

Langenbuch drew the edges of the wound together and sewed it, in order to make his experiment a perfect rehearsal for the operation. "Everything that Sims and Tait have done or will do henceforth," he continued, "is in my opinion incomplete. They do not have the courage to go the whole way; they content themselves with half measures. Although they do free the patients of stones for a while, they leave them partial cripples, with open fistulas and with gall bladders which will continue to form stones. I am interested only in doing a thorough job, and any surgeon who commands the technique of antisepsis should have no fear of the abdominal cavity, and should plunge as deeply as may be necessary. A seriously diseased gall bladder should not be kept in the body. The bile will find its way into the intestines without the bladder, and could even, I imagine, create a new reservoir for itself by widening the hepatic duct or common bile duct at one point."

He put down his thread, and with a kind of quiet deference spread a sheet over the cadaver. Then he removed his apron and washed carefully. In silence we walked toward the door. On the stairs Langenbuch said: "Nevertheless, this is an operation for which the surgeon must prepare himself with the greatest care. I hope soon to have sufficient confidence to operate on the living. I will take the plunge when I encounter a patient who can be saved only by this method. When this time comes you will be the first to hear from me, whether or not the operation is a success."

As we left that cellar I did not suspect that more than two years would pass before Langenbuch would put his carefully rehearsed plan into action, and that it would be a success.

My own gall bladder did not trouble me during 1882, and on July 15 of that year, at the Lazarus Hospital, Carl Langenbuch performed the operation he had outlined for me. His patient was Wilhelm Daniels, a forty-three-year-old Berliner who had suffered from biliary colic since 1866. The man was wasting away and had become a hopeless morphine addict. For years he had been treated by the well-known Berlin specialist in internal medicine, Professor Frerichs. Three cures at Karlsbad had resulted in a deterioration rather than improvement of his condition. The patient had lost eighty pounds by the time he came to Langenbuch. "His increasing weakness," Langenbuch wrote in his report, a copy of which he sent me and which was later printed in the November 27 issue of the *Berliner Klinische Wochenschrift*, "the incessant pain, the serious reduction in intake of nourishment, and especially the growing addiction to morphine, indicated that he was steadily sliding downhill. A reversal of this decline seemed almost impossible. Since the diagnosis admitted of no doubt and the prognosis was so unfavorable, I thought myself justified in telling the patient of the last expedient which remained, and in recommending, after outlining the pros and cons, that he consider carefully this alternative. After some time, during which he apparently looked about elsewhere for advice, he entered the Lazarus Hospital (on July 10) and asked me to perform the operation we had discussed. I had him stay in bed for five days, and purged him in preparation. During this time he suffered two violent attacks daily. The date of the operation was set for July 15."

Langenbuch was aided by his regular assistants, chief among them young Dr. Löhlein, whom Langenbuch, childless himself, later was virtually to adopt as a son. In addition he called in several noted Berlin doctors and surgeons as witnesses, among them the noted gynecologist Martin, with whom he had for a time conducted a private clinic in addition to his work in the Lazarus Hospital. Martin later reported the operation to me in great detail, and through his attitude of confidence made my own decision easier.

Langenbuch removed the affected gall bladder in exactly the manner he had demonstrated to me in the morgue, the single difference being that he first drained it. Except for a minor venous hemorrhage when the bladder was separated from the liver, the operation proceeded without incident. The gall bladder was chronically inflamed and exhibited greatly thickened walls; within it Langenbuch found two cholesterol stones.

The day after the operation Langenbuch found his patient in fine fettle and smoking a cigar. On July 27 the man who had lived in agony for sixteen years left his bed, entirely free of pain and without any lingering fistula. At the beginning of September he was dismissed from the hospital. The first removal of the entire calculous gall bladder—an operation which Langenbuch named in his report "cholecystectomy" to distinguish it from Sims's and Tait's cholecystotomy—had been a complete success.

Langenbuch's first paper on the operation was virtually ignored. When he went before the German Congress of Surgeons in 1883 to report on three more cholecystectomies, of which two had led to a cure, his lecture was not listed among the major papers, and after the demonstration of his patients not a single voice was raised in discussion. Doctors in general made deprecatory remarks on the whole subject. When Tait heard of Langenbuch's operation, he hastened to describe it as "absurd" in an article in the *British Medical Journal* and a year later called it "completely absurd." He spluttered that Langenbuch's theory that the gall bladder produced gallstones was "simply false." And he initiated a campaign against Langenbuch which bore all the marks of Taitian prejudice, stubbornness, refusal to learn, and capacity for violent hatreds.

By October, 1889, Tait was able to report fifty-five cholecystotomies, and commented with prideful brevity: "I have performed the cholecystotomy fifty-five times, and fifty-two patients have recovered." Unfortunately, the data in all his papers were always given briefly, casually, and superficially, and often did not correspond with preceding individual papers on the cases. Thus, seven of his patients were known to have died, and only five cases of complete cures were unequivocally proved. Moreover, Tait regarded all patients who were left with permanent fistulas as cured. Nevertheless, he contrived to prevent the adoption of Langenbuch's radical gall bladder surgery in England, and not only there. To the day of his death he exhibited the same insufferable obstinacy. He died at the early age of fifty-four, partly as the consequence of his gluttonous habits, partly as the consequence of his furious working pace and obsessive pursuit of his various enmities. In his stubborn hostility to Lister he forbade Gilbert Barling, the London surgeon, who had to operate on him for stone in the bladder, to use antisepsis in his own case. And the day after the operation he insisted on leaving his bed, drinking champagne, and smoking a cigar. With the same mulishness he maintained his hostility toward Langenbuch until that thirteenth of June, 1899, when he was carried away by uremia. He who had given surgery of the gall bladder its first great impetus refused to realize that Langenbuch had taken the crucial step toward the ultimate perfection of the operation. His partisans continued his feud long after his death.

By 1890 a mere twenty surgeons (the list includes such names as

Kümmell, Socin, Courvoisier, Koeberlé, Thiriar, Kocher, Credé, Czerny) had performed, all told, a mere forty-seven cholecystectomies as pioneered by Langenbuch. But from then on the number of adherents of the method swelled mightily, inexorably. There was no longer any mistaking the road to true gall bladder surgery.

The entire medical world became involved in the discussion and controversy. In addition to the fundamental struggle between surgeons and specialists of internal medicine angered at the interference of the surgeons in their domain, there was the struggle among the surgeons, which went far beyond the dispute between Tait and Langenbuch. Once the door was open there came a host of proposals for further operations, and a number of these operations were actually performed. These aimed at eliminating stones which had lodged in the hepatic duct or the common bile duct and could not be removed by either Tait's or Langenbuch's operations. Attempts were also made to establish new ducts between the gall bladder and the duodenum or the large intestine, either bypassing bile ducts which had become blocked by growth of scar tissue, or by reinstating such ducts. Still other operations aimed at the removal of tumors of the gall bladder and bile duct. A few even attempted to deal with cancer. Some of these operations were sensible, others senseless, undertaken in that spirit of excessive pride to which I myself had often fallen prey during those tempestuous early years. There was scarcely an important figure in surgery on either side of the Atlantic who did not play some part in the long struggle. Riedel, Körte, the Mayos, Robson, Winiwarter, McBurney, Sprengel, Eiselsberg, Walzel, Kocher, Courvoisier, Kehr —the list is too long to be given in its entirety. But all these entanglements could not alter the fact that Langenbuch's radical procedure became the basic and most common method for treating gallstones surgically, and remained so long after Sims's and Tait's cholecystotomy was forgotten.

At the end of 1884, just as I was coming from the bed of Henderson, the young Scotsman who had been operated on for brain tumor, my gallstone trouble assailed me once more, and in its most vicious form. It was then that I entrusted myself to Carl Langenbuch—not out of desperation alone, but (so I told myself) with a kind of genuine farsightedness. He removed from me a chronically inflamed, misshapen gall bladder which contained several large stones of corklike shape. Never afterwards did I suffer the slightest in the region of my liver.

Langenbuch died on June 9, 1901, just two years after Lawson Tait—from appendicitis treated too late. By then no one doubted that he had led the way toward modern surgery of the gall bladder. He had worked quietly and unsensationally, had been opposed and frequently calumniated, but in the end he had been recognized as the pioneer he truly was.

The Blue Almond

"It is more than two years since we have seen each other," Hughlings Jackson wrote on April 15, 1887, after a longish period of silence. "I trust you are continuing to feel as well as you did immediately after your gall bladder operation. I would like to continue keeping you informed of developments in our circle during this past year, in so far as these have a bearing on cerebral and neural surgery. I am happy to relate that the situation is quite different from last year, when it seemed as though no one could summon up the courage to follow the footsteps of Godlee and Bennett. This time I have more to report to you than the expansion of our National Hospital to 180 beds, and the installation of a lift and of a gas turbine for the production of electric current to be used in our new electrical treatments. A summary of the past year must include events which can only be described as unusual—at least for the National Hospital—and which will undoubtedly prove to be fraught with consequences. Somewhat over a year ago the decision was made to have one of the younger surgeons permanently attached to the hospital. This would permit us to introduce regular surgical treatment of cerebral and neural diseases. The choice fell upon Victor Horsley, assistant surgeon at the University College Hospital. Possibly his name means nothing to you, for he is barely thirty. At any rate, he joined our staff on

February 9 last year. Since the hospital lacks an operating room, he set up in one of the little-used kitchens, and for a time also used a day-room in the Margaret Higgins division.

"We have come to the conclusion that for cerebral and neural surgery, it is all-important that the surgeon become thoroughly familiar with the functions of the brain and nerves. The first cerebral tumor operation was scarcely an ideal example—after all, a neurologist but nonsurgeon like Bennett had to enlist the services of a surgeon like Godlee who was devoid of any special knowledge of the nervous system and had to be guided through the entire operation. As things stand, this will probably be the procedure for some time to come. But the future neurosurgeon ought to be surgeon and neurologist in one. So far as we know, there is no man in Great Britain who more nearly fulfills this description than Victor Horsley. Horsley has had a thorough surgical training and is complete master of the technique of antisepsis. Moreover, he has from the first taken the keenest interest in Ferrier's doctrine of functional centers, and has himself investigated the functions of the brain and spinal cord. It is significant that as early as 1880 he undertook experiments upon himself at University College Hospital—without the knowledge of the hospital authorities—in order to determine the effects of anesthesia upon the cerebral functions. He had friends place him under anesthesia, and while losing consciousness made notes on the successive losses of physical functions.

"From January, 1884, until his appointment with us, Horsley worked as surgeon and pathologist at the Physiological Institute of University College and at Brown Institution on Wandsworth Road, conducting intensive cerebral and neural research. He has greatly refined Ferrier's picture of the functional centers, determined the centers for ten different movements of the head and eyes, and discovered functional centers for the larynx. He has also investigated the neural paths connecting cerebral cortex and spinal cord, about which so little is known as yet. I also believe that he is the first to have undertaken careful studies of the hypophysis and of the cause of trigeminus neuralgia. We had every reason to think, therefore, that we had chosen the right man. And we have not been disappointed in our expectations.

"Within the year Horsley has performed no less than ten operations upon the brain, and achieved success in nine of the cases. The only fatal termination was the case of a boy who had lain completely paralyzed for a year in consequence of an unusually large tumor extending over both hemispheres of the brain. In a second case Horsley removed, on September 23, a cerebral tumor weighing four and one half ounces from a patient who was paralyzed completely on his left side. This growth was obviously malignant; it re-formed, and claimed the life of the patient after six months of seeming recovery. The other, successful operations included the removal of tuberculous tumors, cysts, and scar tissue which had produced various types of paralysis by pressure upon the motor centers of the cerebrum. Ferrier and I attended most of the operations and can vouch for Horsley's extraordinary technical facility and cleverness. He abjures the chisel for opening the cranium, because of the shock-effect upon the patient. He removes large pieces of bone with bone-shears and a number of special saws he has constructed. In this way he obtains a broad operating field. He also will not hear of the galvanocautery which Godlee—as you no doubt remember—employed for hemostasis, and has invented in its place an interesting method for checking hemorrhage of the periosteum. He seals the bleeding places with modelling wax. At the moment Horsley is occupied with setting up criteria to distinguish between operable and inoperable tumors. He is also engaged in experiments on animals to determine the possibilities for surgical removal of tumors within the spinal canal. As you know, hitherto all cases of tumor of the spinal cord have meant frightful agonies and certain death. There has been no known therapy.

"Horsley's one fault seems to be his impulsiveness. He sometimes fails to practice the necessary restraint in his work and in his utterances.

"Nevertheless, this is a man whom you ought to meet, for I confidently expect some remarkable advances in our branch of surgery from him. I suggest that you make a point of coming to London before long. I am sure you will find a great deal to interest you. . . ."

The letter also contained some remarks on Jackson's progress in his own special field of "clinical-philosophical" investigation of the nervous system; on Ferrier; on poor Bennett, whose health was rapidly deteriorating and for whom apparently nothing could be done; and finally on a Dr. William Gowers, another young neurologist at the National Hospital, who was winning his first laurels. But none of this seemed as significant as the item concerning Horsley. This, after all, tied in directly with my keen interest in the development of cerebral surgery. This being so, I naturally decided that I would visit London first on my next European trip —a voyage I was already planning for June. And of course I would go to see Victor Horsley.

I thanked Jackson, told him of my forthcoming visit, and at the same time chided him for not having let me know of Horsley's first operation in advance. I begged him to inform me in time if Horsley were about to undertake "anything new." As I was about to close the letter, I recalled Jackson's final words concerning Horsley's experiments with spinal cords, and added: "Of course I would not for worlds want to miss the chance of witnessing any attempt to relieve a tumor of the spinal cord by radical surgery."

On May 20 I had booked passage for June 10. At breakfast on May 24, as I opened the morning newspaper, I encountered a headline which claimed my full attention. "Illness of the German Crown Prince," it read. "Cold or severe laryngitis which may require operation. Famous London throat specialist Dr. Mackenzie at Crown Prince's palace in Berlin since yesterday." The news story continued: "According to available information Crown Prince Friedrich Wilhelm, husband of Victoria, the eldest daughter of Queen Victoria, has been suffering since the spring from persistent hoarseness. The Crown Prince is now fifty-five years old. A stay at the German spa of Ems in April and early May did not relieve the affliction. According to confidential information from Berlin, the Prince was treated without success by Professor Gerhardt of Berlin. On May 18 a consultation was held, in which Dr. Wegner, the Crown Prince's personal physician, Dr. von Lauer, personal physician to Kaiser Wilhelm, and Dr. Tobold, a Berlin throat specialist, took part. Interestingly enough, Professor von Bergmann, at the moment one of the foremost surgeons of Germany, also participated. From this, informed persons deduce that the illness is a serious one, possibly a tumor of the larynx which will have to be removed surgically. There is even talk of a possible removal of the entire larynx because of a malignant tumor. Such an operation is not quite without precedent, having been performed some dozen years ago, by the most noted Viennese surgeon of our day, Theodor Billroth. According to reliable sources, on May 19 an operating table was transported from the Berlin Charité Hospital to the Crown Prince's palace, where a room has been re-papered to serve as operating chamber. Why Dr. Morell Mackenzie was called in, is unknown. The results of the first examination by Dr. Mackenzie are being awaited with suspense. Dr. Mackenzie possesses the largest throat practice in London, in spite of his many disagreements with his medical colleagues in that city. He is considered the founder of the specialty of throat diseases in England and a master of the laryngoscope, the new instrument for observation of the larynx. . . ."

I put down the newspaper, for it had become clear to me that I should not wait for my passage but must take the next ship crossing the Atlantic. At this juncture I must be in Berlin, where dramatic events in surgery were about to unfold.

It was true that Billroth, more than a decade ago, had made the first attempt to save a patient with advanced cancer of the larynx, who was doomed in any case. Few had attempted to do likewise, partly because of the enormous danger of the operation in itself and partly because of the rapid recurrence of this type of malignant growth. However, a method of partial excision of the larynx, in cases of cancer recognized at an early stage, had been yielding results. If in this crisis the surgeons in Berlin should decide on operation, and thereby win a place in surgery for the still controversial larynx operation, I wanted to be present. It would be equally instructive if in the end they should give up and acknowledge that surgery could do nothing here.

I knew Bergmann, of course, and had a slight acquaintance with Mackenzie. I was therefore fairly well assured of a comradely reception in Berlin. Jackson's letter, Horsley, the possibilities of surgery of the spinal cord—all this quickly slipped my mind.

I sent my manservant out to find quicker passage to Europe. He returned in an hour, having obtained passage on a fast steamer which, however, was sailing directly to London, and contained only a few cabins for passengers. The vessel was leaving New York the following night.

The weather was good and we had an extraordinarily smooth crossing. But in those days when there was no radio, when to be on a ship was to be cut off from the world, those two weeks meant a period of almost intolerable uncertainty. What was happening in Germany, I perpetually wondered. After a sea voyage one had always to be prepared for surprises, for revolutions, the outbreak of wars, crises and deaths, for upheavals which might change our whole world, or at least parts of it.

The night of June 6 we entered the mouth of the Thames and remained there until daybreak. The pilot boat delivered a batch of newspapers, but the latest of them were already a week old. By the glow of the oil lamp in my cabin I skimmed through headlines and news items. I found one that was pertinent: "Morell Mackenzie returns to London. . . ." "On May 28," the dispatch continued, "Dr. Morell Mackenzie arrived in London, returning from Berlin. After a laryngeal examination of His Royal Highness the Crown Prince of Germany, supplemented by microscopic examination of tissue from the larynx by Professor Virchow of Berlin, Dr. Morell Mackenzie has announced that the Prince's laryngeal disease is not of a cancerous nature and that no operation is necessary."

I searched the other newspapers, but found no further reports or commentary. Laying them aside, I decided to call on Mackenzie next day at his throat clinic on Golden Square, or else to look him up in his manorial house on Harley Street. I had been there once, seven or eight years ago, at a gathering made up largely of actors and actresses who had entrusted their voices to Mackenzie. He himself was seriously ill with asthma and chain-smoked a special type of asthma cigarette; but in spite of his illness he was a cocky man, and full of acrimony toward the other doctors of London who envied his specialization and decried his frank drive for fame and money.

The captain came down from the bridge and approached me. He wished to tell me that he had learned from the agent of a shipping yard that a speedy ship was leaving for Hamburg in the evening. It would take me to Germany faster than the roundabout route across the Channel. If I were still in a hurry, he would be glad to book passage for me.

I hesitated for a moment. But then, out of an old mistrust for newspaper stories, I nodded agreement. "Just give me your London address," the captain said. "The agent will take care of everything else."

I had never been one to form an attachment to one particular hotel, and I could well imagine that accommodations would be short. With Queen Victoria's Jubilee approaching, London had more than its quota of visitors. Where should I stay? Thinking the matter over, I suddenly recalled Jackson's letter. I looked at my watch. I knew that Jackson was something of an insomniac, apt to toss on his bed night after night, unable to free his mind of its preoccupation with the mysteries of the nervous system. He was also an extremely early riser. If I drove to his house, I would surely find him already up. If not, I could ask his housekeeper to receive the papers for the Hamburg steamer when they were delivered in the course of the day. I therefore gave the captain Jackson's address, left the ship, and drove through the early morning streets to Manchester Square.

The cries of a ragged newsboy prompted me to stop the carriage and buy a morning newspaper. During the drive I skimmed through it, and discovered this report: "Dr. Morell Mackenzie has again left London for Berlin to conduct another laryngeal examination of the German Crown Prince. This examination and a consultation with the German physicians are scheduled to take place on June 8. According to our informants, the German Crown Prince intends to seek a change of climate in the near future and to stay for a time in the vicinity of London, probably at Norwood, where he can be under the constant care of Dr. Mackenzie."

Evidently, then, I would not be able to call on Mackenzie. But why this second trip and another consultation if the diagnosis had been so unequivocal? If the Crown Prince were suffering merely from an inflammation why was Mackenzie making this second journey all the way to Berlin? Was it only to ascertain whether the Prince could safely travel? Could not Gerhardt or Tobold or Fränkel pass on that matter—especially Fränkel, director of the Berlin State Polyclinic for Ear and Throat Diseases, whose name was oddly enough not mentioned in any of the accounts?

Still puzzling over these questions, I arrived at Jackson's home and mounted the stairs to the rather old-fashioned, gloomy door with his name on a brass nameplate. He himself opened in answer to my knock.

"Is it really you?" he exclaimed, staring at me utterly confounded. And his second question was: "Are you clairvoyant?"

I did not understand, and we stood gazing at one another for a moment, both of us struck dumb. "Come in," he said at last. "I was just about to send a cable to you in New York."

I stopped in the doorway, stunned.

"Come in," Jackson repeated, "and tell me what has brought you here." I quickly reviewed the reason for my voyage. "Oh," he growled, "I might have known. But I imagine you are going to stop in London for a few days instead of plunging into this highly curious case of the German Crown Prince and the still more curious conduct of Dr. Mackenzie. My cable was to inform you that my young friend Gowers has diagnosed an unusual case of tumor of the spinal cord, and has requested Horsley to operate on his patient." He paused and looked at me with his searching, penetrating, and slightly ironical gaze, taking pleasure in the effect of his disclosure.

"If you can be patient for a little," Jackson said, "I shall take you to Dr. Gowers, who is having a consultation this very morning with Sir William Jenner at the patient's home." His eyes narrowed under his bushy brows. "The case of the Crown Prince will not run away from you," he said with his old sarcasm. I was later to remember his prophetic words. "The Crown Prince, I would judge, has a carcinoma of the larynx. Carcinomas cannot be talked away; they can only be operated on—if luck is with you. But a merciful lie is preferred to the truth, especially at court. You will see. . . . Would you like to go with me to visit Gowers?"

It was plain that he knew more, or at least had been able to guess more, about affairs in Berlin than I. I agreed to accompany him.

It was approaching nine o'clock when we left Manchester Square. "You don't know William Gowers yet," Jackson said. "To save you a possibly unpleasant surprise, I'll tell you a few things about him in advance. Some people say that he and I are basically much alike. I don't know whether that is altogether flattering to me. But perhaps these people are right. Possibly. . . . Gowers is forty-two now. He comes from Hackney. Do you know Hackney?" I indicated that I did not. "Well, you have not missed much. It's a miserable, dreary district. But as a birthplace it explains a good deal in a man's character. Gowers's father died when he was eleven. As an adolescent the boy studied under a certain Dr. Simpson in Essex. As far as I know, his interest in neurology dates from this period. Among Simpson's patients was a family of five children who all suffered from the same nervous motor disturbances and the same morbid enlargement of the tongue. This naturally stirred Gowers's curiosity. After completing his medical studies he worked as Sir William Jenner's assistant and secretary for a time. Afterwards he set up practice as a neurologist, opening an office on Queen Anne Street, and eventually taking over a section in the National Hospital." Jackson paused and glanced at me out of the corners of his eyes. "Constant intercourse with patients suffering from nervous disorders makes everyone crazy, cynical, or eccentric," he muttered. "I myself am no exception. Nevertheless, after you meet Gowers I would appreciate your telling me frankly what degree of resemblance there is between us. At any rate, don't let his manner put you off. He is as biting as sulphuric acid. Moreover, he suffers torments from sciatica, which makes him still more acidulous. And to crown it all, he thinks very little of any medical man but himself."

Number 50 Queen Anne Street, where Gowers's shingle hung, was one of those narrow brick houses with but two windows to a story and consequently little interior light. An assistant admitted us. Although he greeted Jackson courteously enough, he had evidently assumed some of his master's cold and superior manner. We sat in the office waiting room. Jackson pointed out the electric light and the telephone—both inventions possessed by few persons in those days. "He rigs these things up himself," Jackson whispered to me.

He fell silent, as a man of angular features and singular pallor appeared in the doorway. I noticed the long, soft hair and square-cut beard. If Jackson's eyes were cool and sardonic, this man's were cold as ice; and the bloodless lips expressed condescension, self-assurance, and utter lack of illusion. He was slight-bodied and dressed in a frock-coat of striking elegance. Although Jackson was the older man, Gowers nodded to him with an air of lofty condescension, and approached the two of us with an awkward, limping gait, at the same time throwing a keen look in my direction. "I am glad to see you," he said to Jackson in a grating voice, ignoring my presence. "I assume you want to accompany me to the consultation with Sir William. Sir William will decide whether Dr. Horsley is to be asked to operate. Of course it is not certain that Horsley will consent to perform the operation."

"I have little doubt about Horsley's response," Jackson said. He turned his head toward me and continued: "I should like to introduce you to a colleague from the United States, Dr. Hartmann. We are old friends. Dr. Hartmann is particularly interested in neurosurgery, and I should be grateful to you if you would show him your patient, as a contribution to his studies of the subject. I am unfortunately unable to go today."

Jackson emphasized the phrase "studies of the subject" so strongly that I guessed his intention: he wished to make it clear that I had not the slightest intention of interfering in the case in any medical capacity. Gowers glanced swiftly at me once more. "You are interested in neurology?" he asked warily, with a kind of cunning mistrust. One could sense that he was by no means delighted with the prospect of taking me to the consultation.

I felt that a simple explanation of my interest in the development of surgery would not especially move him. A man of his cold, dry nature would not understand my passionate involvement with the cause of surgery, and would certainly not sympathize with my restless peregrinations around the world. Jackson had warned me that Gowers had a low opinion of all but a few physicians. Perhaps some of my distinguished friends could be counted among these few, however—Charcot, say, or Weir Mitchell of Philadelphia, who knew more about nervous diseases than anyone else in America. I therefore replied that I was a friend of Charcot's and Weir Mitchell, and well acquainted with Sir William Jenner.

This last name evidently carried weight. "Aha," he said with deliberation. And then: "Well, I shall not prevent you from accompanying me."

Jackson nodded impassively. "We will see each other later at Queen's Square," he said to me. We left the house together. In the vestibule Gowers was suddenly surrounded by four children who addressed him as "Papa." Instantly, his whole manner changed. He stooped, and hugged and kissed the children. I began to suspect that like most aloof, cold people's, his heart was softer than his exterior.

During the whole ride in the carriage which had been waiting outside Gowers did not say a word. Later, when I knew more about him, I often thought back upon this ride. The studied silence was characteristic of Gowers's whole nature, as a person and as a physician. He hated needless talk, senseless discussion, and above all he hated theories. His was not a philosophical mind; in this regard the comparison with Jackson did not hold. Gowers was a collector of facts and symptoms. For hours he would sit at the bedside of his patients, holding a small pad and noting down in shorthand the slightest clinical observation. He listed and arranged all the symptoms, and in this way had succeeded in describing several hitherto unknown diseases of the nervous system with extreme exactitude. As a result he had acquired the reputation of being a remarkably accurate diagnostician. Like Charcot, Gowers was not particularly interested in therapy.

We stopped in front of a rather old but well-kept house on a tree-lined street. From the other direction another carriage drawn by two uncommonly fine horses approached us. Now Gowers opened his set lips for the first time. "My patient is Captain Gilby," he said churlishly. "A former army officer and businessman, with quite a bit of money. This is his home. Since you are so well acquainted with Sir William Jenner, I take it that I need not introduce you. There is Sir William's carriage."

I detected in his words a certain disbelief in my boasted acquaintance with Sir William. I had met Jenner many years ago, at a soirée, and subsequently spent many hours talking with him about American medicine and my experiences in various parts of the world. His bluff, autocratic, candid personality was not easily forgotten.

Jenner stepped out of his carriage, gazed searchingly at me with knitted brows, but remembered instantly when I mentioned my name and the time of our meeting. Gowers watched in silence as we shook hands. There was no occasion for further exchanges, for at that moment a cry of pain from the house reached us. It was so loud that it could have been heard some distance down the street, and was repeated several times. Jenner asked: "The patient?"

Gowers nodded. Morphine was virtually ineffective, he commented. Then he limped ahead of us. A heavy-set, bald man opened the door. He looked exhausted, as though he had spent the night without sleep. "Dr. Percy Kidd, the patient's friend and personal physician," Gowers said. "Dr. Kidd," he continued, "could you show us to a room where I can speak with Sir William about the background of this case?" Kidd nodded. From all the walls in the dim vestibule grinning masks looked down upon us. Evidently the owner of the house was a much-travelled man who had brought home trophies from many countries.

Glancing uneasily about him, Kidd opened a door hung with heavy Asiatic ornaments. We stepped into a room somewhat brighter than the vestibule, and Kidd closed the door behind us.

"I must thank you for coming so soon, Sir William," he said. "The captain's sufferings have reached such a degree that in spite of his advanced paralysis I have hidden every weapon in the house to forestall his somehow obtaining one of them and putting an end to his life. The servants left the house yesterday, except for one maid, because they could no longer endure his screams. Much as they pity him, the neighbors' nerves have about reached the breaking point. This latest attack has been going on for an hour. At the same time the captain is fully conscious and demands that I tell him whether there is any hope of improvement in his condition. If not, he wants nothing more than a quick death."

This room too was crowded with masks, bronze figures of the Buddha, temple utensils from India, Burma, Ceylon, and Japan. "What conclusion have you arrived at, Dr. Gowers?" Kidd wished to know. It was evident that he, too, was near the breaking point.

Gowers ignored his tone of urgency. Turning to Jenner, he said: "Captain Gilby is now forty-two years of age. Until 1884—that is, three years ago—he enjoyed excellent health. Then he and his wife were involved in a severe accident. In the spring of 1884 the captain's wife was run over by a carriage and fatally injured. Gilby had the presence of mind to hurl himself backwards and was only grazed by the vehicle. At the time he felt only a dull pain in the lower back; this lasted for several weeks, but ultimately cleared up without treatment. In June, 1884, however, he began to experience pain below the left clavicle, which was intensified by riding in carriages. Physical examinations produced no clue to the cause. The pain disappeared at times, but recurred in the autumn and winter.

"In the spring of 1885 Captain Gilby made a business trip to China. Before his departure he had himself examined once more, by a London colleague whose name we need not mention. This colleague diagnosed his trouble as intercostal neuralgia, prescribed mustard plasters, and assured him that it was safe for him to travel. During the railroad journey to Genoa, however, he suffered considerable pain, and the pain became increasingly violent in the course of the sea voyage. After arrival in Asia it reached such a pitch that the patient scarcely dared to walk. A German doctor from Shanghai suspected aneurysms with pressure upon the spinal nerves. Two English doctors rejected this diagnosis, however, and prescribed large quantities of potassium iodide and digitalis. Instead of improving matters these medicines produced fainting spells reminiscent of epileptic fits. In October, 1885, the patient left China to return to England. He spent most of the voyage in bed, and improved sufficiently so that he could go about a little after his arrival in London. Several of our London colleagues were thoroughly perplexed, and in their helplessness prescribed a winter in southern France. This actually seemed to help, for by the spring of last year Captain Gilby felt well enough to go to Constantinople. On his way back to London, however, the trouble recurred with renewed violence. On the advice of several physicians he then went to Aix-la-Chapelle to try the sulphur baths there. After a few baths the pain became so intense that morphine injections became necessary for the first time. Thereafter his condition deteriorated to such an extent that he lost all control of himself and suffered repeated fits of despair. Various doctors who could find no cause for his pain ended by calling it a mental illness. Two of our London colleagues flatly denied that there was any organic affliction at all.

"Toward the end of the winter, during February and March of the current year, the patient for the first time felt a weakness in his legs, first in the right and subsequently in the left leg. Another trip to the south was advised—Dr. Kidd, by the way, had not yet been consulted. The patient attempted to follow this advice, but collapsed during the journey. His legs would no longer support him at all. Shortly afterwards they became completely paralyzed. Still worse, this was followed by paralytic symptoms in the abdomen, with all the well-known miseries of that condition. These symptoms were accompanied by extraordinarily intense pain which proved resistant to morphine. Such was Captain Gilby's state when he arrived in London just four days ago. This time, fortunately, Dr. Kidd was consulted. In contrast to all the British and foreign doctors who had previously been consulted—whose diagnoses seem to be a telling indication of the paucity of knowledge of nervous diseases in the medical profession—Dr. Kidd suspected an organic disease and invited me to examine his patient."

Gowers paused and gave a dry cough. The wailing of the patient, which had accompanied Gowers's whole speech almost without interruption, rose once more to shrill heights, as though the poor man's torture had reached a climax of intolerable suffering. Immediately afterwards it relapsed into an exhausted moan. Jenner's florid face betrayed a certain uneasiness.

But Gowers calmly resumed his explanation. "At my examination yesterday," he said, "I found the patient in a truly desperate state. Both legs and the abdomen were completely paralyzed, and the skin of those parts was insensitive. Sensitivity to pain, however, had not diminished. The muscles of the legs convulsed almost continually. The site of severest pain was in the region of the sixth and seventh intercostal nerves which start from the spinal column and encircle the entire chest. No external changes in shape were apparent in the spinal column itself. Evidently the connections between the nerves of the cerebrum and abdomen are interrupted or severely irritated somewhere about the middle of the spinal cord. Since there is no external injury, the only possibility is a morbid development within the spinal canal. I exclude the possibility of morbid changes in the bones, since these usually manifest themselves externally as well. And since the prolonged treatment with potassium iodide was unsuccessful, I exclude syphilitic focal centers. To my mind all the evidence points to a tumor which has developed inside the spinal canal, and since the paralysis began with the left leg I believe the trouble lies on the left anterior side at about the fifth, sixth, or seventh vertebra. Possibly an encapsulated tumor has grown between the spinal cord and the wall of the spinal canal, displacing part of the cord, or possibly a malignant tumor has grown into the spinal cord. One way or the other, in the present state of therapy, the prognosis is fatal."

Gowers inclined his head in a listening attitude toward the direction from which the low moaning sounded. For a moment there was an oppressive silence in the room. Then his grating voice resumed:

"Hitherto, no one has ever thought of surgery in such a case. Erichsen and certain others have, I believe, attempted to remove splinters of bone that had penetrated to the spinal cord as a result of wounds. Generally the outcome was death by shock or infection. Since their work no one has ever operated upon the spinal cord, and only last year Page declared that such operations have no place in the field of practical surgery."

Gowers paused briefly. "I hold differently," he said. "Some time ago I expressed the view that surgical removal of spinal tumors should be less dangerous than the removal of intracranial tumors. Antisepsis has made such progress that there is no longer any reason for fatal infection. Operation upon the tumor offers the sole chance to relieve the patient of his torments, and perhaps even to restore him to health by removing the obstruction in the spinal cord. Even if it should develop that the tumor is malignant and cannot be excised, it ought to prove possible, by the removal of several vertebrae, to provide room for it to expand outward and thus relieve the pressure upon the spinal canal. In my opinion the patient's condition justifies even the most desperate of operations, since his pain is otherwise beyond relieving. The young surgeon Victor Horsley will in all probability be willing to venture it."

Jenner had listened with half-shut eyes, putting no questions. "May I suggest," Gowers now said to him, "that you come to the patient's bedside and judge for yourself."

Still Jenner did not speak. He only nodded. I could not discern whether he, member of an older generation who had grown up with the conviction that the spinal cord was inviolable, really understood the audacity of his pupil. But would Gowers have called Jenner in for consultation if he had not counted upon him for support and perhaps for protection against attacks by conservative physicians?

Dr. Kidd, who had waited all this while with every sign of impatience, opened the door to the vestibule and led the way. When he opened another stout oaken door, the dull moans sounded much closer. We passed through a third doorway and found ourselves in a half-darkened room.

Captain Gilby lay propped up on pillows, a weird skeleton of a man. His sunken eyes turned slowly toward us. Their overcast gaze slid from Kidd to Gowers, from Gowers to Jenner, from Jenner to me. I could see that he had once been a powerful, good-looking, and strong-willed person. Even now he fought manfully against his pain, and repressed his moans. His colorless lips twitched, and finally, with grinding teeth, he managed to speak a few words: "What do you bring me, Dr. Gowers?" And then: "I've had enough of doctors' follies. I need immediate help, or an immediate end to my sufferings. As it is, I'm a living corpse from whom everyone flees in horror."

Gowers went up to the bed. He waited until Gilby had struggled through these words.

"Captain Gilby," Gowers said formally, "you see beside me Sir William Jenner, personal physician to Her Majesty the Queen. I have asked Sir William for advice because I believe I have discovered the cause of your condition, and see a chance to allay the pain, perhaps, and possibly to make you sound again." Gilby's half-shut eyes opened. He tried to speak again, but was unable to produce a word.

"Sir William must subject you to one more examination," Gowers said. "It will be painful. Do you consent to this examination?"

Gilby's eyes flickered, veering between distrust and hope, from Gowers to Jenner and back again to Gowers. He hesitated. But then he nodded, his head moving convulsively. Kidd turned back the blanket and revealed a pitiable sight. The lower part of the man's once athletic body lay lifeless before us. It was no longer capable of any movement. Gilby could not control his muscles, intestines, or bladder. But because only the motor nerves, not the pain-conducting nerve-paths to the brain, had been interrupted, this immobile, dying part of his body was the cause of the unspeakable pain he suffered.

As carefully as possible, Kidd rolled the patient onto his side. Gilby, in fearful agony, gasped between clenched teeth. He choked and screamed, until at last he was in such a position that Jenner could examine the entire length of his spinal column. Without a word, Jenner sat down on the edge of the bed and began the examination as it was conducted in those days, without X-rays, lumbar puncture, or any of the other diagnostic tools we have at our disposal nowadays. His muscular hands were his most important instruments.

Jenner's fingers slid from vertebra to vertebra. I cannot say how much time passed. I only know how slowly it passed, while scream after scream forced its way through Gilby's clenched teeth and bitten lips. Would Jenner confirm Gowers's diagnosis? Would he approve an operation which to his way of thinking might seem sheer heresy, an irresponsible adventure upon the part of a member of the younger generation, and would he exert the weight of his influence and personality to win the patient to it?

Jenner's expression was wholly opaque. His fingers groped along the patient's back. They reached the eighth, then the seventh vertebra. Jenner probed hard, harder at any rate than Gowers could have done with his slender, anemic-looking hands. His fingers reached the sixth vertebra. Now he pressed deeper, first on the right, then in the middle, then on the left. At that moment Gilby screamed again. Jenner stopped, then pressed again. An even more violent scream broke through Gilby's clenched teeth. At that moment Jenner straightened up. He signed to Kidd to roll the patient back to his former position. Then he turned to Gowers, his right eye squinting shut—a little tic of his. He looked at Gowers with his left eye alone, and said slowly: "I find a spot sensitive to pressure on the left side of the sixth vertebra." He paused. "I think you are right." Turning once more, he looked down at Gilby, who lay on his back once more, eyes closed, colorless face covered with sweat.

"Do you want the absolute truth, Captain?" Jenner asked.

Gilby moved his lips, then his jaw, as though he had difficulty opening his mouth. "Yes," he breathed at last. "The absolute truth."

"My young colleague Dr. Gowers," Jenner said, "has concluded that a tumor has formed in your spinal column. By its increasing pressure this tumor has probably caused the symptoms from which you suffer. I believe his diagnosis is correct."

Gilby opened his eyes. They were badly inflamed, as though a number of capillaries had burst from the strain of the examination. Almost immediately he closed his eyes again, as though to shield them from the harsh glare of reality. "A death sentence, then," he murmured. "Thank you, Doctor."

"My young colleague thinks differently," Jenner said. "Many fatal diseases have been overcome in recent years. Dr. Gowers believes there is a chance to help you, although the chance seems as desperate as your disease itself."

There was a moment of silence. Then Gilby said with surprising clearness: "What is this chance?"

"Dr. Gowers believes it would be possible for a surgeon, using the latest surgical techniques, to open the spinal column and re-move the tumor. To our knowledge no such operation has ever been performed. It would be the first of its kind. No one can predict how it will turn out. It may result in cure, or at least relief —or in death. I cannot venture to say. I can only imagine what I would do if I were in your predicament."

Gilby still kept his eyes tightly closed. "What would you do?" he gasped.

For a moment there prevailed that portentous silence which by right precedes the decision upon the life or death of a human being, precedes a reaching out into something new, a possible step forward on humanity's long road. Every breath in the room could be heard, and the quiet scuffing of Jenner's shoes. Then Jenner said: "I would risk it."

Gilby looked up. He regarded Jenner and Gowers. Then he said: "I have always played for high stakes. . . . Call the surgeon. But call him at once."

Half an hour later Gowers and I were already on our way to see Horsley. That drive to Horsley's and the meeting that followed have remained branded upon my memory with especial vividness— as an example of how small the world was in those days, how much more personal and intimate, without the technical apparatus of communication which in these days not only connects but sep-arates people. The medical world, too, was smaller and more in-timate. How otherwise would that conversation with Horsley have been possible?

Gowers seemed to be troubled by a slight nervousness, now that the first step into the unknown had been taken. He took me along in his carriage without further explanations or questions, but once more he said not a word during the entire drive.

In those days, Horsley lived and practiced at 80 Grosvenor Square. (He was not yet living in the big house on Cavendish Square into which he moved a few years later, and where I was a frequent guest.) Unfortunately, we did not find him in. Gowers decided to return in an hour, unless Horsley called on him in the meantime. He left a message saying that the matter was of the greatest importance.

We returned to the carriage and drove in silence again along Park Street. Just as we were turning into a side street, Gowers suddenly stopped the carriage. Though he was as taciturn as ever, his whole manner suggested to me that he had just caught sight of Horsley. I looked around in vain for another carriage. There was none in sight, and not even a pedestrian on the street. Instead, I saw a young man riding one of those high-wheeled bicycles which were just coming into fashion. He was travelling at a speed which would certainly have been considered high in those days, and it did not for a moment occur to me that this was the man we were seeking. What respectable London physician would have made a spectacle of himself on a wheel? But Gowers leaned out of the carriage and waved to the rapidly approaching cyclist with that peculiarly stiff dignity of his.

The cyclist braked immediately, and drew up to the carriage, his youthful face flushed by the exercise. He looked the picture of health. Tall, limber, broad-shouldered, he had strikingly attractive though irregular features, gleaming white teeth, hypnotically piercing, gray-blue eyes, and a refractory forelock of pale straw-colored hair falling over his forehead.

This was Horsley.

His strong hands, stained brown by the acids he used in his physiological studies, lay easily on the handlebars. He was not wearing tails—the sole garment for any physician of standing—nor the traditional top hat.

"Ah, Dr. Gowers," he exclaimed, undaunted by Gowers's marked formality or their ten years' difference in age. "I have just come from a consultation. An interesting case of Jacksonian attacks. You look as though you had something important to tell me. Have you just been to my house?"

"Yes, I have," Gowers replied stiffly, leaning back in his seat once more. "But these are scarcely matters to be discussed in the street."

"Why not?" Horsley thrust both hands into the pockets of his sack coat. "There is not a soul in sight."

"As you wish," Gowers said, slightly discomfited. "Professor Jackson tells me that you are interested in spinal tumor and might be willing to undertake surgery if the diagnosis were unequivocal."

Horsley suddenly took on a look of keenness I was later to recognize as highly characteristic of him. He possessed, as I later had many occasions to observe, an innate love of audacity. It drove him to undertake the sort of thing from which others shrank in fear or horror. This passion dominated him all his life, whenever he took a scalpel into his hand. It, too, was the trait which subsequently gained him so many enemies. For he did not know how to hold his tongue and would rail at surgeons less adventurous than himself as "cravens" and "bunglers."

"Do you have such a case?" he asked.

"Yes," Gowers replied. "My diagnosis has just been confirmed by Sir William Jenner. The patient acquiesces to the operation. Jackson tells me that you have already dealt with the problem by experimenting on animals and cadavers. . . ."

"So I have," Horsley said.

His experiments, I was to discover, had already ranged far beyond those that Jackson had described to me in his letter. Although Brown Institution, where Horsley preferred to experiment, was constantly under surveillance by the antivivisectionists, Horsley had escaped their chivvying. This may have been due largely to that fortune which follows the brave, and which seldom deserted him in later years. Eventually Horsley was haled into court, charged with cruelty to animals. During the trial a cat wandered into the courtroom, and to the amusement of judge and spectators chose to settle in Horsley's lap. After that, his acquittal was a foregone conclusion.

Now, however, Horsley did not expatiate on his experiments. He asked tersely: "When can I see the patient?"

"At any time," Gowers said. "My patient's condition is so

wretched that he would want to have the operation this moment, if it were possible."

Horsley considered only for a few seconds. "In an hour I must go to Southampton for a consultation and operation. I will be back by twelve o'clock the day after tomorrow. On that day, then, June 9 at one o'clock, I will see your patient."

"Let us assume that you do decide to operate," Gowers said. "How much time will you need for preparations?"

"Time for preparations?" Horsley looked surprised. "If I operate I shall do it that same day. Let me have your patient's address. We'll meet there."

Gowers gave him Gilby's address.

"Thank you," Horsley said. "Day after tomorrow, then, at one o'clock. Please excuse me now. My train, you know."

Like an acrobat, Horsley swung up onto his bicycle and rode off.

"I take it," I heard Gowers's grating voice saying to me, "that you wish to be present at this operation, should it take place."

"I most certainly do," I replied, my eyes fixed upon Horsley's swiftly receding figure. "This will be something I would not want to miss!"

During that two-day wait, which seemed very long to me, I found more newspaper accounts concerning the case of the German Crown Prince, which had almost slipped my mind in my excitement over the impending operation for spinal tumor. It was reported that Dr. Mackenzie had once more made an examination of His Imperial Highness's larynx, and that Professor Virchow, the famous pathologist, had been called in for consultations.

I thought immediately of Jackson's prophetic words. If Virchow were in fact involved, he could have been called only to determine the benignancy or malignancy of the tumor.

Nevertheless, my interest was chiefly in Gilby's fate and the decision that was soon to be taken.

By two o'clock in the afternoon on June 9 I had not yet received any further information on Horsley or any further developments of his case. I sent a messenger to Gowers. He was not at home. I was just considering whether to send the messenger directly to the patient's house when there was a knock at the door.

A boy appeared with a note from Jackson stating that Horsley had decided to operate and would do so at three-thirty.

I left at once. Although the National Hospital had changed somewhat since my last visit, I had no difficulty finding the operating room—that is to say, the small, rather musty kitchen which Horsley was using for this purpose.

When I entered, Gilby was already lying on his side, half doubled up, on the operating table. In addition to Horsley, Gowers, and Kidd, Jackson and David Ferrier were present. There were also three assistants who were hastily introduced to me as Drs. White, Stedman, and Ballance. White had already begun anesthesia with ether. The acrid smell of ether and carbolic acid permeated the overheated air. Ballance was washing the operating field along the spinal column with ether and carbolic. Stedman started up the carbolic spray apparatus. Horsley, in shirt sleeves, with his muscular arms bare and an apron about his waist, reached into the carbolic solution in which the instruments lay. I was startled to see him do this with his left hand. Jackson whispered into my ear that he was left-handed. However, he soon transferred the scalpel from his left to his right hand.

The scalpel made a long incision through skin and tissue from the third to the seventh vertebra. As in so many cases before and since, in which the first stride into unknown territory was being taken, I felt my breath catch, felt my heart beat like a hammer. The acanthae—the spinal processes—appeared one after another, and the origins of the back muscles, only slightly dabbed with blood from the incision. The first step had been taken. Now there could be no turning back.

There was virtually no bleeding. Horsley bent lower. He began working through the muscles and acanthae in order to reach the spinal canal. For all that he may have practiced a hundred times on animals or cadavers, have penetrated again and again into the marrow of the spine, here he had before him a breathing human being, a living body governed by its own peculiar laws.

Horsley cut through the first sinew, then another and another. The bleeding increased. Ballance caught the bleeding vessels with pincers. The last sinew was severed. Horsley proceeded to lift out the strands of muscle, freeing them from the spinal processes and vertebrae. He worked first on the right side. The bleeding increased.

Ballance and Stedman stuffed the deep incision with sponges while Horsley began freeing the muscles on the left side, proceeding with calm, sure movements, as though he had not even seen the spurting blood vessels.

Fresh intense bleeding began on the left side. More sponges. Horsley waited until the last trickle of blood had ceased. Then he ordered Ballance and Stedman—with a mere nod of his head— to draw the edges of the incision far apart. He himself removed the sponges and ligatured the blood vessels. A few more swabs, and then, at the bottom of the incision, the naked bony structure of the spinal column appeared, in front the protruding chain of acanthae, and behind them, in a series, the vertebrae, the bony shield of the deeply hidden nerve channels constituting the spinal cord.

Horsley asked for a bone shears. Stedman picked the stout instrument out of the bowl of carbolic acid. Horsley placed the blades against the spinal process of the fourth vertebra and squeezed. There was a brief, cracking sound. The acantha was cut off precisely along the line of attachment to the vertebra. It fell to the floor, disregarded. The acanthae of the fifth and sixth vertebrae followed. Deprived of its anterior protection, the bony shell around the spinal marrow was now exposed. The prelude was over; the decisive act had to begin now—opening of the spinal canal, exposure of the cord.

Horsley threw a quick, questioning look at White, who was holding the patient's pulse. White nodded. Horsley reached for a trepan. He applied it to the arch of the fifth vertebra, and slowly turned it. Bloody bone meal welled up. In the breathless silence only the grinding, scraping noise of the instrument was audible. Horsley lifted the trepan, removing with it a small disk of bone. Through the drilled hole the dura mater could be seen, that hard membrane separated from the inner bony wall of the spine only by a thin layer of fatty tissue. With bone forceps and scalpel, Horsley removed the remainder of the posterior wall of the fifth vertebra. The arches of the fourth and sixth vertebrae followed. Then he cut through the surrounding fatty tissue, pushed it aside, checked the slight bleeding. In a moment the dura mater all the way from the third to the seventh vertebra was revealed—for the first time the spinal cord of a living human being lay exposed.

I took a deep breath. The speed with which everything had

been done seemed incredible, and equally incredible Horsley's sureness of touch, as though he had done nothing for years but perform this selfsame operation.

I heard him speaking, his voice apparently somewhat choked up, so that he had to cough and clear his throat. "I am now about to cut into the dura mater," he said. "In my experiments on animals, the cerebrospinal fluid poured out of the incision immediately and flooded the whole area alarmingly. It turned out, however, that if there was no movement from the animals the effusion ended quite quickly of its own accord, so that after sponging out the wound I was able to inspect the spinal cord without difficulty. I do not know, of course, whether the cerebrospinal fluid will act in the same way in man, but I see no reason why it should not do so."

I caught a glimpse of Gowers's sallow, almost ill-looking face, and the tense features of Jackson and Ferrier. Horsley took up his scalpel again. Ballance stared down at Horsley's hand, and at the dura mater. Then the scalpel pierced the hard membrane. On the instant, cerebrospinal fluid welled out. It swamped the wound, ran over the lower edges of the incision and onto the table. I was over-come momentarily by terror. Suppose Horsley's deduction from his experiments on animals did not apply? Suppose this vital fluid poured away, bringing death to the patient at the very moment when the way seemed clear for the last stage of the operation?

Fractions of a second later the stream of fluid ceased with re-markable abruptness. Horsley had been right. Stedman was already holding sponges in readiness. He dabbed out the wound, and there now lay before us, plainly visible, the spinal cord from the fourth to the sixth vertebra. I seemed to hear Gowers's diagnosis ringing in my ears and to see Jenner's strong hand probing the region which now lay open before me. Had he not discovered the most sensitive spot at the sixth vertebra, and therefore concluded that the tumor must have its seat there?

The exposed spinal cord showed no sign of morbid discoloration. Carefully, Horsley's fingers, rinsed in carbolic acid, groped along the cord. But they found no swelling, no hardened mass—nothing. Even more cautiously he introduced a curved aneurysm needle around the spinal cord and moved it back and forth. He probed the posterior side, seeking some kind of tumorous formation, pos-sibly a very small one. But he could detect nothing abnormal.

There was such deep silence that the faintest breath could be heard. The first doubts began to creep into our minds. Horsley's head was bent over the wound.

Suddenly he reached once more for the bone forceps. At the lower and upper edges of the incision the arches of the third and seventh vertebrae cracked. The whole process was repeated once more: drawing aside of the fatty tissue, slitting of the dura mater, exposure of the cord. I suddenly recalled having read that sensations of pain, due to the complicated paths of the nervous system, could manifest themselves at places far from the site of the actual cause of the pain.

Horsley did not give up. He continued to search, up and down along the spinal cord. His fingers groped here and there—in vain. The curved needle circled the cord. But not the slightest anomaly, not the slightest hint of a possibly hidden tumor underneath the cord, could be detected. There were no signs of a tumor in the areas of the third and seventh vertebrae either.

In the silence Gowers's almost white lips moved soundlessly. Beads of sweat formed on Horsley's broad forehead. He straightened up, audibly drawing breath. What would he do now? Give up? What false hopes had stirred in the heart of the poor pain-bedevilled man lying there on the operating table?

The silence was broken by Ballance's voice: "I would try further up," he murmured. "The roots of the nerves are considerably higher than the corresponding vertebrae. The sensitivity to pressure at the sixth vertebra . . ."

Horsley glanced at Ballance. I waited in painful suspense. Would he follow his assistant's advice? At the time I was not aware of the unusually close relationship between Horsley and Ballance, a man of his own age. Rebellious as Horsley was toward his elders, and poor though he was as a teacher of younger men, he got on well with his contemporaries. His hesitation lasted only a few seconds. Then, without a word he took up the bone forceps. He threw a questioning look at White. The anesthetist nodded reassuringly. Horsley applied the forceps. At the upper end of the wound he broke open the second vertebra. He reached for the scalpel, prolonged the incision through the dura mater. The edges of the incision gaped apart.

At that moment it happened—and I was never to forget it. At

the upper margin of the incision, on the left side, there appeared a dark, bluish spot, barely an eighth of an inch wide. Its appearance contrasted markedly with that of the spinal cord. Someone sighed, as though released at last from suspense that had become unendurable. Was this tiny spot the dreadful tumor that Horsley was seeking? Was it the lower pole of the deadly growth?

Horsley's hands had fairly leaped for the bone forceps. Now he broke out the posterior side of the first vertebra also. Once more the scalpel prolonged the incision through the dura mater, once more the hard membrane gaped wide, and the bluish spot could now be seen more clearly. It proved to be a swelling, rather purplish in color, about the size of an almond, squeezed between the dura mater and spinal cord on the left, below the uppermost root of the fourth dorsal nerve. The growth was pressed deep into the spinal cord. Here it was, Gowers's tumor! Horsley had found it.

I can no longer say what moved me most at that moment: the simple joy of having witnessed this historic operation, or a sense of the enormous delicacy of the spinal cord, so that this tiny thing no larger than an almond was sufficient to ruin a man's life and to produce those agonies I had observed at Gilby's bedside.

I caught only a glimpse of Gowers's face, its sudden return of color and the flash of satisfaction at this confirmation of his diagnosis. Then I fixed my attention upon Horsley, who had already begun examining whether the tumor had grown into the spinal cord or was only embedded in it; whether, that is, it could be lifted out without complete destruction of the cord. Once more I was conscious of almost unbearable suspense.

This time, however, it did not last long. With almost absurd ease Horsley's fingers freed the tumor from its adhesions at both ends. Even more easily, he lifted it out of the bed it had formed in the spinal cord. Only an oval hollow remained. It showed no disposition to fill out, however. Horsley ligatured a number of vessels that had begun bleeding when he freed the tumor. Ballance removed the trickles of blood and dabbed all exposed parts of the spinal cord with carbolic solution. But the hollow where the tumor had lain was still present. Did this mean that the cord was no longer capable of repairing the damage it had suffered? Had the pressure of the tumor gone on too long? Would its removal perhaps eliminate the pain, but fail to alleviate the paralytic symptoms? These questions hung almost tangibly in the hot, heavy air permeated with carbolic vapors.

Horsley pressed the incised edges of the dura mater together without sewing them. He closed the great longitudinal incision with deep stitches running through all the severed tissues. Inserting two drains, he drew the edges as close together as possible. Then he stitched the skin and applied the dressing. White raised the mask from Gilby's face and stepped back. Two attendants carried Gilby into the bed in the adjoining room. Horsley watched him until the door closed. Only then did he notice all the hands outstretched in silent congratulation.

Driving home from the hospital, I cursorily read the latest newspaper report from Berlin: "We learn from reliable sources that the examination by Professor Virchow has banished the rumor attributing the illness of the German Crown Prince to a malignant growth. Dr. Mackenzie is returning to England. His Imperial Highness is expected to arrive in London on June 14 for his planned vacation."

In so far as my thoughts dwelt at all on the curious ups and downs of the news stories about the Crown Prince, this piece of intelligence reinforced my decision to remain in London and watch the further developments in Gilby's case. The following morning there began a dramatic series of alternations between hope and despair, fresh hopes, new confidence, and new setbacks.

Five critical days passed. The healing of the operative wound proceeded without complication. Gilby ran no temperature higher than 99° F. There was not the slightest sign of infection. But his pain did not diminish. Every movement remained a torment for him. At times it seemed as if the cramps in the paralyzed limbs attained a greater intensity than before the operation. The abdominal paralysis remained. Disappointment followed hard upon disappointment.

Then, on June 15, Horsley suddenly discovered that the surface sensitivity of the lower part of Gilby's body was beginning to return. For the first time Gilby reported sensations of heat and cold in the paralyzed parts. The following day there was a partial return of bladder control. Were these the first signs of regeneration of the spinal cord, of slow recovery? The following days, however, were once again highly variable. The pain refused to yield to any measures. There were times when Gilby cried out in despair that he was suffering worse torments than before the operation.

But on June 22 there came, surprisingly, a first movement of his hitherto totally paralyzed leg. Gilby—mortally terrified of self-deception, arming himself against false hope—insisted that these movements were only the accidental consequences of a muscular cramp. But a few days later there could no longer be any doubt: muscular power was being restored in the entire right leg. It moved slowly down to the foot. Simultaneously, the cramps on the right side, which had heretofore been extremely violent, began to vanish. Now all cramps were restricted to the left side. But these, too, manifested themselves at increasingly longer intervals. On July 20 the left leg for the first time displayed the beginnings of the capacity for movement. On August 13 Gilby was given a steel brace and two armpit crutches, with the aid of which he undertook his first attempts at walking. The pains in his left side steadily diminished. By now the operative wound was virtually healed. The incision in the dura mater had closed so tightly that not a drop of cerebrospinal fluid exuded.

Three months later, on November 17, Gilby began taking daily walks in the garden, although he still needed two crutches. On January 24, 1888, Horsley presented his patient to the Medical and Surgical Society in London. The scar of the incision by now was completely closed, and was in sections almost as hard as bone, as though the body were attempting to replace the missing vertebral arches. By this time Gilby was able to walk three miles with ease. His gait was still a little stiff. A month later even this stiffness disappeared. Gilby went back to work, and on June 6, 1888, approximately one year after the operation, he wrote to Horsley that he was enjoying his former good health and was active sixteen hours a day, both standing and walking a great deal.

That operation, therefore, of June 9, 1887, proved the foundation of Horsley's world-wide fame. It marked also one of the fateful moments in the history of human suffering when the curtain was once again lifted from a part of the body hitherto barred to surgery. One more disease no longer spelled certain death.

Almost thirty years later—on July 16, 1916—Victor Horsley, then serving as consulting surgeon to the British Expeditionary

Corps in Mesopotamia, died of sunstroke in Amara on the Tigris. By then the operation which he had been the first to venture had been markedly improved and had become a standard feature of neurosurgery. Horsley's whole life had been lived in keeping with the principle of boldness which had inspired that first operation. He had always plunged straight ahead, refusing to consider himself or others, refusing, at last, to heed the warnings of friends who predicted an early death if he needlessly subjected himself to the hardships of the campaign in Mesopotamia. He survived William Gowers by little more than a year. Gowers was carried off by a malignant disease of the nerves which he himself had observed and methodically described during the best years of his life, although he had never been able to determine its cause. This disease produced deterioration of the spinal cord which more and more affected his capacity for movement and co-ordination. A precise diagnostician even in his own case, unemotional and unseduced by false hopes, he observed the progress of his own disease as he had the diseases of his patients, and waited for death. On May 4, 1915, he died.

Imperial Tragedy

In the long, slow struggle to extend the domain of surgery to the various organs of the human body, the history of throat surgery has no parallel. I can think of no other branch in which developments were so vitally influenced by the fate of a single patient, in which world-wide attention was magnetized by that one patient's story. The tragedy of the German Crown Prince, later Emperor Friedrich III, casts a peculiar and lurid light over this particular segment of surgery's history.

As it turned out, I had a closer view of the vicissitudes of Friedrich's disease than was granted to others. Partly, of course, this was due to my knowing the most important medical actors in the drama before the curtain rose. But principally I owed my privilege to my meeting and later friendship with a man who played a vital role in the tragedy, but whose importance has to this day been seldom and imperfectly described. I am referring to Sir Felix Semon, the internationally recognized leader in the field of laryngology during the last decades of the nineteenth and the first decades of the twentieth century.

On June 14 I heard the London newsboys crying: "German Crown Prince arriving today. Attending Her Majesty's Jubilee on June 21. Dr. Morell Mackenzie to cure his laryngitis. . . ."

At Horsley's I met a tiny man of about thirty-seven, with a remarkable head. His face was adorned with a mustache of truly heroic dimensions, but every visible feature, and in particular his eyes, bespoke unusual intelligence. Horsley introduced this person to me as Felix Semon. He and Semon had worked together searching for the functional centers in the cerebral cortex which governed the movements of the vocal cords.

Horsley turned to Semon and said: "Dr. Hartmann happened to be a witness of Gilby's operation. What brought him to London, however, was something else entirely. He read the first accounts of the German Crown Prince's illness back in New York, and wanted to find out about it on the spot from Mackenzie."

I detected Semon's sudden acute interest. "Yes," I confirmed, "I met Mackenzie years ago when he first established his throat hospital, and have been to see him several times. But the case of the Crown Prince now appears to be not a surgical matter at all."

Semon looked at me with a peculiar expression. "Oh," he said, "do you really think so?" Then, as we walked on, he added in the faintest German accent: "I am not of your opinion. Should you be interested in the latest developments in laryngeal surgery and their possible relationship to the Crown Prince's case, I shall be happy to aid your researches. Horsley knows where I can be reached."

Outside, Semon bade us goodbye and entered his handsome carriage drawn by an equally handsome pair. Horsley took me with him in his own conveyance. At the next intersection another newsboy was bawling out his monotone: "German Crown Prince in London . . . Dr. Morell Mackenzie . . . Mackenzie . . . Mackenzie . . ."

"The stories have certainly run the gamut of contradictions," Horsley said. "If you really want a look behind the scenes, take advantage of Semon's offer. Mackenzie is a bit of an outsider who has virtually not a single friend among us. Heaven knows how he happened to be called to Berlin. Moreover, he is too deeply implicated to be a reliable source of information. If anyone in London really knows the details of this case, it will be Semon. Incidentally, he is German by birth."

During our ride I learned that Semon had studied in Berlin, learned the use of the laryngoscope in Vienna, and devoted himself to the new specialty of diseases of the throat. He had been a cavalryman during the Franco-Prussian War, had later come to London to enlarge the scope of his studies, and had stayed on. His personal practice included some of the most prominent persons in London. Two years previously he had treated Gladstone, and had cured him of a laryngeal inflammation in such short order that Gladstone had been able to speak during the election campaign. Moreover he had been able to recognize many cases of cancer of the larynx in their early stages, and arrest them for a goodly number of years. In some such cases he had achieved complete cures.

But how should Semon have special knowledge of the case of the German Crown Prince, I asked. "That is very simple," Horsley replied. "He grew up with the two sons of German Chancellor Bismarck, and is still on intimate terms with at least one of them. He knows the Berlin medical profession well, and especially the throat specialists of that city. As to Mackenzie, he served for some time as his assistant at the Golden Square Throat Hospital. That was his first post in London, and it was while working there that he decided to make London his headquarters. Mackenzie's best-known book on diseases of the throat was translated into German by Semon, who supplemented it with extremely detailed and careful commentary. For some time, however, Semon's relations with Mackenzie have been cool. If you call on him he will no doubt explain the reasons himself. At any rate, he is one of the most unbiased, honest, and courageous men I know. He has a beautiful home and an even more beautiful wife, likewise German. He himself has considerable talent for the arts, and composes music. All in all, an exceptional person. Look him up—you will not regret it."

Two days later I went to see Semon at his house on Wimpole Street. Here I learned the background of the German Crown Prince's illness, which was known to scarcely anyone at that time.

Later, talking to other witnesses, I was able to piece together the complete story as I set it forth here.

Some three months before, on the morning of March 6, 1887, Karl Gerhardt, professor of internal medicine at Berlin University, received an unexpected summons to the Crown Prince's palace. Gerhardt came from the Palatinate. He had worked for many years in Würzburg, and there made a name for himself as a pediatrician. He owed his appointment to Berlin University primarily to Ernst von Bergmann, who before his rise to world fame had likewise worked in Würzburg. The Crown Princess, too, had seconded Gerhardt's appointment because she wanted a top-notch pediatrician in Berlin.

When Gerhardt arrived at the palace, he took it for granted that he had been called in connection with some medical problem concerning one of the Crown Prince's four daughters, or the Crown Princess herself, who was now forty-seven. He did not even think of the fifty-six-year-old Crown Prince, who was the very picture of a handsome, healthy man.

Gerhardt was received by the Crown Prince's personal physician, Surgeon-General Wegner. From him he learned that the patient was the Crown Prince himself. Since January, His Highness had been suffering from a stubborn hoarseness, to which at first little attention had been paid. His respiratory passages had been sensitive since childhood, and all his life had constituted a weak point in his otherwise robust constitution. Wegner had originally assumed that the Crown Prince had caught cold at Monza the previous year, during a drive with the Italian royal couple. The coachman had lost his way and the drive in the open carriage had continued for a long time in damp cold. But the persistence of the hoarseness had in time alarmed Wegner. That was why he was now requesting Gerhardt to make a thorough examination of the Crown Prince's throat.

The Crown Prince was on his feet when Gerhardt was admitted. Tall, lean, but strong and broad-shouldered, with thick blond hair and beard and bright blue eyes, he was the ideal image of a Prussian Prince. I had encountered his portrait time and again in German houses. He wore the uniform of a Prussian general, as he had done fifteen years before during the Franco-Prussian War—from which he had emerged, because of his kindness and humanitarianism, as the most popular of Prussian generals.

Gerhardt had come to Berlin too recently and had too few connections to suspect that back of this picture of hale success there lay a kind of tragedy which had nothing to do with disease. For here was a man approaching his sixtieth year who was still only the Crown Prince. In a few days his father would be celebrating his ninetieth birthday. Nor could anyone guess how much longer the present Emperor, who had been a sickly child never expected to live long, would continue to reign. Since those days in Scotland in 1854 when the romantic youth had given a bouquet of heather to the then barely fifteen-year-old English Princess Royal, Victoria, and had asked Queen Victoria for the hand of this pampered eldest daughter, the Crown Prince had been dreaming of a new Germany—a Germany released from the harshness of the Prussian authoritarian state represented by his own father and by Chancellor Bismarck.

The Crown Princess had been given a thorough political education by her father, Prince Albert. These teachings, implanted in her passionate and ambitious nature, had formed a personality which, though less richly endowed in emotional values than the Crown Prince's, was far superior to his in will power, purposiveness, and resolution. The Crown Prince's attachment to his wife struck observers in later years as verging on psychological servility. Certainly her influence upon his ideas and aims grew steadily. On the other hand, his distaste for Bismarck's policies accorded with the mildness of his disposition. He had hoped for the day when he could create a genuine German parliament and realize his idealistic dream of "freedom and justice for all." He had hoped also to establish a lasting amity with England, in place of Bismarck's overtures to Russia. But for decades his and the Princess's dreams had remained mere visions. He was a public figure permanently on display, powerless and without influence. In his gloomier hours he even believed that his father would outlive him, and the Crown Princess alone, with tenacious obstinacy, nourished his hopes, which were her own. She—more and more disliked at the Berlin court, and unable to win the affection of the Germans—had untiringly encouraged the Crown Prince and imbued her weaker husband with constantly renewed faith in their common future, in which great changes would be made.

Gerhardt knew nothing of all these psychological complications that day in March when he confronted the Crown Prince for the first time, and conducted his examination. At this time the larynx was a comparatively new field for medical exploration. Egyptian and Roman physicians had had some knowledge of the anatomical construction of that deep-seated organ invisible from the mouth except by the use of special instruments. Only at the beginning of the nineteenth century did a Dr. Mende have occasion to observe the functions of the vocal cords in a living human being—a suicide who had cut his throat and nevertheless survived for a day. Somewhat later Liston, the British surgeon whose introduction of ether anesthesia into England I had witnessed, conceived the notion of inspecting the larynx with a dentist's mirror. In 1854, finally, a Spanish singing teacher, Manuel García, succeeded in peering into the functioning larynx, using two mirrors, and the sun as source of illumination. A few years later two Viennese doctors, Türck and Czermak, independently introduced the laryngoscope into medical practice, and substituted artificial light for the rays of the sun. Since then examination of diseases of the larynx had become possible. Treatment, however, remained virtually hopeless, and all serious illnesses generally ended with loss of the voice and slow asphyxiation. Starting in Vienna, the special field of laryngology had nevertheless developed. Gerhardt, too, although not exclusively a specialist in the field, had had a great deal of experience in the diagnosis and treatment of diseases of the larynx.

In the mirror the Crown Prince's vocal cords showed a distinct, evenly spread reddening. At the edge of the left vocal cord Gerhardt discovered a longish, shallow, pinkish nodule. The mobility of the cords seemed to be unobstructed—a finding of particular importance because experience had shown that impaired mobility generally indicated malignancy. The nodule itself strongly resembled a benign growth.

Gerhardt proposed to remove this polyp through the mouth, working by mirror—an operation frequently performed in those days. Throat specialists had developed a whole minor branch of surgery for such operations, and possessed a number of unique instruments: delicate, curved forceps, wire nooses, and above all electrically heated platinum wires with which such tiny tumors of the vocal cords could be burned away. Moreover, for some years cocaine had been used as a local anesthetic. The use of cocaine had enabled physicians to overcome many of the difficulties that had previously constituted insuperable obstacles—above all, the extreme sensitivity to pain of the region of the throat, a sensitivity which had hitherto compelled ultrarapid and therefore frequently improper operations.

By March 14 Gerhardt had made several attempts to get at the small tumor with wire loops and circular scalpels. He did not succeed. On the evening of March 14 he attempted for the first time to use a red-hot platinum wire. In spite of all his care these operations were extremely painful, and followed by consistent sore throat, difficulties in swallowing, and hoarseness. The tumor proved to be hard. It broke into fibers in an unusual manner. Its appearance changed from day to day.

On March 20 Gerhardt burned it away completely. Two days later, however, when the Crown Prince went to congratulate his father on his ninetieth birthday, he spoke thickly. The following week Professor Gerhardt discovered that the tumor had regrown to its full size. He had never known a benign tumor to come back with such speed. For the first time he had the glimmering suspicion that he might be dealing with a cancerous growth. The Crown Prince had reached the age at which, according to the experience of the day, cancer of the throat most frequently appeared. Since even now, however, Gerhardt observed no impairment in the mobility of the vocal cords, he tried once more to extirpate the tumor through the mouth. In a number of daily sessions continuing until April 7 he succeeded in burning away completely the morbid nodule. Since before the treatment Dr. Wegner had proposed a cure in Bad Ems, one of the foremost German spas for throat conditions, Gerhardt agreed that the trip should be taken at this time. He hoped that after the Crown Prince's return he would be able to arrive at a final diagnosis.

On May 15 the Crown Prince returned. That same day Gerhardt went to the palace to examine him. He found his worst fears confirmed. Frederick's voice was hoarser, the tumor larger than before. But the most menacing of all the symptoms was a new one: the mobility of the vocal cords had distinctly diminished.

The Crown Prince, still unsuspecting, insisted on another cauterization. Gerhardt, now quite sure that this method of treatment would be fruitless, instead proposed consultation with a surgeon. As he later assured me, he had no doubt that the tumor was a carcinoma and that only immediate removal of the entire tumor offered a chance to save the Crown Prince's life. In his experience only the smallest part of such a tumor could be reached through the oral cavity. Nor did he know of any cases in which it had proved possible to remove even extremely small laryngeal cancers through the mouth without their growing back in a very short time. Here the techniques of throat specialists no longer had a place. Only major surgery could accomplish anything.

Gerhardt was by no means fully informed on the subject of major laryngeal surgery, which had been developed only during the previous fifteen years. But he knew of two cases in which an immediate operation from outside—that is, through the throat—had led to lasting successes. One of these cases involved a physician, Dr. Fromm, who had been operated on by the Berlin surgeon Küster seven years before. Küster had removed the part of the larynx attacked by the cancer. The patient was left with a hoarse voice, but otherwise had recovered completely. The second case concerned a patient named Zygan in whom an incipient cancer of the larynx had been removed in the same fashion. This patient, too, was still living, and had likewise emerged from the operation with nothing worse than hoarseness. The surgeon in this case was Professor von Bergmann, who later had taken me to see his patient.

Gerhardt therefore proposed a consultation with Bergmann, but said nothing about the nature of the case to him, in order not to prejudice his judgment. On May 16 Bergmann went to the Crown Prince's palace and conducted an examination. Afterwards, alone with Wegner and Gerhardt, he declared that the tumor was a malignant epithelioma (cancer of the mucous membrane) which must be removed as soon as possible.

Bergmann was intimately familiar with the history of laryngeal surgery. He knew what his proposal involved. The first attempts to approach the larynx from the throat side, to penetrate the shell of cartilage to reach the interior of the organ, had been made some hundred years before. The French surgeon Pelletan in 1778 had split the larynx of a patient in order to remove a piece of meat that had become lodged between the vocal cords. He succeeded in opening the larynx, inserted his finger, and pushed the obstruction back into the pharynx. In spite of the lack of anesthesia and antisepsis, the victim of this somewhat comic misadventure came through splendidly. Nevertheless, some seventy years passed before such an operation was attempted more frequently, with the aid of anesthesia and antisepsis. Extraordinary difficulties had arisen to hamper such operations under anesthesia because the operating field lay right in the path which the anesthetics had to travel from mouth and nose to lungs. Tracheotomy was revived—a desperate expedient on the part of the boldest of the old surgeons in cases in which the passage of air through the larynx was blocked by tumors, diphtheria, tuberculosis, or syphilis. In the sixteenth century the Florentine physician Bonviene had opened the windpipe of a suffocating patient. Some time afterwards another surgeon, Fabricius, had invented a short length of pipe which he inserted into the incision in the trachea, facilitating the intake of air. Later this tube—the cannula—was provided with a valve.

With the first laryngeal operations under anesthesia, tracheotomy had been resorted to in order to provide a passage for the anesthetic below the level of the operating field. Above the cannula the trachea was tamponed in order to stop blood from the operating field from entering the trachea and producing coughing and asphyxiation. The slitting of the larynx and the limited removal of parts of the organ, in particular of single vocal cords, had been accomplished without any great difficulty as early as the seventies. The wounds, in spite of the lack of antisepsis, or its incomplete application, had been inclined to heal. This healing was the more lasting the earlier the operation was performed, the smaller the carcinoma was, and the more completely it could be excised. The voice remained hoarse, to be sure, but the patient lived and had the use of his vocal cords.

After these successes a few surgeons had gone several steps further. They considered removing the entire larynx in cases of far-advanced carcinomas. In 1870 Czerny, one of Billroth's assistants in Vienna, had experimented in removing the entire larynges of dogs and sewing the trachea directly to the pharynx. This seemingly impossible operation succeeded. Except for the loss of voice, all the functions of the throat, the whole apparatus of swallowing and breathing, were restored. On December 31, 1873, Billroth himself performed the first complete removal of the larynx of a human being, a thirty-six-year-old patient.

An address delivered by Gussenbauer, another of Billroth's assistants, at the Third Congress of the German Surgery Association, had acquainted the medical world in general with this operation of Billroth's. When the patient first went to Billroth, the surgeon diagnosed an extremely advanced case of laryngeal cancer. Nevertheless, Billroth had at first hoped that laryngotomy would suffice, and that he would be able to save one vocal cord which appeared to be inflamed but not cancerous. The operation was performed on November 27, 1873. From the start there had been complications. The cannula (for the anesthetic), which was introduced into the trachea through an incision below the cricoid cartilage, was found not to fill the incision completely. Blood from outside had run into the trachea, causing coughing. The vertical incision made above the cricoid cartilage into the larynx had been insufficient for the removal of the tumor on the left vocal cord, which was large and lumpy and extended below the right vocal cord. Billroth had been compelled to sever the cricoid cartilage also. As a result, the cannula had lost its support. The tampon in the trachea leaked. Only by hasty work with a succession of sponges had Billroth prevented the blood from pouring into the trachea. Nevertheless he succeeded in removing the visible part of the tumor with a fluted shears and scraping out the bed of the tumor with a sharp spatula. Healing followed with amazing speed. Within two days the patient was breathing almost exclusively through the pharynx and speaking in a hoarse voice. The suppuration of the wound, which at that time was still considered natural and inescapable in Billroth's clinic, passed quickly. An examination with the laryngoscope on December 16 showed good healing. The right vocal cord had been preserved. The distinct reddening and swelling of the mucous membrane in the larynx was still considered mere inflammation. The patient left his bed. The incision in the throat, too, had healed except for a tiny opening.

Then, on the night of December 29, Gussenbauer was called to the patient. He found him struggling for breath. Gussenbauer had to insert a cannula as quickly as possible into the still partly open throat incision, in order to prevent asphyxiation. An immediate examination with the laryngoscope showed a fresh knobby tumor diffusely distributed over the entire larynx. What had been considered an inflammation was likewise a cancerous growth.

Billroth had to inform his unfortunate patient that the carcinoma was again rampant and that a more thorough operation would be necessary. The despairing young man agreed. On December 31 the scarified wound was again opened. At first Billroth had thought only to scrape out the entire interior of the larynx. But immediately after he cut through it he was forced to recognize that the whole cartilage of the organ was attacked by cancer. It was now a question of abandoning the operation entirely or for the first time attempting upon a human being the operation which Czerny had performed on dogs: total extirpation of the larynx. Billroth had the anesthesia temporarily interrupted and asked the patient, when he came to, whether he consented to an attempt at total extirpation. With a look that expressed nothing but a plea for rescue, the patient nodded his consent, and was promptly anesthetized again.

Billroth prolonged the incision upwards as far as the hyoid bone and freed the soft tissues on either side of the larynx. In the course of his attempt to draw out the larynx, the cricoid cartilage was torn several times. The cannula slid out of the trachea and had to be repeatedly replaced. Several times the patient awoke, and a tormented cough sprayed blood over the operating field. The operation had already lasted a full hour before Billroth was at last able to sever the trachea by a diagonal cut below the larynx. Violent bleeding from the upper arteries of the larynx forced him to work fast. The cricoid cartilage and the arytenoid cartilage were separated from the esophagus and the larynx was severed from back to front. It then became apparent that the epiglottis was also cancerous, and the larger part of it had to be removed likewise. Finally the loose end of the trachea was sewed to the pharynx.

The unfortunate patient had already lost a great deal of blood. Four hours later a postoperative hemorrhage from an artery developed, and before Billroth succeeded in finding and ligaturing the source the patient was already in a deathlike coma. Nevertheless, healing progressed so rapidly that the patient was able to take solid foods by the eighteenth day, and shortly afterwards managed to speak in a feeble whisper. Thereupon Gussenbauer undertook to replace the larynx by an artificial device. Soon the patient was able to speak loudly enough to be heard at the other end of a large hospital ward. On March 7 he was released as cured; but a few months later, by the time I visited him, his doctors held the shattering suspicion that cancerous metastases had already formed. The patient still suspected nothing. Shortly afterwards, however, he died of diffuse new growths in the pharynx and in the scars which made any subsequent operation pointless.

At the time Bergmann entered the Crown Prince's palace these two operations lay some fifteen years in the past. The optimism aroused by Gussenbauer's lecture in April, 1873, on the successful complete removal of the larynx had not lasted long. The patient's death soon afterwards had had the inevitable sobering effect. Further attempts at total extirpation had followed, to be sure, and the operational technique had been improved each time. These operations no longer took the unexpected and distressing turns of the first. But in the end the results had been the same: shortly after each operation the patients were killed by metastases and new growths. From these events the conclusion had been drawn that no operation, however thorough, could save the victims of cancer of the larynx once large portions of the organ were involved. On the other hand, it had been demonstrated with equal certainty that where cancer was recognized in its early stages, surgery upon the affected parts gave the patient an extended lease on life and, frequently, a permanent cure. More or less severe vocal deterioration—hoarseness and reduction in volume of the voice—was the price paid for these cures. The operation itself involved no greater risks than those of any other operation since the introduction of asepsis.

Immediately after his examination, Bergmann proposed laryngotomy and removal of the parts affected by the tumor. He argued that, given the deep-seatedness of the tumor, one could not determine its extent when working through the mouth alone; this could be done only by laryngotomy. There was every indication that the tumor was still limited, and that the impairment of the voice would be no greater than would follow from continuation of the inadequate operations through the mouth.

The Crown Princess was informed by Wegner, Gerhardt, and

Bergmann. Although she had already had dark premonitions, she now felt the ground quake beneath her. The aged Kaiser had just passed his ninetieth year. Never had the Crown Princess seen him looking as weary and exhausted as he had on his birthday; never had the hour of fulfillment seemed closer. It would be a fulfillment of an odd sort, to be sure, for the Crown Prince was by now at an age when other men had the fruits of their lives long since stored in the granary. Nevertheless, it would represent some fulfillment. As yet, none of the doctors had openly spoken the word "cancer." But the Princess sensed something ominous in their very gravity. She stood by, inwardly numbed but mastering herself with all the force of her iron character, when Bergmann broached the question of the operation to the Crown Prince. Of course not a word was said about cancer at this point either. Nevertheless, the Crown Prince paled. He too was prey, perhaps for the first time, to an obscure, vague, terrifying premonition. But he too pretended composure. "Something must be done about the swelling in any case," he declared. "If it cannot be burned away from inside, you will have to cut it out from outside."

Wegner, a somewhat vacillating person without any great medical experience, quailed before the responsibility which suddenly reared before him. He said that in any case another prominent international laryngologist ought to be consulted, in order to secure the confirmation of a specialist in so important a matter. The Crown Princess, feeling a spark of hope, was at once of his mind. Gerhardt and Bergmann naturally assented, for they too felt the tremendous burden of their responsibility and were glad to have it shared by other doctors. They never doubted that no matter what laryngologist came to Berlin for the consultation, the result of his examination would correspond to theirs. They themselves proposed Professor Schrötter of Vienna or Professor Rauchfuss of St. Petersburg. At this time, however, no decision was taken.

When the Crown Princess was left alone with Wegner, she asked him: "Who is the leading English specialist for diseases of the throat?" Given her English background, and her long-standing lack of rapport with things German, she was naturally inclined to place her hopes and confidence in the doctors of her native land. Wegner, however, could not at once give her a name.

That evening Wegner, as he later related to me himself, rummaging in his study, found Felix Semon's German translation of the two-volume textbook on diseases of the nose and throat by Morell Mackenzie. He opened it, read Semon's foreword, and came across the following sentence: "Convinced as I am that a scientific work proves its *raison d'être* by its contents and not by the meager addition of a foreword, I would send into the world this translation of the views and experiences of the man who is undoubtedly the foremost English throat specialist without a word on my part, if it were not that . . ." etc. At that moment Wegner made the decision whose full import was to be revealed only much later. The name of Mackenzie meant virtually nothing to him. But the name of Semon meant a great deal. And if Semon referred to Mackenzie in these terms, then he, Wegner, could justifiably recommend Mackenzie as the foremost British laryngologist to the Crown Princess.

Wegner did so with no more ado.

The Crown Princess had never heard Mackenzie's name before. But that same day she requested her mother to send Mackenzie to Berlin at once, and to send him as an emissary from the Queen of England—for the Crown Princess did not wish to arouse the impression in Germany that she, being English, wanted at all costs to consult an English physician.

On Wednesday, May 18, Queen Victoria's physician in attendance, Dr. James Reid, hastened from Osborne, where Her Majesty was staying, to London. At Harley Street he routed out the throat specialist, who was on the point of going to bed, and relayed Her Majesty's command that he go at once to Berlin to examine the Crown Prince, and inform the Queen of the outcome of this examination. Reid gave no details whatsoever, so that Mackenzie departed in complete ignorance of the case, and without taking his instruments. He set out without a moment's demur—not only because the Queen was sending him, but above all because he would never have let slip a case of such enormous international importance.

Somewhat over fifty, Mackenzie was undoubtedly the most prosperous, famous, and also controversial throat specialist in England. My present description and my later judgment of his personality and his conduct are based upon personal impressions of my meet-

ings with him, but also upon the opinions of others who knew him
and were quite capable of objective verdicts.

Mackenzie was the son of a physician, and one of eight children.
His father was killed in a carriage accident while the boy was still
at school. Morell, the oldest of the children, a rotund, enterprising
chap with a strikingly large head, was found a situation with an
insurance company. On the side, however, he studied his father's
medical books. At night he would tie his right thumb to the big
toe of his left foot, so that if he fell asleep while studying, the
tugging would awaken him. This imitation of the proverbial Chinese
student suggests something of his purposefulness and drive. At last
an aunt provided him with the means for formal medical studies,
in the course of which he journeyed to Vienna. There he learned
about the laryngoscope and, with his keen scent for career opportunities, perceived that he would be able to make his way by
using this instrument, which in England was scarcely known. All
that was necessary, he realized, was to be the first or one of the
first to employ so novel a technique. Back in London he told the
conclave of his brothers and sisters—this was a family group of
unusual cohesiveness: "If I am ever to make anything of the throat,
I must see more patients." This businesslike formulation suggests
something of his direct, commercial attitudes. He rented several
rooms in a rather low-class London neighborhood, on King's Street.
Subsequently he was to take over the entire building, acting as land-
lord, and thereby enjoying rent-free quarters. Over the door he
hung a shingle reading: "Metropolitan Free Dispensary for Diseases
of the Throat and Loss of Voice." He conducted this clinic entirely
alone, pretending to have assistants by slipping into an adjoining
room after the examination of a patient and there, behind frosted
glass, playing the part of laboratory technician, apothecary, and
so on. This little stratagem, too, throws light upon his personality.
Soon he was working fourteen hours a day. Patients came to him
in droves because his specialty was unique in London. His commercial sense, moreover, was linked with fantastic industry, high
intelligence, and considerable manual skill. Within a few years he
commanded an income such as normally fell to the lot of a successful London physician at the end of a long career.

Naturally, envious voices were raised against him. London's
doctors were hostile on principle to specialization, and diseases of

the throat had hitherto been considered of such minor importance that no doctor cared to take over a department limited to these diseases in any of the hospitals. Instead, the youngest assistants had fallen heir to such positions, inasmuch as they had to take what was given them. Mackenzie's success made him hated. It must be said, however, that whatever the merit of his work, he acted in such a way as to provoke this hatred. He worked more than the other doctors, although he was bothered by asthma and never felt entirely well. He amassed a degree of experience and skill in the field of throat diseases such as no other London physician possessed. He soon became an artist in the use of the laryngoscope, and was able to make his diagnoses in seconds. He worked in several consulting rooms at once. While one patient was still unwinding a scarf from his throat, Mackenzie would be giving gargle to another, spraying powder into the larynx of a third, and then darting back to the first and removing the patient's tonsils without anesthesia, with two lightning-fast movements. His publications during the first decades of his practice, including the book whose German translation had resulted in his call to Berlin, contained a great deal of new knowledge acquired by infinite pains. In private life he had that profound and touching affection for his family which often characterizes the self-made man, and I had seen him, both in his handsome house on Harley Street and at his modest country place in Wargrave, on the banks of the Thames, playing with his three daughters, Ethel, Olga, and Hilda, in a manner which was quite endearing.

Nevertheless, the darker sides of his nature showed through every crack and cranny in his outward demeanor. One conspicuous trait was the ruthless energy with which he advanced his career and exploited people, conditions, and things for his own ends. He had a brutal way of casting aside everything that had served its purpose for him. He loved publicity and used it to advance his fame, to an extent which many respected physicians considered undignified. In 1878 Mackenzie's private clinic came under attack on grounds that it was badly administered and was only a money-making institution for Mackenzie. The Prince of Wales, who had assumed sponsorship of it after Mackenzie's early successes, withdrew his name. This was regarded as proof that things were not all they should be—although the Prince may well have been led to this action by malicious rumors spread by envious colleagues. Yet I myself had known Mackenzie to pay a daily professional call upon a sick man whose death was only a matter of time; he confined himself to asking hastily whether the patient had taken a useless medicine. When the reply was "Yes," he said, "Very well, good-bye," pocketed two guineas, and left the house. And this farce he repeated day after day. He maintained, it is true, that he had explained to the patient the uselessness of his visits, but that the patient insisted on them. This did not, I thought, justify his conduct. Finally, in his medical work Mackenzie was courteous to his colleagues, but excessively self-assured. He relied heavily on his virtuoso skill, a heritage from the days before the discovery of cocaine when the throat specialist was obliged to work with the greatest swiftness. This enforced speed had resulted in the physician's being prepared for a large percentage of errors. The mortality in Mackenzie's hospital was high, and this fact was certainly not due solely to his receiving virtually hopeless cases from other hospitals and doctors. It was due also to the superficiality of much of his treatment; he was too self-confident. In later years he no longer bothered to keep up with the general progress of medicine, above all in the realm of major surgery of the throat and larynx, which lay outside his field of minor surgery. Indeed, he treated surgeons as intruders into his private specialty. At the time Wegner in Berlin read Semon's preface, and gave the name of Mackenzie to the Crown Princess, he did not know that Semon in the meanwhile had parted company with his teacher—and not only on grounds of personality and disillusionment with Mackenzie's human frailties. Semon was more put out by Mackenzie's failure to develop scientifically, and by his famous self-assurance, which by now had become downright arrogance.*

* In a book published nearly thirty years after Henry Steven Hartmann's death, sections of the diaries of the Crown Princess and later Empress were presented, together with portions of her correspondence with her mother, Queen Victoria. Included in the latter was the letter Queen Victoria dispatched to Berlin at the time she sent Mackenzie. She wrote to her daughter: "I hope Dr. Mackenzie has arrived. Not knowing him at all (and I had never heard of him) I thought it best to send Dr. Reid up to see him and send him off. Sir William [Jenner] said Dr. M. Mackenzie certainly is very clever in that particular line about throats; but that he is greedy and grasping about money and tries to make a profit out of his attendance. And that the Professors dislike him for that. I only mention this that you may know whom you are dealing with." From *The English Empress. A Study in the Relations between Queen Victoria and Her Eldest Daughter, Empress Frederick*

In Berlin, meanwhile, there had been another full-scale examination of the Crown Prince on May 18. This had taken place at the request of the old Kaiser, to whom the sad news had been broken. The Kaiser's personal physician, von Lauer, Surgeon Major General Dr. Schrader, and Tobold, one of the oldest laryngologists of Berlin, participated. They unanimously agreed that the Prince's condition was due to cancer of the larynx, and that immediate laryngotomy offered the sole chance to save his life. It was decided to wait for Mackenzie's arrival, but to make all preparations for the operation so that it could be performed by May 21 at the latest. The Crown Princess, wearing an air of composure while in her husband's room and surrendering to wild despair or desperate hope in her own apartment, consulted with Bergmann on what was to be the operating chamber. Table and instruments were brought to the palace. The Crown Princess gave Bergmann the keys to a side door of the palace, so that he could enter at any time. He was also given a key to a desk in which he could place confidential memoranda for her.

At five o'clock in the afternoon of May 20 Mackenzie arrived in Berlin. As soon as he had changed from his travelling clothes he was taken to the Crown Prince, who addressed him in a hoarse but quite distinct whisper.

Mackenzie was then introduced to the German doctors, who waited in an adjoining room. From the first he behaved with his characteristic slightly offensive self-assurance. Vanity speaks in every line of the account he later wrote of this meeting—although, it must in fairness be added, his tale is colored by the accumulated resentments of a later period. Yet on the whole the account indubitably reproduces much of the attitude he displayed on that May 20. He regarded Gerhardt as a man who had found "some" time for throat diseases in addition to his usual medical work. Bergmann was "a surgeon from Petersburg" who had taken the chair of surgery in Berlin after other great surgeons had rejected it. Moreover, Mackenzie had "never heard of Bergmann as an operator on the larynx." Mackenzie regarded Tobold as a broken-down old man.

He listened to the summary of previous examinations, which Wegner read aloud. Then he went to the Crown Prince, and in a

of Germany, by Egon Caesar Conte Corti, translated by E. M. Hodgson. Cassell and Company, Ltd., London, 1957.

darkened room proceeded with his examination of the Crown Prince's throat. He worked with the amazing speed for which he was noted. According to his own statement and the testimony of the other witnesses, he observed a pale pink growth about the size of a split pea in the posterior section of the left vocal cord. The mucous membrane of the surrounding area was red. Mackenzie also observed the lessened mobility of the diseased vocal cord. Then he again withdrew to talk with the German doctors. Gerhardt, Tobold, and Bergmann gave the reasons for their decision to operate. They were still certain that Mackenzie would agree with them and recommend operation as the sole possible hope of saving the Prince's life.

But they were to encounter an extraordinary surprise. Mackenzie declared that the appearance of the tumor was not at all typical of cancer. He was convinced that if the patient had been an ordinary person, not the Crown Prince, Bergmann would never have thought of cancer. Emphatically he stated that his experience was extremely wide and that he had seen more of these matters than "any other living man"; he had more than once encountered identical cases which had been cured by careful treatment through the mouth. Gerhardt countered that at the beginning of the illness, weeks before, he had thought the same, and had been taught his error by the growth of the tumor. Thereupon Mackenzie replied that he could not advise so dangerous an operation, whose consequence was almost certain to be fatal, as long as tumorous tissue had not been proved cancerous by microscopic examination. Bergmann protested that the operation was by no means dangerous, that he had performed it seven times with only one failure. He invited Mackenzie to visit his patients. Mackenzie arrogantly disregarded all this. Here, he felt, major surgery was invading the domain of his specialty. Nor was he moved by Gerhardt's argument that it was impossible to remove through the mouth portions of the tumor of sufficient extent and depth to tell one anything under the microscope. Mackenzie understood this argument—as he later wrote—as an admission of the Germans' inability to do the sort of thing his own virtuosity rendered commonplace. Of course he did not say this during the consultation, but his private opinion was not hard to guess.

If the Germans had taken a closer look at Mackenzie's earlier

published work, they would have found four sentences contradict-
ing his present stand, such as: "In these cases, should particles be
expectorated or removed during life with the aid of the laryngoscope, the microscope cannot be relied on for differential diagnosis.
Several cases have come under my notice where the histological
features were decidedly those of cancer, whilst the clinical history
was of a totally different character, and vice versa." They might
then have demanded of Mackenzie what, at this fateful time, made
him deny his own knowledge and appoint the microscope as arbiter?
There is no answer to this question. Mackenzie's insistence on a
microscopic examination was quite justified as long as the results
were regarded in the light of the existing status of histology and
not held as decisive in themselves. If Mackenzie's skill allowed him
—contrary to Gerhardt's view—to remove deeper-lying tissues
through the mouth, there was every reason not to neglect an immediate microscopic examination as a prime aid to corroborating
the diagnosis.

I still maintain that it is unfair to charge Mackenzie—as was
often done subsequently—with initial dishonesty and with having
played an ambitious, irresponsible gamble for the favor of the
Crown Prince and Princess. On May 20 he was undoubtedly convinced that the clinical findings did not point to cancer. The question was only how far his excessive specialist's vanity and concomitant carelessness would lead him into the kind of error from
which there would subsequently be no escape without admitting
his mistake and endangering his whole prestige.

The German physicians agreed to the microscopic examination.
Since they believed firmly in their diagnosis, they were convinced
that Virchow would only bear witness in their favor. Moreover,
they had to accede or expose themselves to the just reproach that
they had not done everything possible to substantiate their diagnosis.

Nevertheless, this first consultation had already sown the seeds
of antipathy and distrust. Bergmann, too, was a man who had risen
high from lowly origins. His was an entirely different personality
from Mackenzie's, quieter, firmer, more retiring, more conscious
of the dignity and responsibility of the medical profession. But
he too had a good deal of that self-assurance which grows along
with a man's career, although he exercised it in a less obtrusive

manner. Mackenzie's superior tone had offended Bergmann's vanity. Gerhardt, too, though less famous and less complex a person, and perhaps for that very reason more sensitive, was similarly affected.

Mackenzie, who had come without instruments, obtained a laryngeal forceps in Berlin. On May 21 he removed, on the second attempt, a piece of the tumor from the Crown Prince's throat. With utmost suspense, the result of Virchow's histological examination was awaited. The verdict was indeed a shaking one.

Virchow stated that he had been unable to find any evidence of malignant growth in the tissue presented to him. Privately he commented that the tumor might be "a warty growth resulting from a chronic inflammation of the larynx." Some writers on the subject have conjectured that Virchow was carried away by his sympathy for the Crown Prince and his hopes of the latter's acceding to the throne, and that his examination was perhaps too careless. There is no doubt that Virchow's results corresponded with his hopes. But it is surely mistaken to suspect that this dry, precise scientist had been led into error by wishful thinking. As chance would have it, Virchow had received for examination a piece of tissue free of cancer—this being precisely the kind of chance which could always enter into histological examination, as Mackenzie had fully recognized in his earlier writings.

Virchow's report struck the German doctors like a bolt from the blue. It was a horrible blow to their self-confidence and their conviction of the rightness of their diagnosis. But they were correct in declaring that Virchow's report was not decisive. The total clinical picture, which they had unanimously recognized as evidence of malignancy, remained unchanged. It was also noteworthy that Virchow asked for further samples of tissue. On the other hand, Mackenzie could rightly greet Virchow's report with feelings of triumph, for it bore out his interpretation of the clinical picture. This was, however, only a tentative corroboration, as he should have been the first to recognize. Instead, he leaped to immediate conclusions. His specialist's pride, his sense of his own infallibility, and his condescending attitude toward the Germans prompted him to throw off all restraint.

Since he had from the first been quartered in the Crown Prince's palace and was able to speak privately with the Princess in English, he had the opportunity to communicate his views directly to Victoria. His optimistic comments even before Virchow's report had won the confidence of the Crown Princess. Now he hastened to inform her of his triumph. In his craving for recognition he forgot all caution. He declared that the disease was a harmless one, although he could not yet diagnose it precisely, and that he could cure it within a few weeks without a dangerous operation. Confronted with the choice of believing the pessimistic Germans or her own optimistic fellow countryman—corroborated, moreover, by Virchow—the Crown Princess naturally began to rely completely upon Mackenzie. The Crown Prince himself followed her example.

On May 23 Mackenzie undertook a third operation in order to obtain the additional tissue that Virchow had requested. This operation was performed in the presence of the German doctors. Already there was a distinct tension in the atmosphere. Mackenzie took no trouble to conceal his feelings of triumph. But this time his operation failed. The forceps was empty when he withdrew it. In the subsequent examination with the laryngoscope Gerhardt established that Mackenzie's forceps had injured the previously sound right vocal cord. Two days later Bergmann and Tobold confirmed this injury to the cord. Mackenzie was already in ill-humor over his failure. The Germans' observation was correct, for all that a measure of perfectly human satisfaction doubtless accompanied it. But Mackenzie felt that his honor as a master of the technique of laryngoscopy had been gravely impugned. Henceforth there was profound antagonism between himself and Gerhardt, although for the time being it remained hidden. But Mackenzie's position with the Crown Prince and Princess had already become unassailable.

Since both Friedrich and Victoria had long been planning to attend Queen Victoria's impending Jubilee in London, the Crown Princess, after her first conversations with Mackenzie, resolved to take advantage of this opportunity to decamp from Berlin and the German doctors, and entrust Mackenzie with the task of healing the Crown Prince's illness on English soil. Mackenzie encouraged this idea by speaking of the favorable influence of the English climate upon diseases of the larynx. The Kaiser, of course, would have to be approached for permission for the trip to England.

When the German doctors heard of this latest development they naturally recognized an intent to spirit the patient away from them. Their subsequent conduct was partly governed by germinating rivalries, nationalistic resentments, jealousy of the preference given to a foreigner. But it cannot be denied that the Germans acted primarily out of a sense of medical responsibility. They reaffirmed their diagnosis. To their minds, the carefully observed clinical picture pointed so indubitably to malignancy that Virchow's analysis, based as it was upon a tiny fragment of tissue, could not alter their conclusion. Mackenzie's predictions of a cure seemed to them false and frivolous. They therefore asked Mackenzie for a more detailed statement of his plan of treatment. How was he going to remove the tumor which was undoubtedly present? Mackenzie thereupon spoke in superior tones of removing the tumor with forceps or cautery—the same methods which Gerhardt had already applied in vain. When the Germans objected that this had already been tried, he gave the prideful rejoinder that his handling of this method was different and backed by more experience.

It was at this time that the first mentions of the disease began appearing in various German, English, and French newspapers. I had read some of these items in London, as I have mentioned elsewhere. While the German doctors had hitherto maintained strict silence, in keeping with the tradition of the medical profession, the journalists began speaking quite openly of cancer. What is more, they suggested that Gerhardt and Bergmann had been victims of a fearful error; that they might have killed the Crown Prince with their projected operation if Mackenzie had not been called in. Even the most respected of English journals carried hints along these lines. Mackenzie wrote openly to the editor of the *Deutsche Revue* on July 1: "I am happy to inform you that the microscopic examination of Professor Virchow has now demonstrated completely that the disease was not cancer." Mackenzie was indulging his old and incurable mania for publicity.

These were the reports which alarmed Semon, who as yet knew nothing of his unwitting part in the case—his translation which had resulted in Mackenzie's being called in. He immediately intervened, writing to the Bismarck family and to those doctors in

Berlin with whom he had closer associations. But it was already too late. In vain he advised the greatest guardedness in dealing with his former teacher, whose merits and weaknesses he knew only too well. In vain he and Henry Butlin, the foremost English laryngologist, publicly contested the accounts in the *British Medical Journal*, which were already reproducing Mackenzie's version of the affair. On the basis of their extensive experience with laryngeal carcinoma the two men issued a warning, on June 4, against jumping to conclusions from microscopic examination, and pointed to cases of their own in which such microscopic examination had proved deceptive. But it was too late. The trip to England had already been decided on.

Bergmann also pleaded with the Kaiser to veto the trip to England—not only out of nationalistic feelings, but above all out of fear that precious time was being irrevocably lost and that afterwards it would be too late for an operation. His efforts were vain. "I cannot do it," the ninety-year-old Kaiser explained. "My son is not a child. If he hopes that this treatment will save him, I cannot forbid him; all I can do is ask for assurances that no valuable time will be lost during Mackenzie's treatment." Mackenzie, who in the meantime had returned to England temporarily, came back to Berlin on June 7. On June 8 he once again succeeded in plucking out a piece of the tumor with his forceps. This time he had arranged matters so that neither Gerhardt nor Bergmann was present. Only Wegner, whom Mackenzie did not regard as a rival to be taken seriously, observed the operation. The tissue was immediately turned over to Virchow. On June 9 Virchow reported—and it was as if destiny held its hand over Mackenzie. Once again his forceps had encountered a nonmalignant piece of tissue. Virchow declared that this time as well he had found no sign of carcinoma. However, he added—by now cautious—that the nature of the whole tumor could not be deduced from the available tissue.

With difficulty, Gerhardt and Bergmann obtained a promise from the departing Mackenzie that he would continue to send further pieces of tissue from England to Virchow, and that he would instantly cease treatment if his efforts should prove inadequate. They were also anxious to have one other German doctor trained in laryngoscopy, in addition to Dr. Wegner, accompany the Crown Prince and Princess. Mackenzie, in speaking to the Crown Princess, referred to this demand as espionage. Since the Crown Princess trusted him completely, his view became hers. Nevertheless, the doctors' wish prevailed. The choice fell upon one of Gerhardt's young assistants, Dr. Landgraf. An extremely careful, objective observer skilled in the use of the laryngoscope, he at least would provide reports on the further course of the disease which would not be colored by Mackenzie's opinions.

On June 12 the Crown Prince and Princess set out for England.

June 21 was a warm, radiantly fair day. The London streets were swarming with people. Her Majesty's loyal subjects had turned out in force to honor the fiftieth anniversary of their Queen's accession to the throne. Felix Semon had invited me to join the party which was watching the parade from the home of one of his friends, Sir Ernest Cassel. While the procession moved slowly past, we stood with Semon's wife and the other ladies at a big window of Cassel's home on the corner of Bennel Street, St. James.

"This will be the first time I have seen the Crown Prince since the beginning of his illness," Semon remarked. "You know how much can be read in a patient's face."

"I am most eager to know what you will find in it," Cassel murmured.

At that moment there was a surge of music and cheering. There was the Queen's golden coach, glittering in the sunlight, drawn by six slowly stepping ponies. Twelve Indian officers in brilliant costumes preceded it. Then followed an animated and brightly clad group consisting of the Prince of Wales and his two brothers, the Queen's five sons-in-law and nine grandchildren. We had no difficulty making out the man we were waiting for. Mounted on a white horse, wearing a white cuirassier's uniform with silver breastplate, lustily cheered by the crowd, the German Crown Prince took his place among Queen Victoria's sons-in-law. Majestic upon his white horse, the Prince came closer and closer to us. Semon's tension was visible on his little face with its preposterous mustache.

Now the cheers rang out directly below our window. The Indian officers trotted by. The white cuirassier was still ten yards from our window. "Lohengrin!" Mrs. Semon exclaimed. And the other women, overcome with admiration, echoed the epithet: "Lohengrin!"

They saw only the white figure. They did not perceive all that Semon's trained eye glimpsed in that one moment. The Crown Prince's face looked white also, but it was a sallow white. Stiffly upright upon his horse, he resembled a white statue more than a living man. His eyes were deep-sunk, and it seemed to me that they were filled with the premonition of a sad leave-taking rather than pride in the warmth with which he was greeted.

When the Crown Prince had passed, and then the royal coach containing the stout little figure of the Queen, dressed in black and adorned with pearls and orders, Semon turned silently away from the window. For a while he looked at the floor. Then our eyes met. "That is not Lohengrin," he murmured. "Rather the Commendatore from *Don Giovanni*."

A few days later I was invited to a party at Semon's stately house on Wimpole Street, famous for its magnificent mantelpieces and ceilings. The date, I remember, was the twenty-eighth of June, 1887, precisely one week after the Jubilee procession during which we had had our glimpse of the German Crown Prince. In the course of the evening the conversation touched repeatedly upon the illness of the distinguished visitor, his present stay in London, and Morell Mackenzie.

When the guests began departing, toward midnight, Semon asked another man and myself to stay. This man had been introduced to me as a London solicitor by the name of Montagu Williams, but I had not exchanged a word with him all evening. As we crossed the room to the fire, Williams addressed me for the first time—and I began to comprehend why Semon was bringing us together. Williams's speech was perfectly understandable, but it had that somewhat hoarse quality usually due to damage to the larynx.

"Do you understand now?" Semon said, as his puny figure almost disappeared in the depths of an easy chair. "Mr. Williams is the most recent of my patients who has undergone a laryngeal operation. We can speak with utmost frankness. From the start Mr. Williams has insisted on no concealments, and has been kept fully informed of all the factors of his case." He glanced from under his bushy eyebrows at Williams. "Mr. Williams will gladly corroborate everything I have to say. The operation was performed on May 3, 1887.* My friend Professor Hahn, of Berlin, whom I had asked to come to London, was the surgeon. The left half of the larynx was removed. The operation lasted twenty-five minutes. Within ten days the surgical wound closed without complications. On May 22 Mr. Williams was able to leave Fitzroy House, where the operation took place. He has since ceased to appear in court, to spare his larynx the strain of long speeches. But to this day not the slightest trace of a recurrence of his complaint has appeared. I know that this does not necessarily mean final and complete cure, as it would in other diseases. But without the operation Mr. Williams would no longer be alive."

I looked at Williams, who nodded silently. Then he said: "It is so. I find, too, that I can do quite a bit of talking every day. It does not seem to me that a Crown Prince or Emperor should shun the only operation which can save him."

Semon looked worn. It was clear that he was tormented by a sense of responsibility, and by the helplessness to which he was condemned in the case of the Crown Prince. "There are mysterious correspondences," he murmured. "When Mr. Williams consulted me for the first time a year ago, the tumor on his left vocal cord looked like a simple papilloma, and the usual symptoms of carcinoma were not present. I removed a fragment of tissue with the forceps and had a very careful microscopic examination done. There were no signs of cancer. But, mindful of my experience that a single result of that sort does not necessarily define the nature of the growth, I extracted other specimens of tissue. Not until April 23 was one found which indisputably displayed cancerous characteristics. We operated ten days later with the result that you see."

There was no need for him to say more. The parallel to the Crown Prince's case and to Mackenzie's brash diagnosis was so plain that it could not be missed.

"This afternoon I had a painful experience," Semon remarked a

* Semon, like all the throat specialists of the time who had been trained only in minor surgery, turned all his cases requiring more radical surgery over to a surgeon. Only in later years did he also perform major operations himself.

little later. "I drove down Harley Street, past Mackenzie's house. I admit, I did not take that route by chance. But what followed was a matter of chance. As I drove past, a majestic figure of a man in civilian dress came down the steps in front of Mackenzie's door. It was the Crown Prince. He looked so pale and troubled that my heart went out to him. I felt as though I ought to have called out a word of warning to him."

The day we sat at Semon's fire, the day on which Semon happened to see the Crown Prince in front of Mackenzie's house, marked the beginning of the second act of the tragedy. It determined, in so far as such a decision lies within human powers, whether the Prince was to live or to die.

On that June 28 Mackenzie began his treatment. Aided by the laryngoscope, he attempted to remove the tumor of the left vocal cord with forceps. Present at the operation in addition to Dr. Wegner was one of Mackenzie's assistants. He was Dr. Wolfenden, a young man who some years previously, at the time of the scandal involving Mackenzie's hospital, had risen with surprising swiftness to a leading position—the other doctors having left the hospital. I must deviate from strict chronology here in order to throw some light upon Wolfenden's competence as a throat specialist. In the *British Medical Journal* for April, 1888, Wolfenden described the case of a patient which he diagnosed as chronic inflammation of the larynx and cartilage. Since the patient was in danger of asphyxiation, he had performed a tracheotomy, and in addition to the incision into the trachea had opened a tumor which he referred to as an "abscess." Barely a week later in the same journal it was demonstrated that he had not opened an abscess but a cancerous growth. His patient, who had meanwhile gone to another physician, actually suffered from cancer of the larynx, and died of it.

Mackenzie not only appointed this same young doctor his assistant in the treatment of the Crown Prince, but also installed him as his official representative in the Crown Prince's household.

Dr. Landgraf, Gerhardt's assistant, was not present at the treatment. Once in London, Mackenzie had seen to it that Landgraf was excluded as far as possible from the case. Just once he was forced, for appearances' sake, to allow Landgraf to conduct a laryngeal examination of the Prince. This took place on June 18.

Landgraf noted, in addition to the plainly visible tumor of the left vocal cord, inflammation, beginning of swelling of the posterior wall of the larynx, defects in the right vocal cord, and increasing rigidity of the left vocal cord. Mackenzie had dismissed Landgraf's findings with his usual superior smile. When Landgraf attempted to point out that glandular swellings should be looked for, as these usually indicated cancer, his comments were received with equal condescension. Mackenzie had already begun to belittle him to the Crown Prince, and especially to the Crown Princess. Perhaps Mackenzie really did not know that Landgraf had recently published an important scientific paper on "major catheterism of the respiratory passages," a paper testifying to considerable technical skill. Mackenzie may not have been aware of this because he had for so long ignored latest developments in his field. But perhaps he also preferred to ignore the paper. In any case, he and Wolfenden represented Landgraf as a man who knew nothing of laryngoscopy and whose opinions were to be taken no more seriously than those of a "third-year student." It was not difficult to push Landgraf to the sidelines because Landgraf was no prestidigitator with the laryngoscope, no acrobat seeking applause. Rather, he was a highly conscientious physician who took his time, and whose examinations, therefore, seemed to the Crown Prince far more irksome and protracted than Mackenzie's.

After the operation on June 28 Mackenzie was convinced that he had removed the entire tumor.

Wegner sent the pieces of tumor to Virchow in Berlin immediately. On July 4 Virchow's reply arrived. In truly mysterious fashion the farce was repeated for the third time. Once again Virchow found no indication of cancerous growth. This time, however, he wrote with even greater caution: "On this occasion deep layers of tissue were not removed, as was the case with the first and even more with the second operation." These words made no impression upon Mackenzie. Virchow's report once again confirmed his faith in his diagnosis, and intensified his vanity and therefore his carelessness.

Mackenzie's and Wolfenden's reports of their examinations seemed to me, when I read them later, almost inconceivable examples of vagueness and lack of factual content. In the meantime, at the Crown Princess's urging, the Crown Prince moved to Norris Castle on the Isle of Wight. Dr. Wegner and Landgraf were left behind in London. Their sole sources of information were newspaper reports that the Crown Prince was steadily improving. These bulletins sounded more and more as if they were directly dictated to the reporters by Mackenzie himself. Not until July 22 did Landgraf arrive at Norris Castle. He was treated with contemptuous condescension, especially by the Crown Princess, but obtained leave to examine the Crown Prince's larynx. At the spot which had been operated on June 28 he found a saddle-shaped swelling. The tumor had grown back in the very place where Mackenzie had removed it. Even more important than this, it seemed to Landgraf, was the swelling and reddening of the posterior wall of the larynx. These signs of a still half-hidden extension of a cancerous tumor had indubitably increased.

Mackenzie and Wolfenden declared that they did not see this swelling. It seems incredible, but perhaps in their haste and carelessness they really did not see it. Otherwise, the only possible explanation is that they did not want to recognize it. For Landgraf had seen correctly, as later developments proved. At any rate, the following day both the English doctors had to admit that there were "some signs of recurrence at the site of the excised tumor." Mackenzie now decided to do exactly what Gerhardt had vainly attempted months before in Berlin. He burned the tumor with the electrocautery. This was done on August 2. Five days later Wegner obtained permission for Landgraf to check the results. Landgraf "quivered with horror." He observed that the tumor had enlarged. It now had a lumpy, irregular surface. In the middle was a blackened spot where Mackenzie had used the cautery. The swelling at the back of the larynx was unchanged. The left vocal cord had lost almost all power of movement. Aghast, Landgraf heard that Wolfenden and a second assistant of Mackenzie's, a young man named Hovell, had corroborated the complete destruction of the tumor and absence of all inflammation. On the same day Wegner learned from the Crown Prince's adjutant that the Prince experienced constant pain when swallowing, as well as intermittent pain from heavy breathing. Nevertheless, the following day the newspapers printed the information that Mackenzie had given them—that the Crown Prince was making satisfactory progress and was well on the way to complete recovery. It was alleged that his voice had regained much of its former strength and resonance and was almost entirely free of hoarseness, and that free movement of the vocal cords had been restored.

Landgraf was confronted with an enigma. He now implored Wegner to do all in his power to have the German surgeons called to London for a consultation. He pointed out that Mackenzie's treatment had led only to a deterioration of the condition, and that there was no time to be lost if an operation was to have any prospect of success. He insisted that the disease was cancer, no matter what Mackenzie maintained, no matter what the results of Virchow's tissue examinations were.

Wegner was torn between fear of the immensity of his responsibility and fear of a quarrel with the Crown Prince and Princess. He was too weak to make a decision on his own, and called on Semon for advice. Semon could only support Landgraf's view. With horror he saw that his worst forebodings were becoming reality. Mackenzie persistently ignored the truth. Semon could not understand why he should be doing so. Were carelessness and arrogance the sole reasons for his strange behavior? Or was he suppressing his own doubts by leaning on Virchow, who had three times confirmed his optimistic view? Or could he not bring himself to confess his own mistakes in Berlin and admit the inadequacy of microscopic examination? Did he crave to remain in charge of this sensational case which set the entire world astir, to be the man everyone was talking about? Or was he carried away simply by his dislike of the German doctors?

Semon counselled Wegner to request authorization to report the true state of affairs at once to Berlin, or else to offer his resignation. Wegner asked for an audience with the Crown Prince. In the end he actually fell to his knees and begged permission for Landgraf to make another examination, to be followed by a consultation with the Berlin doctors. But the Crown Prince stamped his foot impatiently. He cried, "No!" and left the room. Wegner was not the man to take the logical next step—resignation. It was as though a wall had been erected around the Crown Prince and Princess, a wall with only one gate. And Mackenzie stood guard in front of this gate. When Mackenzie advised the Crown Prince to go to Scotland for a few weeks, so that the change of air would hasten the healing process, his suggestion was followed immediately.

The Crown Prince and Princess went to Braemar. Wegner and Landgraf were permitted to accompany them only as far as Aberdeen. Dr. Hovell was the only physician in attendance at Braemar. Hovell's reports were full of involved phrases that sounded favorable. Wegner and Landgraf, meanwhile, spent two weeks oppressed by fears and doubts. At last, on August 23, after much pressing, Landgraf was permitted to make a further examination in the presence of Hovell. The Crown Princess made it quite clear that she regarded him as a troublesome intruder. As far as she was concerned, the German doctors were nuisances and enemies who wished to block her husband's prospects of a happy future and ascension to power in Germany. Mackenzie alone was the man who promised her the future she had waited for these many decades —and this he remained even when she herself began to see that the Crown Prince was not improving and that Mackenzie made promises he could not keep.

When Landgraf—deathly pale—finished his examination, he knew that it was already too late. On the tumor he found excrescences which already obstructed his view of the posterior portion of the larynx. The left vocal cord was no longer capable of any movement. He felt a spasm of hatred as he looked into Hovell's face and heard him state that he could observe no sign of a regrowth of the tumor. Landgraf was no psychologist. But he understood that it was pointless to continue fighting to have the surgeons from Berlin called in again. Any such proposal would be rejected, would be regarded as simple hostility. Mackenzie had an explanation for every deterioration of the Prince's condition. One time it was a mere matter of Friedrich's straining his voice, then a cold caused by Scotland's raw climate.

As evidence for future use, Landgraf recorded the results of his examination in writing. He felt crushed by the knowledge that he could do nothing but look on helplessly. Nevertheless, he was a man raised in the Prussian tradition, just like Wegner, and as such could do nothing insubordinate. He was incapable of sending his report to Berlin without "His Highness's permission." And Wegner gave him no support; Wegner merely went to Semon again with his lamentations. Disgusted, Semon broke off relations with him—as he told me the following day in a voice quivering with rage and contempt.

Meanwhile, Mackenzie suggested to the Crown Princess another change of climate. Oddly enough, he suddenly did not consider Germany out of the question. But the Crown Princess rejected the mere thought of a return to Germany with an uneasiness bordering on panic. She decided that Toblach, in the Tirol, would be their next destination. At the end of August, after another examination, Mackenzie for the first time began forging a line of retreat. He informed the Crown Princess, in uncommonly involved language, that although it appeared that the disease could be regarded as cured and that only a period of convalescence was necessary, there nevertheless could develop a condition of "multiple papilloma" which could also be mortally dangerous. He still utterly disavowed a diagnosis of cancer but did not exclude the possibility that the condition might later develop into cancer, as in the case of other chronic inflammations. At the same time he made it plain to the Crown Prince's lord chamberlain, Radolinsky, that he desired some recognition of his services—not the conferral of a German decoration, but knighting by Queen Victoria. Before the departure for the Tirol he wrote a report for Berlin which could only be construed as a sign of the Crown Prince's unquestionable recovery. This report read: "The condition of His Imperial and Royal Highness the Crown Prince has made good progress recently, since His Highness's general health is excellent. . . . Care in regard to the use of the voice and avoidance of damp and cold air are the most important prophylactic measures to be taken for the near future."

Once again Wegner pulled himself together. He succeeded in having added to the report the one sentence: "The Crown Prince's voice is still hoarse." Landgraf was permitted to see the report only on condition that no further emendations were to be made. It pained him deeply to read this message of false optimism when he himself was convinced that the cancer had already reached a hopeless stage. It was even more harrowing to see that the Crown

Prince, for all that his complaint remained unchanged, himself believed in his recovery because the Crown Princess wanted to believe in it.

When this report was published in Germany on September 2, it was generally concluded that the Crown Prince was well, and that his recovery was due to Mackenzie. Innumerable newspapers, with the influential *Berliner Tageblatt* taking the lead, now launched diatribes against Bergmann. The story was that he had not only made a wrong diagnosis but would certainly have killed the Crown Prince by his operation, had Mackenzie not intervened. Mackenzie, meanwhile, was knighted by Queen Victoria. Had he not come to the rescue of her son-in-law? Her Majesty wrote the Crown Princess: "To think that he should have recovered his dear health so much in London and still more in dear Scotland is an indescribable cause of joy and thankfulness to us."

On September 3 the Crown Prince and Princess left London. Before their departure they dispensed completely with the services of Wegner and Landgraf. Young Hovell alone was chosen to accompany them; Wegner and Landgraf were sent back to Berlin. The doctors left with a sense of utter helplessness in the face of certain disaster. There was nobody who could support them, for Bergmann and Gerhardt themselves had difficulty withstanding the storm of blame and vilification.

Two months later the world began to understand what was in truth taking place. During those two months the newspaper accounts occasionally sounded a somber note, though on the whole all the talk was of improvement, convalescence, recovery.

The Crown Prince and Princess, Dr. Hovell, and retinue arrived in Toblach on September 7. Then and later I followed every detail, every phase of the tragedy. In Toblach, at an altitude of some forty-five hundred feet, no sunlight awaited them—rather, a cold, autumnal wind. En route the Crown Princess had received a telegram from Toblach warning her of the bad weather and advising her against continuing the planned journey. But she ignored it. This was her way of compelling fate to do her bidding. Seven years before, in the case of her eldest son—the later Kaiser Wilhelm II—she had simply refused to admit that the boy had a crippled arm. She had forced an education upon him as if he were in perfect health. Now she was playing the same defiant and ruthless game with her husband. She wanted the whole world to think him healthy. Rumors had reached her that in Berlin there was talk of her husband's being excluded from the succession on grounds of illness. She saw her highest ambition threatened. To counter this, she forced the sick man to lead the same life he had led when he was well: to breakfast out of doors, keep windows open, take long walks at her characteristically brisk pace, and engage in endless conversations on political matters.

When Mackenzie went to Toblach on September 20 he found the Crown Prince weak, without appetite, suffering from slight fever and swelling of the larynx. The doctor blamed this deterioration on a cold and recommended a still more southerly climate. The Crown Princess suggested Venice because she herself loved Venice. There the couple remained until October 6. But the liveliness of social life in the city led to further strains upon the Crown Prince. On October 7 they continued their journey to Baveno on Lake Maggiore. There Mackenzie turned up again.

For the first time he spoke more plainly, although still in circumlocutions, of the complete immobility of the left vocal cord, which Landgraf had observed long ago, during those last fateful weeks in England. He likewise spoke of an "elevation" of the posterior portion of the larynx. Suddenly he was seeing things to whose existence he had been blind only a few weeks before. But once again he ascribed all the symptoms to inflammation, overstrain, catarrh—at least, he did so when speaking to the Crown Prince and Crown Princess. He did so also when he spoke with the journalists who followed him to Italy or lay in wait wherever the Crown Prince was staying. On October 21, however, he wrote a curious letter to Professor Oertel of Munich. In this letter occurred the sentence: "Valuable as were the examinations by Professor Virchow, these of course provide only negative evidence, and I shall not feel entirely free of concern until six months have passed since the application of electric cauterization. I need scarcely assure those who know me that I have never refused to meet with my German colleagues, and if unfortunately any unfavorable symptoms should develop, I should be the first to request the co-operation of one of your countrymen."

Mackenzie intimated that he would not be opposed to publication of this letter. Certainly the letter looked very much like a belated effort to establish an alibi. Was Mackenzie beginning to feel uneasy? Was he conscious of the approach of that fateful hour in which he would have to admit that the long-banished German doctors had been right in the first place?

Mackenzie left for England again. But this time the respite lasted barely ten days. Then Hovell for the first time was startled out of his blithe optimism and sent a letter of alarm to London. He reported that the left wall of the larynx was swollen and that a swelling was visible along the right vocal cord. Even before Mackenzie could receive this missive, the Crown Princess took the Prince still farther south, to San Remo. She rented the Villa Zirio, a spacious modern building, gleaming white, set among the palms and olives.

They had barely arrived in San Remo when the swellings in the Crown Prince's larynx assumed such proportions that Hovell sent an urgent cable to London—a cry for help. Late in the evening of November 5 Mackenzie reached San Remo. On the morning of November 6 he sat facing the deathly pale Crown Prince. When he removed the laryngoscope, his fluent tongue fell silent for a moment. What he saw, and could no longer ignore, unquestionably pointed to an advanced stage of cancer. With effort, Mackenzie forced out the sentence: "Unfortunately, an unfavorable change has taken place in Your Highness's throat."

For a moment there was a ghastly silence. Then, according to the witnesses who have described this scene in detail, the Crown Prince asked only, in a tired, almost inaudible voice: "Is it cancer?" The question showed that in spite of all his pretended trust in Mackenzie, in spite of all the concealments and deceptions, there had always existed a hidden fear of the reality.

Once more the silence prolonged itself. Then Mackenzie murmured: "I am sorry to say, Sir, it looks very much like it. . . ." He then added hastily: "But it is impossible to be certain." After another moment of silence, the Crown Prince's bloodless hand reached out for Mackenzie's. He said, thickly and with an effort: "For some time I have feared something of the sort. Thank you, Sir Morell, for being candid with me."

Weird thanks for belated candor. The Crown Prince held himself proudly erect until Mackenzie had withdrawn. Then he broke down. The Crown Princess—likewise informed by Mackenzie in a succession of euphemisms—found her husband weeping; all trace was gone of the proud posture of confidence which she herself had for so long nourished. His softer nature emerged. "Why must I have so horrible, disgusting a disease!" he lamented. "A burden and a thing of horror to you all. . . . Why is Heaven so cruel to me? What have I done to be so stricken and so condemned?"

With incredible fortitude, the Crown Princess fended off this renewed threat to all her hopes. She rallied the Crown Prince, reminded him that he had obligations toward her and their children, and likewise toward the political aims to which they both were dedicated. Her keen mind had instantly sensed the equivocation which even at this moment Mackenzie continued to practice. And she seized upon this evasion. She pointed out to the Crown Prince that Mackenzie was by no means certain, and that there was no microscopic proof. Until such proof existed, no cancer existed. Let him trust to her and to God.

Then she went to Mackenzie. She coaxed out of him the statement—which he was only too ready and relieved to make—that without microscopic examination there could be no absolute certainty, and that right now the removal of tissue from the swollen and extremely inflamed larynx would be impossible.

But Mackenzie was now terrified of bearing sole responsibility for the Crown Prince's treatment—the very thing he had fought for so stubbornly in the past. Now he refused to forgo consultation with other doctors. He would not call in Gerhardt or Bergmann: his hatred of these men must have been stronger than ever, now that he sensed the approach of his own defeat and their coming vindication. He suddenly asked for other German or German-speaking doctors to share the responsibility with him. Of the well-known throat specialists in Berlin who had not yet been consulted, there were Professor Fränkel, chief of the University Throat Clinic, and a young *Privatdozent* named Dr. Krause. Perhaps Mackenzie knew that Fränkel owed his position in part to the backing of Felix Semon. Perhaps he also knew that Fränkel, according to Semon's later estimate of him, was himself a difficult and designing person. Mackenzie's choice may have fallen on Dr. Krause because he felt that a young man would be subordinate to him. Among Viennese throat specialists, Mackenzie knew no such younger man. He had to pick Professor von Schrötter, one of the deans of Viennese laryngology. The Crown Princess gave her consent. She was ready to consent to anything, so long as Gerhardt and Bergmann did not turn up in San Remo.

Meanwhile, however, news of the apparently sudden turn for the worse had reached Berlin. Ninety-year-old Kaiser Wilhelm, utterly perplexed by the conflicting reports, ordered his grandson, Prince Wilhelm, to go at once to San Remo, accompanied by a doctor, and determine what his father's condition actually was. Bergmann was, of course, the logical and first choice as the doctor to go with the Prince. But then he was dropped in order not to affront Mackenzie and the Crown Princess. Instead, Dr. Schmidt, the well-known Frankfurt laryngologist, accompanied young Prince Wilhelm.

On November 8 and 9, Professor Schrötter and Dr. Krause arrived at the Hôtel Méditerranée in San Remo. Mackenzie, on edge, constantly smoking his asthma cigarettes, led them to the Villa Zirio, opposite the hotel. The Crown Prince received them standing, but looking extremely worn. The examinations were conducted in silence, in an atmosphere of terrible suspense. The Crown Princess waited outside the door, pacing back and forth, her features frozen. When the other doctors withdrew, Schrötter declared without hesitation that the disease was cancer, and that he wondered how there could still remain the slightest doubt about it. Mackenzie struggled against his asthma. He looked haggard and pale. Cautiously, he repeated his most recent stand: that every sign pointed to cancer, but that microscopic proof was still lacking. Krause, too, could not deny that every single symptom indicated cancer. But Mackenzie had evidently picked the right man, for Krause, like Mackenzie himself, endeavored to evade any clear-cut decision.

That same evening Prince Wilhelm and Dr. Schmidt arrived in San Remo. The Crown Princess, distrustful of her own son and of any emissary from Berlin who had not been called by herself or Mackenzie, was determined to preserve the Crown Prince's pretense of health to the last, and not to make any admission which could be interpreted as a sign of imminent and certain death. She objected strenuously to Prince Wilhelm's being apprised of the true situation, for she knew that the Prince was an admirer of Chancellor Bismarck, whom she detested. But at the moment she could do nothing to keep from him what was now common knowledge. Nor could she prevent Dr. Schmidt from confirming the diagnosis of cancer.

On November 11 the doctors settled upon their verdict: far-advanced cancer of the larynx. Schrötter rejected Mackenzie's stubborn suggestion that before any decision was taken he cut still another piece of tissue from the larynx and send it to Virchow. He pointed out the known unreliability of histologic examination. In this case, where the symptoms had only one possible meaning to any experienced physician, microscopic examination was superfluous; moreover, experience showed that in this stage of the disease removal of tissue only led to accelerated development of the tumor. Mackenzie had to bow to this authoritative voice.

In regard to treatment, the doctors saw only two possibilities. The cancer had advanced so far that laryngotomy and removal of the cancerous parts—the operation proposed in May by Bergmann —was no longer possible. Only complete removal of the larynx now offered a chance of total excision of the carcinoma. But since experience showed that this chance was insignificantly small, and since the operation was difficult, the doctors were opposed to it. When Mackenzie, obviously seeking a new alibi, remarked that his whole endeavor from the start had been directed toward preserving the Crown Prince from the deadly peril of this operation, Schrötter sharply reproved him, pointing out the differences between early operation and complete extirpation of the larynx. He declared bluntly that it was the duty of the responsible physician to tell his patient the absolute truth and to leave to the patient the decision of whether or not he wished to submit to an operation. Accordingly, he now insisted that the Crown Prince must make this choice himself, after being truthfully informed of his condition. All the others agreed, and Mackenzie had no recourse but to vote with them.

If the Crown Prince rejected the perilous major operation, Schrötter continued, there remained only a second course of treatment. It offered the possibility of making the Crown Prince's life endurable for a number of months. If the tumor of the larynx developed to such a point that there was danger of asphyxiation, then the windpipe must be surgically opened below the larynx—in other words, a tracheotomy must be performed, thus providing an artificial respiratory passage. Naturally, this would not mean cure; it would merely provide a measure of relief until death inevitably ensued.

Schrötter was appointed to be the spokesman. In order to make this task less painful, a written report was drawn up; this was to be handed to the Crown Prince.

Throughout all the long consultation the Crown Princess had kept vigil. She now insisted on being present during the doctors' report to the Crown Prince. The poor woman looked like a caricature of her former self—and at the same time conveyed the impression that she regarded the Crown Prince's life as her personal property.

The Crown Prince received the doctors standing, as usual. As he listened to Schrötter's report, he did not at once understand the circumlocutions in which the doctor clothed the cruel facts. He understood all the less when Schrötter, desperately seeking to offer some kind of hope, said that he had had a patient of seventy in whom a tumor of the larynx had spontaneously regressed. The Crown Prince said: "Oh, after all, I am only in my fifties."

At that moment a loud sob was heard. One of the doctors had been unable to suppress his emotion any longer. Now, at last, the Crown Prince understood. He stammered hoarsely, wearily: "Tell me, my dear Professor, is it cancer?"

Here was the same, agonized question he had put to Mackenzie. Schrötter held his breath. Then he pulled himself together and managed to speak plainly; although he still could not bring himself to say the word "cancer," his statement was clear enough: "Your Highness," he said, "it is a malignant growth."

For a second the Crown Prince's bloodless hands gripped more tightly the written document the doctors had handed to him. He turned and went into an adjoining room. After a short while a servant brought to the doctors a sheet of paper on which the Crown Prince had written, in his steeply slanted handwriting: "Extirpation? No. Tracheotomy? Yes, if necessary." He had decided in favor of waiting for death.

On November 15 the *Deutsche Reichsanzeiger* published the following statement: "After repeated examination the assembled physicians are certain that His Imperial Highness is suffering from cancer of the larynx. In regard to therapy the various possibilities were likewise discussed. His Imperial Highness was informed of these, and deep tracheotomy when necessary has been recommended to him. Signed: Morell Mackenzie, Schrötter, Schrader, Krause, Moritz Schmidt, Mark Hovell."

In Germany and the rest of the world there began a tremendous awakening. The German doctors were suddenly restored to honor. How, the Kaiser demanded, had it come about that the timely operation had been neglected so that the present verdict was "too late"? Bergmann reminded everyone that in assuming responsibility Mackenzie had promised to consult him and his colleagues in case his treatment failed or the tumor grew back. In spite of Landgraf's repeated urgings, Mackenzie failed to do so. The very last possible date for the operation had been the beginning of August. It should therefore be clear, he said, whose fault it was that the one known means for preserving the Crown Prince's life for some years, and possibly for many years, had not been employed.

The German doctors were mistaken, however, if they thought that this was the end of the fruitless disagreements and animosity. They underestimated the defiant obsessiveness of the Crown Princess, and they underestimated the tenacity with which Mackenzie, his back to the wall in the tight corner into which he had maneuvered himself, fought to win the newspapers over to his side once more, once more to triumph over the hated Germans, by no matter what means, at no matter what price. During those hours when he quailed before his own responsibility, he had joined with Schrötter and Schmidt in beseeching Bergmann to hold himself in readiness in Berlin to go to San Remo at once if a tracheotomy should prove necessary. He had even agreed to have Bergmann's assistant Bramann called to San Remo, in case there should be sudden danger of asphyxiation and insufficient time to bring Bergmann from Berlin to Italy. The Crown Princess, too, had reluctantly given her consent to Bramann's presence, before Schrötter and Schmidt took their leave. In return she had obtained a promise that the diagnosis of cancer should remain a secret.

Now, when she discovered that it had been made public—how this happened was never clarified—she "raged with indignation." She surmounted her shock at the diagnosis of cancer and almost forced Mackenzie to new falsifications, new attempts at masking the truth. He discovered fresh symptoms which were allegedly not typical of cancer. The Crown Princess, meanwhile, surrounded her husband with still more impenetrable walls. Whatever came from Berlin she regarded as a sign of enmity, as a trick to murder the Crown Prince, to deprive him of his rights. Within a short time she had brought the Crown Prince himself once more to the point of ignoring the diagnosis of cancer. She succeeded in instilling into him renewed distaste for all German doctors. The only exception was Krause, whom Mackenzie—with a keen sense of the man's vacillating temperament—had retained in San Remo. The Crown Prince declared: "I place my trust in God and Sir Morell Mackenzie." When Bergmann's assistant, Bramann, arrived in San Remo, he was received with the usual coldness, and consigned to the role of a more or less troublesome outsider.

Within a few weeks Mackenzie once again had the international press singing to his tune. He recanted his own diagnosis of cancer. On January 7, 1888, the *British Medical Journal* announced with satisfaction that it had heard from an "authentic source" that the symptoms which had caused so much alarm early in November had almost entirely vanished. This report was published only a few days before the Crown Prince was stricken with severe headaches, fever, and respiratory difficulty which could no longer be ignored. Bramann pleaded for permission to send for Bergmann in time, so that the tracheotomy would not have to be performed as a last-minute emergency measure. But he was only an unknown young man, an excellent technician, but simple and uncomplicated in personality. Like Landgraf, he was "lost" from the start amid the intrigues of the Crown Prince's court. His request was met with supreme coldness. Slowly he began to understand that neither the Crown Princess nor Mackenzie desired Bergmann's presence in San Remo. Mackenzie was apparently determined to postpone the operation as long as possible until Bergmann could not be called and Bramann, who was on the spot, would have to take emergency action.

Early in February difficulty in breathing interfered with the Crown Prince's sleep. He had to sleep upright in bed. But still the doctors went through the procedure of checking the growth of the tumor by cold compresses. In vain. On the night of February 8 the Crown Prince appeared suddenly at his valet's bed. "I can no longer bear it!" he choked. "Make a compress for my throat." The afternoon of the following day he suffered an attack of suffocation. Bramann now requested that Bergmann be informed immediately. But this was not done.

A terrible night followed. The cold compresses were utterly ineffective. Early in the morning von Kessel, the Crown Prince's normally quiet, even-tempered, and endlessly patient aide-de-camp, confronted Mackenzie, face flaming with indignation. "If you do not send for Bramann at once," he stormed, "I shall see that you are haled before a court-martial!"

Then, at last, Mackenzie rushed to Bramann. He ordered him to perform the tracheotomy at once. Bramann hurried to the Prince's villa, but again asked that Bergmann be immediately informed. The request was granted. The telegram was written out at 9:20 A.M. Yet by one o'clock in the afternoon, as was later determined, it had not yet been dispatched from San Remo. In vain Bramann waited for some word from Bergmann. He did not know that he would have to go on waiting all day. By three o'clock this young man, placed under every disadvantage, flustered and nervous in this hostile environment, found himself confronted with the inescapable necessity of acting alone, without even authorization from his superior. The throttled breathing of the suffocating Crown Prince could be heard far out into the corridors of the villa. Mackenzie puffed away at one stramonium cigarette after the other.

Mackenzie must have known the possible consequences of deferring the operation until the very last. He must have known how often fatal pneumonia followed from excessive procrastination of a tracheotomy. But his hatred for his German rival had evidently grown stronger than his judgment. Now he confronted Bramann with an ultimatum: "I decline all responsibility if you do not operate at once," he said. Bramann had no choice; he had to give up hoping for a reply from Bergmann.

In great haste he had his instruments taken to a drawing room in the villa. Then he asked for a suitable table on which to perform the operation. But Mackenzie and the Crown Princess—the latter following every action and every word with the suspiciousness of a person possessed—would not hear of a table. They insisted that the operation be performed with the patient lying in a comfortable bed. In vain Bramann pointed out that a bed was too wide and too low, and would only hinder him. The bed was brought into the drawing room and placed opposite a window. From the adjoining room came the sound of the Crown Prince's breathing, more and more painful, more and more rasping. Assembled in the drawing room were the Crown Princess, Bramann, Mackenzie, Mark Hovell, Dr. Krause, and Dr. Schrader, now attached to the Crown Prince's retinue in his capacity of military physician. Bramann asked one of the doctors to help him with the chloroform anesthesia. Whereupon Mackenzie rushed to the Crown Princess and declared that he objected, strenuously and on principle, to chloroform; it was dangerous, and no English surgeon would conduct a tracheotomy under anesthesia. The Crown Princess promptly fell in with his view. She declared: "Under no conditions will I permit chloroform." For some moments the dispute drowned out the gasping sounds of the Crown Prince's breathing in the next room. Bramann countered that he had used chloroform on children and adults in more than four hundred tracheotomies. Since the responsibility for the Crown Prince's life was being forced upon him, he must be able to operate under his accustomed conditions. But Schrader alone backed him up. Hovell seconded Mackenzie; Krause also supported Mackenzie. Whereupon Bramann, in a burst of desperation, declared: "Then I will not operate. Will one of you gentlemen kindly take over."

Mackenzie literally shook. Faced with the necessity to act independently, he went entirely to pieces. Between clenched teeth he exclaimed that he could not operate. Hovell and Krause made similar statements. Vexed and dismayed, the Crown Princess looked from one to the other. Then she went in to speak to the Crown Prince. But the poor man, fighting for his life as he was, did not care who operated on him, or whether it was done with or without anesthetic. If only someone would save him from asphyxiation! Staggering into the drawing room, he held out his hand toward

Bramann. With indescribable effort, his words barely intelligible, he managed to say: "Operate at once. I put myself into your hands; operate in whatever way you think best."

Bramann therefore asked the Crown Prince to lie down on the bed. Once more he requested assistance. But only Schrader volunteered to handle the instruments. No one wanted to hold the chloroform mask. Mackenzie had but one thought: to clear himself of all responsibility. He exclaimed that Bramann would have to bear full responsibility for everything that happened under the anesthesia. I was later to speak with people who went so far as to believe that during the operation Mackenzie had hoped for the Crown Prince's death, in order to be able once and for all to shift all blame to the Germans and extricate himself from the situation he had created, whose end could only be his own defeat. Hovell, with trembling hands, held two bowls of sponges and forceps. Bramann had no choice but to initiate the anesthesia himself. Several times respiration faltered. But then, quickly and without further difficulty, deep anesthesia ensued. At this point Krause consented at least to assume the task of holding the chloroform mask and the head. Bramann thrust a bolster under the Crown Prince's shoulders. He could not tilt the head lower because near-asphyxia immediately followed. The position was extraordinarily difficult. The larynx extended very low, and the muscles of the throat, which had to be severed, were very strong. Bramann had to disinfect the operating field himself. He shaved the throat up to the hyoid bone, and cut off the ends of the Prince's beard. Then he incised the skin for about two and one half inches along the median line of the throat. The moment the first drops of blood welled up, Krause let the Crown Prince's head drop. Bramann had to command him sharply to hold tight and to pay attention to the anesthesia.

Bramann checked the bleeding and cut deeper, as far as the thyroid gland. The fascia investing the trachea was densely netted with widely dilated veins. Unless special measures were taken, the danger of a severe hemorrhage was great. Bramann ligatured the blood vessels on both sides of the trachea, severed them, and was able to press the thyroid gland down far enough to expose the windpipe as far as the fifth tracheal ring. At that moment the Crown Prince's face turned a shade paler. With trembling, almost unintelligible voice, Mackenzie uttered cries of warning. Bramann himself felt the patient's pulse, and was obliged to take over the anesthesia. He suspended it for two minutes; then the heart resumed its normal activity. Bramann attended again to the bleeding. Then he incised the trachea. With two hooks, he drew the edges of the wound apart. At that moment the Crown Prince's lungs greedily sucked in the air. Bramann introduced a large silver breathing cannula into the trachea, stuffed iodoform gauze into the incision all around it, and placed a simple bandage around the wound.

Exactly twenty minutes had passed. Mackenzie staggered off to one side, poured himself a glass of wine, and downed it at a gulp. A few seconds later the Crown Prince awoke from the anesthesia. For the first time in weeks he was able to breathe freely. He became aware of this at once, and pressed Bramann's hands. He tried to thank him. But then he realized that he would never again be able to speak, because his breath no longer passed through the larynx. He was handed a writing pad, which henceforth was always to be at his side, and wrote a few lines of thanks to Bramann. Mackenzie still stood by, somewhat unsteady on his feet. Then, with that dissimulation of which he was always capable, he expressed his own thanks with exaggerated formality. The Crown Princess also spoke some words of gratitude. Then she hastened to the side of the Crown Prince, who had been carried to his bedroom.

Back in Berlin, Bergmann had but one hour ago received the telegram calling him to San Remo. Even before he could finish his preparations for departure, news of the completed tracheotomy reached Berlin. The old Kaiser sent for Bergmann. He ordered the hesitant surgeon to go to San Remo and to remain at the Crown Prince's side until the wound closed. He furthermore commanded him to report regularly from now on, and to prevail upon the Crown Prince to go to Berlin as soon as it was safe for him to travel. During this interview Bergmann had the impression that the sovereign was weary and ill.

Bergmann set out with Count Radolinsky, and arrived in San Remo the evening of February 11. Like Bramann, he was received with cold courtesy, and was installed in a small room in the Hôtel

Méditerranée. The Crown Princess's instinctive aversion to Bergmann had only grown in the interval, for she saw him more than ever as the spokesman of a truth she did not want to recognize. Nothing could now alter her blind faith in Mackenzie.*

When Bergmann called upon her, she received him with courtesy —and expressed her regret that he had come so far for nothing, since the operation was already over. She thereupon turned the conversation immediately to the use of chloroform. She wanted to hear Bergmann say that this had been a major error. Bergmann replied: "Your Imperial Highness, it would have been a crime had he failed to use chloroform." The Crown Princess held her peace for the moment. Then she said—and her words betrayed her cognizance of the dangerous game Mackenzie had been playing: "I hope that you will be able to convince yourself that the tracheotomy was performed at exactly the proper time, neither too soon nor too late." Bergmann bowed slightly, and said nothing.

The Crown Princess accompanied Bergmann to her husband's room. The Crown Prince lay back on his pillow, looking wasted and worn. Since he could not speak, he pressed Bergmann's hand, and held it for a long time.

Upon leaving the room, the Crown Princess turned to Bergmann with some vivacity. "Doesn't he look well?" she said. "Don't you think he looks well? Once the cannula has been in for two weeks, we can hope that the reduction of the perichondritis will be complete." She said not a word about the incontestable diagnosis of last November, not a word about cancer. With a shudder Bergmann realized that the Crown Princess refused to admit of any other diagnosis but perichondritis (inflammation of the membrane surrounding the cartilage of the larynx)—Mackenzie's original diagnosis, to which, evidently, he had now reverted. To Bergmann, no greater demonstration of unscrupulous and unprincipled medical misconduct was possible.

Bergmann could guess what awaited him during the next few weeks. His premonition became a certainty when he encountered

---

* According to Conte Corti, the day before Bergmann's arrival, in spite of the wretched role Mackenzie played during the operation, she had written to her mother: "Sir M. Mackenzie is the greatest comfort and help in the world. He is the oldest and wisest and the steadiest head in this house. . . . Tomorrow Professor Bergmann arrives which is not what I look forward to." (Op. cit., p. 262.)

Mackenzie, who was just coming from a conference with the journalists at the Hotel Victoria. Mackenzie greeted Bergmann with "the friendliness of a reptile," and graciously but emphatically urged him to concern himself solely with the incision in the Crown Prince's throat, not with the larynx or with diagnosis of the disease. These matters were exclusively his, Mackenzie's, province. The front lines were being carefully staked out around the unfortunate victim.

The surgical wound healed satisfactorily. A doctor was in constant attendance at the patient's bedside. The watches were changed every six hours, and included Bergmann and Bramann. These vigils were strenuous, and frequently the doctors had no rest at all, less because of the undemanding Crown Prince than because of the Crown Princess, whose drawing room adjoined the Prince's sickroom. Even during the night she rose repeatedly to listen at the door or to come in. She regulated the room temperature by the thermometer, and sprayed the air with eau de cologne and eucalyptus oil from an atomizer. Her manner toward the Crown Prince was interpreted by some observers as boundlessly loving and solicitous; but all less kindly witnesses called it domineering. Certainly it was trying to all concerned. "Didn't he cough? Isn't he coughing too much? I'll go now, but you will give me your word, won't you, that everything is all right?" Such questions, together with her unyielding optimism, could be extremely annoying.

The Crown Prince certainly was coughing. The violence of his coughing expelled through the cannula a brownish or blood-colored mucus, mingled with particles of degenerative tissue. When Bergmann first observed this process during his watch, and took some of the expelled material for microscopic examination, he went to speak with the Prince's valet in the next room. "Schulz," he asked, "how long has His Imperial Highness been coughing up brown phlegm like this?" The valet replied: "Since January 15, Herr Professor, I have seen this several times a day. Everything that has come up has had the same threadlike look, brown, with little black dots like coagulated blood in between."

When Bergmann called Mackenzie's attention to the phlegm, the Englishman pretended that this symptom was extremely recent. He quickly took his departure. Bergmann and Bramann set about making the microscopic examination themselves. In almost every specimen they found three, four, as many as eight concentrically layered spheres, large epitheliomas in onionlike layers. Here was unmistakable microscopic proof of the presence of laryngeal carcinoma, the proof which Virchow had never been able to find, and the absence of which Mackenzie had made one of the pillars of his case.

Bergmann and Bramann sent for Krause. They showed him their results. He could not help but recognize these results for what they were—at least in the presence of the other two. But when Bergmann and Bramann also asked Mackenzie and Hovell to examine the slides, they declined. They knew nothing about microscopy, they declared; in England it was the business of anatomists, not of surgeons. It was plain enough that Mackenzie did not want to see proof of the correctness of the diagnosis of cancer. For if cancer was present and if he had to acknowledge it again, it meant the beginning of the end for him. His unprincipled mind went leaping far ahead; he began instantly taking countermeasures and securing his position for a time at least. The morning of February 14 he began a dispute with Bergmann. His argument, it must be granted, had been conceived by an infernally ingenious mind. Bergmann was pointing out that the phlegm coughed up from the disintegrating larynx was falling down into the trachea. Mackenzie contended otherwise. He asserted that the cannula used by Bramann and Bergmann scraped the back of the trachea until the blood came, and caused inflammation; that, he insisted, was the source of the inflamed particles of tissue. Bergmann, after removing the bandages over the incision, asked him to look through the cannula and convince himself that there was no bleeding or irritation at the other end of it. Mackenzie pretended to be satisfied. He ended the consultation, and at once ran off to the Crown Princess. The Crown Princess sent for Bergmann and informed the startled surgeon: "Your cannula scratches; that is why there is blood in the phlegm." Hard on the heels of this, Mackenzie, who with each passing day was growing paler and more nervous, resumed his attack. He asked Bergmann to remove his cannula and use a cannula which he himself had devised many years before and which, he alleged, caused no irritation. With incredible determination he repeated the charges he had made that morning: "I have been using this excellent instrument for twenty-five years. Its advantage is that it never causes bleeding, whereas the friction of your instrument produces a flow of blood into the trachea."

"The blood does not come from the friction," Bergmann repeated. "Since it is decomposed and dark brown, it comes from the tumor of the larynx higher up. Your instrument has the following flaws: it fits badly because the bend is not anatomically correct; secondly, the lock is too complicated; thirdly, the edges are too sharp. For that reason I do not permit its use in my clinic."

Mackenzie quickly shifted his ground: "Yes, yes, I don't want to interfere in this matter. I wanted only not to neglect warning against the misfortune that might come about through the flow of blood."

But Mackenzie was not giving up so valuable a gambit. Too much was at stake for him. He now made drawings of various types of cannulae. Accompanied by Hovell, he took these drawings to the Crown Princess. Once again he exerted his influence upon her, and of course succeeded. She accused Bergmann for the second time of having affected the Crown Prince's condition adversely. At this same time Mackenzie was talking to the reporters waiting in the Hotel Victoria. Next day the London, Vienna, and Berlin newspapers carried reports that the condition of the Crown Prince's larynx was perfectly satisfactory, but the state of the trachea, "due to the German surgeons' errors in choice of cannulae and treatment of the wound," was very grave; a bloody secretion was being produced in the trachea.

There followed five days of protracted, incredible quarrels which Mackenzie renewed daily, his voice shaking, his face of a corpselike pallor. The pressure upon Bergmann mounted so greatly that on February 20 he at last yielded, against his will, and stood by as Mackenzie introduced his own cannula into the Crown Prince's trachea. This was done in the evening. Before introducing the cannula, Mackenzie gave the Prince a heavy dose of chloralhydrate and morphine. The consequence was that he spent a fairly peaceful night for the first time in many days; he scarcely coughed or raised phlegm. The very next day a British newspaper, the *Standard*, published the statement that Mackenzie had been issuing warnings for a full week against the German cannulae, that the Germans had at last yielded on the twentieth, with the result that "the night brought the Crown Prince a refreshing sleep, as the German doctors themselves were forced to admit in their bulletin." A few days later the *British Medical Journal* noted:

"The Crown Prince is now beginning to make satisfactory progress. The cause of the unfavorable local symptoms was mainly mechanical. . . . A tube of large caliber, specially constructed in this country, has now been adjusted and the irritation produced by the ill-fitting tubes has passed away."

In fact, the effects of the chloralhydrate and morphine were by then long past. The Crown Prince was coughing more violently than before. Time and again the cannula was blocked by coughed-up masses of phlegm in which Bergmann's microscope repeatedly demonstrated cancerous tissue. But Mackenzie, since his cannula failed, found fresh reasons for the Crown Prince's poor condition. One of the correspondents, primed by him, wrote: "The true cause of the patient's suffering was the clumsy manner in which the tracheotomy had been performed. The surgeon lost his head. He was so nervous that he had great trouble in finding the trachea, finally opening it much too much to the right side, rather than in the middle. No wonder that there was so much difficulty in finding a suitable cannula. . . ."

When the Prince had an especially bad night on February 23, Mackenzie did not scruple at publicly blaming Dr. Schrader, who had been entrusted with the night watch. Dozens of newspapers, once again led by the *Standard*, declared: "If Dr. Hovell had been permitted to keep the watch over the Prince, there would be no accounts of troubled rest."

In vain Bergmann, in the name of universally recognized principles of medical ethics, protested against this sort of misleading report. The Crown Princess was adamant. There was no eliminating Mackenzie's interviews with the reporters, she replied, and the great English doctor made wise and rational use of the press. Moreover, she took this occasion to demand that Bergmann leave the night watch exclusively to Mackenzie and Hovell.

Once more Mackenzie had won a victory. But it proved to be one he could not enjoy. The Crown Prince went through a fearful night. In his anguish he rebelled one last time against being the victim of this contest conducted with deceptions and lies. He requested Hovell and Mackenzie to stop torturing him and to restore the old Bergmann cannula. Mackenzie had to request Bergmann to change the cannulae. When Bergmann introduced his cannula into the now almost completely healed tracheotomy incision, the Crown Prince wrote on a pad: "This cannula is much better; please stop the changes and decide that I am to keep this one."

For days Bergmann had been troubled by the fear that portions of the cancerous, decaying mass which the Crown Prince coughed up might have penetrated into the lungs. Moreover, he thought that the case no longer belonged in the hands of a throat specialist, nor of a surgeon, but should rather be supervised by a general practitioner who could fend off the general physical degeneration as long as possible. The Crown Prince was already experiencing stomach and intestinal symptoms which were not in the least palliated by the unknown powder that Mackenzie daily blew into the patient's throat. Bergmann therefore seized this moment to demand the consultation of an experienced general physician. Mackenzie agreed—although he made the condition that the new doctor must limit himself to examining the lungs and must not make any diagnosis of the throat disease. Thereupon a telegram was sent to Professor Kussmaul.

Kussmaul arrived in San Remo late in the evening of February 25. The Crown Prince had been getting up for a few hours at a time, and even sitting for short spells on the terrace of the Villa Zirio, but he suffered from severe headaches which medicines only temporarily stilled. Kussmaul was shocked by his appearance. He found no alarming developments in the lung, but this meant little considering how meager were the techniques for such diagnosis— X-rays had not yet been discovered. In spite of Mackenzie's embittered opposition, Kussmaul insisted on examining the patient's throat. Though Bergmann had said nothing of this, he diagnosed an already disintegrating cancer of the larynx, whose decay products were entering the trachea and being expelled through the cannula. Thereupon Mackenzie resorted to his old dodge. He admitted that cancer might be present, but maintained that cancer cells had never been identified by a recognized *anatomist*—he emphasized this word in view of Bergmann's microscopic analyses.

If Virchow should determine the presence of such cells he would, of course, be prepared to bow to the diagnosis and agree to the Crown Prince's return to Germany.

Mackenzie's adversaries later charged that he had gone this far only because he knew that Virchow was in Egypt and would not be available. In any case, Bergmann and Kussmaul proposed calling in Professor Waldeyer, whose reputation in Germany as an anatomist and pathologist was in no way inferior to Virchow's. Mackenzie consented, and promised to abide by Waldeyer's judgment. But what did promises mean to him? That very evening, after Kussmaul's departure, the Crown Princess spoke up, saying: "I have no faith in Professor Kussmaul's opinion; he is a weak old man of an altogether outdated school of medicine." She sent for Bergmann, and said to him with icy courtesy: "You said yesterday that the operation wound has healed."

Bergmann replied: "Happily, the wound has cicatrized rapidly."

The Crown Princess: "Since that is so, I suppose you will be leaving soon and taking Bramann with you."

Bergmann realized that the obsessed woman could think only of banishing from San Remo the Berlin realists who threatened her illusions. On the morning of February 27 the Crown Princess ventured into outright rudeness to make herself plain: "Mackenzie does not care to begin using his methods against the perichondritis as long as you are standing by. He takes it very much amiss that a doctor whose competence for throat diseases he does not recognize wishes to be present like a supervisor."

Bergmann: "Very well, Your Imperial Highness, I shall not be present."

The Crown Princess: "Well, that is not enough. You have had things as you wanted them. Kussmaul has come. . . . Now, by remaining, you deprive me of the hope . . . that Mackenzie will cure my husband. I am afraid that . . . if you stay, he will leave. . . ."

Bergmann: "At your service. I shall request Berlin to recall me."

According to his own account, Bergmann did not know which emotion was uppermost in him, bitterness or pity.

That very evening Bergmann stood on the railroad platform at San Remo, waiting for the train, relieved at the prospect of leaving this hopeless situation in which the sole tragic figure was the Crown

Prince himself. At that moment a messenger handed him a telegram. It was a direct order from the Emperor in Berlin for him to remain in San Remo. The old Kaiser felt that he was close to death. He wanted to see the Crown Prince one last time, and had again sent Prince Wilhelm to San Remo to persuade his father to go to Berlin. Obedient to his Emperor's command, Bergmann gloomily returned to the Hôtel Méditerranée. From there he telegraphed to Leuthold, the Emperor's personal physician, that it would be useless to send the Prince unless Professor Waldeyer were simultaneously dispatched to San Remo in order to confirm the cancer diagnosis with such firmness that Mackenzie and the Crown Princess would be unable to ignore it.

Bergmann's request was immediately granted. On March 2, Prince Wilhelm arrived. He was received by his mother with that air of cold rejection which had been so great a factor in the formation of his refractory character and excessive vanity. Victoria did everything in her power to keep him away from his father. His mission had already failed when, on March 3, Professor Waldeyer arrived in San Remo. During the next two days Waldeyer carefully examined the particles of tissue coughed up by the invalid. He set down the results of his work in writing: "The concentric bodies which were found are indubitably so-called cancroid bodies, and derive from a cancerous growth. An extensive process of degeneration . . . must be present in the cancerous growth. This process has already . . . affected the larynx."

Waldeyer explained his results to Mackenzie in both German and English. Mackenzie smoked without cease while he listened. Then he exclaimed, "Good, I see that it is cancer," and took his leave.

Waldeyer firmly believed that Mackenzie had at last been convinced. Bergmann, too, thought so for a moment. He imagined that Prince Wilhelm would now, after all, be able to prevail on the Crown Prince to hasten to the old Emperor's sickbed, and prevail on the Crown Princess to give way. But he had not yet won his point. That very evening, Bergmann learned, Mackenzie had promptly gone to the Crown Princess with the following arguments: Waldeyer had proved the presence of cancer cells. But this proof scarcely altered matters. Between himself and the Berlin doctors there existed a fundamental difference of opinion in regard to the prognosis and treatment of cancer. He had evolved certain measures to be adopted against this disease, and believed that these measures would keep it effectively in check for a long time to come. But to undertake this treatment with full conviction, he had to be free of interference from doctors who took a hopeless view of the development of cancer.

In the light of all that had gone before, no one should have been surprised that the Crown Princess was once more completely won over. Again she told Bergmann that she wished him to leave at once. At the last moment Prince Wilhelm and Bergmann succeeded in securing Mackenzie's signature to a written pledge that he would, if still more severe symptoms should develop, press the Crown Prince to return to Germany.

On the evening of March 7, when Bergmann entered the train at San Remo, bound for Berlin, the Emperor had already been confined to his bed with a high temperature for several days. Two days later, during the morning hours of March 9, the Crown Prince was taking a slow walk in the garden of the Villa Zirio, the cannula concealed under his beard, when a telegram was brought to him on a silver tray. He read only the salutation: "To His Majesty Emperor Friedrich Wilhelm . . ." and let the slip of paper flutter back to the tray. His father was dead. He himself, a sick man, was Emperor, the Crown Princess was Empress of Germany. The question of a return to Berlin had been settled. He must be there, even though Berlin was undergoing the coldest March weather in its history.

At that time I had already been two weeks in Berlin, and I well remember the icy wind that raged through the streets, whipping clouds of snow before it. Late in the evening of March 11, 1888, I was among the crowd which gathered at the snow-covered Berlin-Westend station to await the arrival of the new Emperor Friedrich. The day before, he had left San Remo in a special train. In Munich his train had made a long halt. Bismarck had ridden as far as Leipzig to meet the imperial couple. The train, moreover, was several hours late because of snow blocking the tracks. The snow was falling continually, and from the gate of the station to the Emperor's waiting carriage a corridor of canvas had been stretched to shield him from the biting wind. I myself had placed my carriage so that I would be able to observe him above the heads of the rest of the crowd as he crossed the short open space between the end of the canvas lane and the door of his carriage.

It was shortly before midnight when the train at last pulled in to the station. The storm had waxed in violence. Nevertheless, the larger part of the crowd had stood fast, determined to catch a glimpse of the Emperor's face. These people wanted to find out for themselves whether or not he was deathly ill. But all of us were disappointed, because of the canvas lane and the celerity with which the Emperor vanished into his carriage. We saw little more than the silhouette of his face. Perhaps a few of those who were standing right up front had a better look, and perhaps the intense cold had brought a faint flush to his cheeks. That sufficed to send rumors galloping around Berlin that very night: the Emperor looked well, healthy and vigorous. Mackenzie must be right.

Ten yards away from me, closely surrounded by the "Garde Corps," the Emperor rode into the snow-covered city. He rode to the old Charlottenburg palace, which had been prepared in the greatest haste for the arrival of the imperial couple. This palace had not been occupied for decades. The lighting was poor; the fireplaces gave scarcely any heat. Iron stoves had to be placed in the Emperor's bedroom in order to raise the temperature to a bearable level. Thus, even here in Berlin, Friedrich was placed in a kind of ghostly isolation.

He was only able to watch, not to participate, in his father's funeral, which was conducted with great pomp. While the procession moved past the windows of the Charlottenburg palace, the Emperor's figure could be seen behind one window which kept misting over because of the biting cold. This time I saw his face, a thin, deathly pallid spot against the darker background of the room. Close to him stood Mackenzie, who was now living in the castle, along with Hovell. Even before the couple left San Remo the Empress had seen to it that Mackenzie was put in sole charge by imperial decree of her husband's treatment. Mackenzie had unquestionably received this appointment with mixed feelings. He knew how much hostility awaited him in Germany. But he had reached the point of no return.

Only on being bluntly warned of the animosity aroused by the partiality shown to English doctors—an animosity directed against the Empress herself—did the Empress consent to occasional examinations by Wegner, their one-time companion on the trip to England, and by Bergmann, the surgeon who was the particular object of her hatred.

Mackenzie's familiars among the German and international newspaper correspondents had followed him to Berlin. I met several of them, whereas in Berlin I did not again have a chance to see Mackenzie himself. They did not deny that Mackenzie himself gave them bulletins on the Emperor's illness. According to these reports the Emperor's health was definitely improving. He could not leave the palace, it was true, because the weather continued cold and miserable week after week. But it was reported that he worked from morning until night, coughed very little, brought up virtually no phlegm, and during breaks in his work went for strolls in the palace orangery. The glass-enclosed orangery ran along one side of the palace garden, and the people who gathered day after day in front of the palace gates could see the dim outline of their Emperor across the broad intervening yard. But the newspaper reports fed their hopes. Improbable as it may seem, from week to week the opinion gained ground that the Emperor's illness was not really cancer.

In reality, the disease was progressing rapidly. When Bergmann examined the Emperor on March 18, he found a spreading of the carcinoma in the larynx and a growing area of hardness along the trachea down as far as the cannula. The phlegm increased, and microscopic examination showed that it contained more cancerous cells than before.

On March 25, Bergmann was permitted another examination. He found that the tumor was still more enlarged toward the trachea. The Emperor was now suffering increasingly painful headaches. Bergmann had no opportunity to see Mackenzie. But on March 29, when the Emperor suddenly coughed up a necrotic piece of cartilage, Mackenzie suddenly became accessible again. He had shown this piece of cartilage to the Empress and convinced her that it was proof that he had been right all along, that the disease was a nonmalignant inflammation of the cartilage. So thoroughly did he inculcate the Emperor as well as the Empress with his dishonest

Ernst von Bergmann (1836–1907), who diagnosed Friedrich III's cancer.

Sir Morell Mackenzie (1837–92), controversial British throat specialist, the key figure in the tragedy of Friedrich III.

The German Empress during the last weeks of Friedrich III's life.

German Crown Prince and, later, Emperor Friedrich III.

Emperor Friedrich III, on one of his last drives, shortly before his death.

Eduardo Bassini, who laid the foundations of modern hernia surgery.

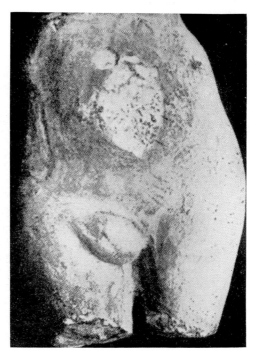

Ancient Greek terra-cotta sculpture, showing inguinal hernia on the right.

Carl Koller, discoverer of the analgesic effect of cocaine on the eye.

Sigmund Freud (1856–1939), with his fiancée and later wife, Martha Bernays, in 1885.

Paul Reclus (1847–1914), champion of cocaine anesthesia when it was under severe attack.

William Stewart Halsted (1852–1922), discoverer of infiltration anesthesia with cocaine, whose experiments led to his addiction.

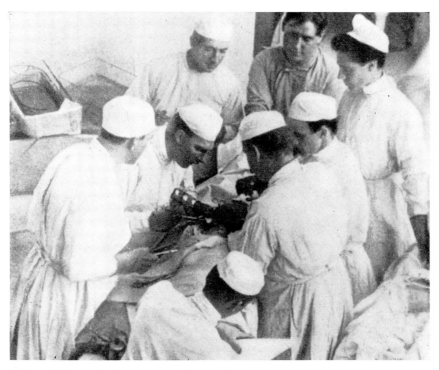

Halsted shown during an operation under total anesthesia, in 1904.

Carl Ludwig Schleich (1859–1922), twenty years after his dramatic appearance at the Berlin congress of surgeons.

August Hildebrandt, Bier's assistant in his experiment on himself.

August Bier (1861–1949), inventor of lumbar anesthesia, talking with Sauerbruch (seated).

John B. Murphy (1857–1916). Independently of Forlanini, he surgically attacked pulmonary tuberculosis.

Christian Fenger, Professor of Surgery at the University of Chicago, Murphy's teacher and friend.

Carlo Forlanini (1847–1918), inventor of the artificial pneumothorax.

Nicholas Senn (1840–1908), one of Murphy's most vehement opponents.

optimism that Friedrich scribbled on a note to General Winterfeldt: "Since Thursday a crisis has ensued which once again leads
my doctors to hope for the best."

At the end of the month of March, the weather turned warm
and sunny. Toward noon on Good Friday the Emperor went driving for the first time in an open four-in-hand with postilions. He
drove on Unter den Linden. The news spread like wildfire. I, for
example, heard of it one minute after the Emperor was first seen.
The few telephone subscribers in Berlin had their day of glory.
Hordes of Berliners assembled in no time. In a moment all the
flower shops of the vicinity were sold out. The Emperor sat upright, almost unnaturally erect. What with his beard and high hat,
only a small part of his face could be seen. But that part was gaunt
and waxen. (The painful sound made by the cannula hidden under
his beard could not, of course, be heard in the street.) Nevertheless, the sunlight and the flowers created a scene of confidence and
security. Once again I witnessed a demonstration of wishful thinking, and how it could blind people to what was before their eyes.

The weather remained fair, and the Emperor took drives into
the city more frequently. Reports that his improvement was continuing came thick and fast. In reality, Bergmann on April 8 found
distinct signs of hardening below the cannula. The entire area
around the cannula swelled. The lymph glands thickened. Mackenzie's comment was: "That is certainly not cancer, merely granula-
tion of the wound." Bergmann pointed out that the unusually short
cannula which Mackenzie was using was being pressed out of the
trachea by the growth of the tumor. Mackenzie passed over this
observation.

Four days later, on the morning of April 12, one of the Emperor's attendants informed Bergmann that the Emperor was having extraordinary difficulty in breathing. After the cleaning of the
cannula it had proved almost impossible to insert it into the trachea
again.

That same afternoon, at three o'clock, a palace messenger located
Bergmann at a consultation and handed him a note from Mackenzie: "We are having trouble with the cannula, and I would be
grateful to you if you could come with me to see the Emperor as
soon as possible." The words "as soon as possible" were under-

lined. Bergmann, who happened to have Bramann with him, rushed home for his instruments.

At the Charlottenburg palace Bergmann found Mackenzie busy with an instrument maker, trying to fashion a lead tube into a temporary long cannula to be introduced into the Emperor's trachea. In the adjoining room the Emperor's gasping respiration could be heard. The short cannula no longer extended into the trachea. Bergmann had brought a longer cannula with him. He and Bramann found the Emperor sitting up in a chair. His cheeks and lips were already blue. At a glance Bergmann could see that the tumor had grown by leaps and bounds. It was impossible to see the posterior wall of the trachea through the tracheotomy incision. Everything was swollen and overgrown. And Bergmann now failed in his attempt to introduce his cannula. The only choice, he quickly explained to Mackenzie, was to draw the tracheotomy incision apart with clamps. In this emergency Mackenzie was ready to accept anything. Bramann held the clamps. There was slight bleeding, but then the cannula was inserted and the Emperor saved from suffocation. Only later did Bergmann learn that the Emperor had been having fever for days, but that nevertheless the outings had been continued so that the Emperor might be displayed to the public. On this morning he had a temperature of over 100° F. Nevertheless Mackenzie insisted on the daily drive, and refused to issue a bulletin on the change of cannulae. He repeated his argument that it was necessary to reassure the populace by letting the Emperor be seen. The Empress thought likewise.

That evening the Emperor suffered chills and fever. By the fifteenth his temperature had reached more than 102°, and it remained on that level for several days. Two additional Berlin doctors, Senator and Leyden, were called in for consultation. At this consultation Mackenzie, to Bergmann's utter incredulity, declared that the fever was due to Bergmann's violent insertion of the cannula. He said not a word about there having been fever and headaches before this. Bergmann, having learned his lesson from his experiences in San Remo, realized that Mackenzie was again trying to make him responsible for a deterioration in the Emperor's condition. Above all, in the face of all evidence, Mackenzie seemed determined to avoid recognizing the inevitable course of development of a cancerous tumor. To cover himself, Bergmann went to a newspaper with his side of the story; Mackenzie did likewise, and a newspaper war developed. The *British Medical Journal* commented: "From information we have received from a trustworthy source we have reason to believe that a false passage was made in replacing the tracheotomy tube, as this operation was followed by considerable hemorrhage, but it can, we are informed, be clearly proved that neither of the Emperor's English medical attendants is responsible for this unfortunate occurrence."

On April 25, Bergmann handed his adversary a letter stating that in view of Mackenzie's violation of the physician's oath of silence and his practice of spreading calumnies, Bergmann would in the future speak with him only in so far as medical consultations required. Simultaneously, he asked the Empress to relieve him of his post. The Empress was delighted to do so.

Early in May the Emperor experienced one more of those deceptive spells of improvement which so frequently characterize the last stages of cancer. His fever vanished. On May 16 he was able to sit in his garden once more, although his posture was hunched and bowed. During the following days he was driven about in a low pony cart. He forced himself to receive delegations, to listen to reports, and submitted to the Empress's impassioned expositions of political matters. He was displayed to the populace of Berlin several times. But on such occasions there could be terrible incidents. Once the cannula became clogged. Mackenzie had the carriage driven swiftly to the gardens of Bellevue Castle, intending to clean the cannula there. But all the buildings were locked up. Finally Mackenzie obtained the use of a gardener's room long enough to save the Emperor from suffocation. On May 24, feverish and dull-eyed, the Emperor witnessed the wedding of his son, Prince Heinrich. On June 1 the Empress had him moved, aboard the steamer *Alexandria*, down the Spree to the New Palace in Potsdam, which was to be his residence. It was a sunny summer day. All along the route people stood waving, children singing, bands playing. But the Emperor and Mackenzie had only a few more days in which to foster the optimism which had become, for the Empress, a form of madness.

On June 7 some milk which the Emperor was drinking ran back out through the cannula. Mackenzie had to resort to artificial nourishment with rubber tube and probe. And yet on June 9 the *British Medical Journal*, drawing its information from Mackenzie, published an incredible report which spoke of the continued improvement in the Emperor's condition, of symptoms so atypical for cancer that the physicians no longer were certain of the true nature of the illness, an enormous relief compared with the disastrous diagnosis of November, a change in views not yet officially made public.

Mackenzie, however, had run out of time to announce this "change in views." On June 10 he felt compelled to inform the Emperor in the circumlocutory form he affected: "I regret that I must tell you that you are making no progress." The Emperor wrote on a slip of paper: "I am very sorry that I am making no progress. . . ." When he was alone with the Empress, however, he broke down: "What will become of me? Do I seem to be improving? When shall I be well again? What do you think? Shall I be ill long?" This was the result of the irresponsible hypocrisy with which the poor man had been treated day after day.

Next day the Emperor, streaming perspiration, eyes sunk deep in their sockets, staggered about his room. He wanted to don his cuirassier's uniform in order to receive King Oscar of Sweden. The effort caused him to collapse several times. In the presence of the other monarch, he was able to hold himself upright only for a minute. Then he had to be carried out, to return to his bed. Mackenzie felt compelled to telegraph Queen Victoria in London: "The Emperor is sinking." During the night of June 14 the Emperor tossed sleeplessly, struggling for breath. At eleven o'clock in the morning on June 15 he sat up once more. He wrote in a barely legible hand: "Victoria, I and the children . . ." That was all. At eleven-fifteen he drew his last breath.

The drama was over for the unfortunate Emperor but not for the Empress, who that morning saw herself cheated of the meaning of her life, banished into the nullity of widowhood. It was also not over yet for Mackenzie or for the German doctors. Amid all the muddle of diagnoses and counter-diagnoses, recriminations and slanders, there had been no clear, decisive statement that the disease had been cancer and that the German doctors had been right from the very first when they proposed the only thing which might have prolonged Friedrich's life. That clear-cut statement was only possible now if an autopsy were performed.

In Berlin, Bergmann, who had been the most attacked of all the German doctors, insisted most strongly upon autopsy. That alone could confirm the correctness of his diagnosis; that alone could prove that the cannula which he had inserted after Bramann's tracheotomy in San Remo had never caused injury to the patient's throat; that alone could dispel the false charges of the alleged injury he had caused with his insertion of a new cannula on April 12.

On the afternoon of June 15, Bergmann appealed to Dr. Schweninger, Bismarck's personal physician, to pass on to the Chancellor his request for an autopsy of the deceased Emperor. The following night Bergmann was invited to the Chancellor's palace. He spoke with Bismarck and Dr. Schweninger. Bismarck refused to intervene since he was aware that the Empress would not hear of an autopsy. Schweninger thereupon pointed out that post-mortems had been performed on all the Hohenzollerns, since it was the rule of the royal household that the cause of a monarch's death must be determined beyond question.

Upon hearing this, Bismarck sent for his son Herbert. Herbert Bismarck confirmed the existence of such a directive. Bismarck then declared his readiness to ask the former Crown Prince and present Emperor for permission to order the autopsy. Bergmann himself went to see the young Kaiser on the morning of June 16. Wilhelm had been on Bergmann's side all along, if only out of opposition to his mother, and he gave his consent. The Empress was horrified. "I was mad with sorrow, anger, and agitation that they dared to touch his dear, sacred mortal remains," she wrote.

Before the autopsy Mackenzie, who was still at the palace, was requested to write a final report on the cause of the Emperor's death. Even if he was not aware of the impending autopsy (as he later wrote), and if he really was asked to be present at it only after having written his report, it is evident that his nimble mind anticipated the result. He wrote: "In my opinion the disease of which Emperor Frederick III died was cancer. The circumstance that perichondritis and caries of the cartilage played an active and important part in the development of the disease undoubtedly contributed greatly to the difficulty of forming any specific opinion on the nature of the disease until quite recently."

An hour later Mackenzie and Hovell were witnesses at the autopsy, which was performed by Virchow and Waldeyer, the two pathologists whose authority Mackenzie had never questioned. Among the other witnesses were Wegner, Bardeleben, Leuthold, Bergmann, and Bramann. The dissection demonstrated unequivocally that the patient had died of cancer of the throat; and that there was no sign of any injury to the trachea, such as Mackenzie had accused Bergmann of several times. Mackenzie and Hovell signed the minutes of the proceeding. Then, bidden a warm goodbye by the Emperor's widow, they departed for London.

As yet the official report of the German doctors had not been published. Mackenzie undoubtedly knew that his great reputation as a diagnostician would suffer after all that had happened, unless he could fabricate some overall excuse for his conduct. Stopping in Holland on the way home, he had an interview with a reporter of The Hague's *Dagblad*. He now averred that he had always known the disease to be cancer, but that he had concealed this diagnosis in order to keep the government from declaring Emperor Friedrich physically unfit to reign.

On July 11 the official report by the German doctors appeared. It was entitled: "The Illness of Emperor Friedrich III, Depicted from Official Sources." And even now Mackenzie's luck held good. The German doctors, with Bergmann at their head, had allowed their bitterness at past slanders to get the better of their scientific objectivity. Gerhardt and Bergmann in particular were carried away into personal attacks upon Mackenzie which shook the factual foundations of their case. Humanly speaking, their actions were understandable. But all those newspapers, journalists, and doctors who for more than a year had sworn by Mackenzie, and were now reluctant to lose face, were helped by the obvious weaknesses in his adversaries. They came very close to at least halfway rescuing his reputation. If at this point Mackenzie had confined himself to a very few intelligent, highly factual comments, he would have been saved from a terrible debacle.

At that moment, however, all the unscrupulousness of his character came to the fore. First, as Semon informed me from London, he attempted to intimidate the publisher in order to suppress the English translation of the German doctors' pamphlet. Then he launched a counterattack which surpassed anything that had ever been done in the way of medical polemics. In October, 1888, he published a book, *The Fatal Illness of Frederick the Noble.* It was a collection of vicious slanders and insults to the German doctors, a testimony to surpassing arrogance. The crux of it was a fresh attempt to explain his own conduct. This time he stated that he had recognized the disease as cancer from the start, but that in view of the terrible mortality statistics and consequent hopelessness of laryngeal operations he had saved the German Emperor from quick death by concealing the true nature of the disease. Mackenzie supported these views of the deathly peril of a laryngeal operation by publishing statistics which were later shown to be distorted. He was careful to blur over the distinction between early operation and total extirpation of the larynx. And he was even more careful not to touch on a crucial point which might have justified his conduct if he had really been motivated by the desire to save the Emperor from an operation which in his opinion was mortally dangerous. Had he ever, during the period when an operation was still feasible, honestly informed the Crown Prince or Princess of a diagnosis of cancer? Had he ever told either of them that the only chance lay in an operation—which, however, he regarded as almost certainly fatal? Had he ever honestly explained that, aside from operation, there was no chance for even temporary salvation, but that he must advise against the operation and would prefer to await the natural end, and to make it as easy as possible? Had he ever honestly given the Crown Prince or Princess a chance to decide? He had not, and for that reason his own attempt at subsequent justification stood condemned as a feeble fraud.

Publication of his book marked, for Mackenzie, the beginning of his rapid fall from the pinnacle of fame. He was requested to resign from various professional associations in England. It availed him little that certain outstanding actors, who had entrusted their voices to his care, stuck by him, and that a newly founded British Laryngological Society elected him its first president. Nor did it avail him that the Emperor's widow steadfastly supported him. Indeed, she had no choice, for if she were to condemn him, she would condemn herself.*

Soon thereafter, little more was heard about Mackenzie. His name appeared in newspapers only occasionally—he who had recently filled columns. He attended quietly to his practice, and did some travelling. In the late autumn of 1890 I was flabbergasted to meet him at the Athens home of Heinrich Schliemann, the famous German archaeologist. It seemed Mackenzie was taking a Mediterranean cruise aboard the British steamer *Chimborazo*. Although somewhat tanned from sunning himself on deck, and although the sea air had helped his asthma somewhat, he looked tired out, a changed man. He avoided speaking of Friedrich III. At last, however, I succeeded in putting a question to him about his conduct of the case. His story now was that the Emperor had suffered from one of those rare forms of cancer where the indications are so overlaid by other symptoms that a reliable diagnosis is impossible. Fate had mocked him, he said. He became aware that a comment on the German doctors' correct diagnosis was on the tip of my tongue. They had been fortunate in what they chose to see, he said, heading me off. I made it plain that I was willing to accept his explanation for the beginning of the affair, but not for everything that had happened after his vain efforts at treatment in London. At that, he changed the subject.

At the end of January, 1892, he fell ill in London, suffering from severe bronchitis. His heart proved unable to stand the strain, and a week later he succumbed, dying in his fifty-fifth year.

---

* According to Conte Corti, the widowed Empress wrote to her mother asking her to confer an honor upon Mackenzie, since an order had been awarded to Bergmann by Wilhelm II. But Queen Victoria would not go so far, even for her daughter's sake. In careful but unambiguous language she replied: "The medical Professors here dislike and distrust him, perhaps too much so; still I am afraid his great indiscretion has done great harm."

Bassini

On the morning of July 2, 1888, when for the first time I heard
of Edoardo Bassini and his method of correcting inguinal hernia
by surgery, my thoughts reverted to my father.

If anyone knew the history of hernias, it was he. Rupture was
common among the hard-riding, hard-working pioneers of the
Northwest, West, and Southwest of the United States. It was no
less common in Europe, of course, and had been diagnosed there
for thousands of years. I was as familiar with the various types as
my father had been. Owing to a strain, an awkward movement,
violent coughing, occasionally even hearty laughter, coils of the
intestine are displaced inside the abdomen. Given some weak spot,
their outward pressure can drive through the abdominal walls,
and a piece of intestine, encased by the elastic peritoneum, can
break through and form a more or less sizable protrusion beneath the skin. This rupture most frequently occurs in the inguinal region. The muscles of the abdomen, especially those leading obliquely down from the hips, do not extend into the groin.
They pass first into those thin, wide tendons called aponeuroses
which form the connection with the pelvic ridge. These flat tendons do not have the powers of resistance of thicker muscles and
yield more easily to a sudden, excessive pressure of the viscera,
especially in the male groin. The aponeuroses, moreover, are further
weakened by the two spermatic cords which, coming from the
interior of the abdomen, run diagonally through them down to the
testicles. Through a gateway, the internal inguinal ring, they enter
the aponeuroses, passing through them along the inguinal canal,
and emerge again from the aponeuroses in the lower corner of the
groin, through the external inguinal ring. Thus the male groin
possesses these particular weak spots. Most hernias develop in that
region, loops of bowel pressing through the inner ring into the
inguinal canal and either following the path of the spermatic cord
and producing scrotal hernia or, without penetrating into the canal,
appearing under the skin as a hernial protrusion. The hernial sacs,

which can at times assume extraordinary dimensions, become more and more of a hindrance to the unfortunate sufferers. They become acutely dangerous when the parts of the intestine in the sac are squeezed, or "strangulated." This is likely to occur where the sac breaks completely through the aponeuroses. The ruptured muscles then form a noose around the sac with the gut inside it. The intestinal canal is blocked, the intestine becomes necrotic, and a painful death ensues.

Every time my father reached a new town or a new ranch, the hernia victims used to assemble—for the news of his coming always flew before him. My father would first explain to these petitioners that no surgical method for really curing rupture existed, and that anyone who claimed that he had such a method was a quack. "There is only one remedy," he would conclude. "It was known to the Egyptian pharaohs, who suffered from hernia just as you do. But I have been improving on it all my life."

His method was to force the hernial sac back into the abdominal cavity, and then to measure the patient for a truss. His fingers were skillful, and he really had perfected an excellent truss. It consisted chiefly of flexible steel bands, and was placed around the hips and groin. At the site of the rupture was a leather cushion which kept the spot permanently under pressure, thus replacing the lost counterpressure of the abdominal wall and preventing the re-emergence of the hernia. My father was well aware that this was no cure, only a troublesome makeshift which did not do for all cases. Often it failed. Moreover, the patients had constantly to be on guard against making sudden or violent movements. But there existed no other remedy that provided any relief. Nor did any such remedy exist as yet on that day in 1888 when I heard about Bassini, and the recollection of my father and his trusses rose so vividly before my mind's eye.

The letter concerning Bassini and his "revolutionary discovery" —that was the phrase used—came from Padua, in northern Italy. The writer was Dr. Peter Gallmann, a young German physician whom I had met a short time before at Virchow's house in Berlin, during the last weeks of Emperor Friedrich's life. I had learned that Gallmann was about to depart for a trip to Italy to study at several Italian universities, and had pledged him to report to me on the state of affairs there. But when I read the first paragraphs of his letter I was far from expecting that I would learn anything new or unusual. On the contrary, Gallmann merely corroborated the rather gloomy picture I myself had formed during the past years and decades of the outmoded, ill-equipped Italian hospitals.

"I truly fled from Milan," Gallmann wrote. "In the medieval building of the Ospedale Maggiore, septic and aseptic patients lie side by side in the same bed. Operations (in 1888!) are performed upon the same table on which cadavers have just been dissected. I shall mention no names, but you may believe me when I tell you that the chief surgeon goes from the morgue to the wards without washing his hands. This same surgeon performed a Caesarean section in my presence, discovered in the course of the operation that his assistants had forgotten to prepare the loop for tying the womb, went to the window, cut a piece of string that held the drapes, and used it as a ligature. Another well-known surgeon made a slip-up and cut the aorta, with the result that his patient bled to death on the operating table. I left for Pavia, hoping that this ancient and famous university would offer somewhat better conditions. Far from it! The San Matteo Hospital is a fever-hole. The lecture halls are filthy and dilapidated. While waiting for the lectures to begin, the students roar out obscene songs. Lion-headed Professor Bottini, who undoubtedly has made a great contribution to medicine by his treatment of prostate hypertrophy, repels me by his histrionics. His vanity is such that he pays more heed to his students' applause than to the necessity for clean operations.

"A few days ago I arrived in Padua. At the University Hospital I found the unhygienic amphitheater serving as an operating room, just as in Pavia; I found the same dirty corridors, the same huge and unsanitary wards. Nevertheless I realized that I was breathing a different kind of air; it smelled clean, fresh, impregnated with carbolic acid and eucalyptus. An old man dedicated to 'medieval' surgery ostensibly rules the roost here, too. In practice, however, the place is in charge of a young surgeon who in the past five years has been endeavoring to clean out the backwardness of centuries. He is Professor Edoardo Bassini, a peasant's son from Pavia, who studied with Billroth in Vienna, Langenbeck in Berlin, Nussbaum in Munich, and Lister and Spencer Wells in London. He has thoroughly learned the lessons of antiseptic surgery. When he came here at the age of thirty-nine and took over first the chair of pathological anatomy and then the men's surgical section, he was derided for his insistence on antisepsis. But in the following years pyemia vanished slowly from these stinking old walls. I hear that he has converted his superior, Tito Vanzetti, to modern methods. But Vanzetti is too old and infirm to apply them successfully.

"Most important, however, is the fact that Bassini has been engaged upon a surgical treatment of hernia, particularly inguinal hernia, and has achieved results which ought to create a sensation when they become more generally known—that is, when Bassini decides to publish his results in some internationally recognized journal.

"From what I have heard, Bassini has operated upon 123 cases of hernia since 1884, including hernias of the severest type, and has developed a method which seems to guarantee complete and lasting cures. By his operation he creates in the inguinal region a new, firm muscular sheath which seems to be stronger than the abdominal wall of even the healthiest person. Three days ago I personally witnessed a dual operation upon Napoleon Catteneo, a man of sixty-nine. Catteneo was suffering from a very severe form of inguinal and scrotal rupture on both the left and right sides. Bassini eliminated the hernial sacs and formed the new abdominal sheath in less than half an hour. On the same day, June 21, I visited ten patients who were operated on by Bassini at least four years ago. All of them are regarded as permanently cured; in fact, some of them have been rated fit for military service, which as you know is unheard of. The operation utterly dispenses with the need for a truss. Since as far as I know no method has hitherto been known to achieve a genuine and permanent cure of hernia, Bassini's discovery seems to me of singular interest. If you are still in Berlin when you receive this letter, you may find it worth your while to continue your journey by way of Padua. Since hernias are extremely common in this vicinity, especially among the poorer classes, Bassini operates almost every week, so that it will be an easy matter for him to demonstrate his technique to you. I can scarcely describe it; it is something that has to be seen. Incidentally, you might try to convince Bassini—who speaks both French and German fluently—that his work ought to be brought to the attention of the medical world."

For years I had shunned Italy in the height of summer. More-over, even in northern and central Europe the early days of July, 1888, were unusually hot, and the evenings sultry. But since this trip was to be only to northern Italy, I resolved to go. On July 10 I left Berlin.

I had employed the days since receiving Gallmann's letter in assembling material on the history of hernia therapy. In Berlin, with its large scientific libraries, this was an easy task. All in all, the story was one of the dreariest chapters in medicine.

Incontestably this history was a long one, stretching into the remote past. The mummy of Pharaoh Merneptah, for example, who had reigned to about 1215 B.C., showed a large scar in the groin. The scrotum was completely separated from the body. Probably he had suffered from scrotal hernia, and had been crudely operated upon. The mummy of Ramses V (about 1157 B.C.) showed an unmis-takable hernial sac in the groin. It could be assumed that Ramses had died of strangulated hernia. A Phoenician statue showed a rup-ture on both sides, around which a crude truss had been placed. Thus some three thousand years ago experiments had been made with both operations and trusses. The Babylonians, I read, had advocated wolf's bile in wine. The ancient Hindus, who apparently had suffered greatly from hernias, believed in laying plasters of heated cow dung upon the ruptures. In severe cases, however, they had tried the knife, attempting simply to sever large hernial sacs and cauterize the rift with a white-hot knife—a barbarous procedure which must have killed the patients. The Chinese were even more subject to hernias, probably owing to their over-frequent and crude use of acupuncture in the region of the groin. Excessive pricking with very large needles had, in the opinion of a good many med-ical historians, weakened the walls of the abdomen.

Afflicted in large numbers by this ailment, the Chinese had done no more than develop clumsy trusses and, with Oriental submis-siveness to fate, consign the severely ill to certain death. Among the Romans, however, another attitude prevailed. In Celsus's sur-viving writings on medicine we find some clearer ideas on the nature and origin of hernia, and suggestions for surgical treatment. Celsus erroneously thought that hernia resulted from a tear in the peritoneum, through which the intestines "fell down" to the skin of the abdomen. He enumerated various methods of treatment prac-

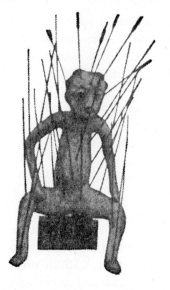

Chinese acupuncture. The excessive application of acupuncture in the inguinal region was considered a cause of the unusually frequent occurrence of hernias in China.

ticed by Roman doctors and surgeons: hot baths; attempts to press the rupture back with the hand; heavy, iron trusses, and month-long pressure exerted by rude blocks of wood against the site of the hernia. This last-mentioned method produced artificial inflammation and suppuration in the groin, and the surgeons hoped that scars would result which would strengthen the feeble abdominal walls. These hopes were, of course, quite vain; but the idea of artificial cicatrization persisted through the centuries. In severe cases Roman doctors also resorted to the knife. According to Celsus, they cut open the abdominal wall in the vicinity of the hernia, until the hernial sac lay exposed. Then they pressed the loops of intestine back into the abdominal cavity, tied the remaining sac close to the site of the rupture, and cut off the protruding portion of the sac. They then permitted the wound to heal. In the course of this a highly progressive step, revealing considerable knowledge of anatomy, was taken. The surgeon attempted to separate the spermatic cord, not to tie it off along with the sac. Thus the effort was made to preserve "masculinity." However, Celsus did not report on the number of those who died after this operation, either of shock from the pain inflicted or from subsequent peritonitis.

Ambroise Paré (1510–90) continued to hold the false conception of the origin of hernia which had been promulgated by Celsus. He burned, scraped, and cut away at his tormented victims for decades in the hope of closing the fatal rent in the peritoneum. From Spain he took over the method of the so-called "golden stitch" in which a small incision was made at the bottom of the hernial sac and a gold wire thrust around sac and spermatic cord. The wire was then drawn tight in the hope that it would prevent further intrusion of the intestines into the sac. In reality it interrupted the blood supply of the spermatic cord and emasculated innumerable unfortunates without preventing the aggravation of the hernias. Paré later returned to the truss, and played with a number of old superstitious formulas. Clearly, he was confessing to defeat.

With Paré's abdication, responsible physicians generally gave up all attempts to cure hernia. At best they recommended trusses. The place of doctors was now taken by those barbers, herniotomists, and quacks against whom my father used so emphatically to warn. Unscrupulous and pitiless, they bore down upon the patients abandoned by the hapless doctors. Pierre Franco, a surgeon born around 1500 in Turriers, France, had acquired his knowledge exclusively from itinerant "cutters of the stone," that is, practitioners of lithotomy. An exceptional man who later became chief surgeon of the city of Bern, he was the first and only surgeon who ventured to treat strangulated hernia, which was regarded as inevitably fatal. Without any way of visually controlling his work, he inserted a probe under the skin to the ruptured spot, introduced his scalpel

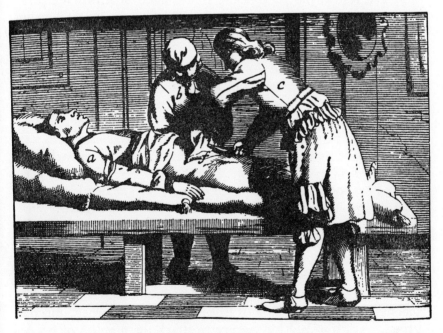

A hernia operation, depicted in Armamentarium Chirurgicum, *published in Ulm in 1653.*

along the probe, and made an incision in the ring of tendons which was responsible for the strangulation of the hernial sac and its contents. This done, he often managed to force the extruded portion of the intestines back into the abdominal cavity. This operation, however, effected no lasting cure, and none of the accounts so much as inform us to what extent the operation wound healed. Yet Franco was nothing if not bold. Wherever his operation for strangulated hernia came too late—that is, where the strangulated piece of intestine had already become necrotic—Franco cut out the necrotic part and sewed the higher end of gut into the abdominal wall, leaving the lower part to atrophy.

Technically, this operation was in advance of its time—but only technically, since the shock of pain, infection, peritonitis, and pyemia killed his patients during or after the operation.

The discovery of anesthesia contributed nothing whatsoever to the development of a new surgical method for curing hernia. However, the tremendous advances in pathological anatomy during the ninteenth century cleared away the ancient error regarding the supposed tear in the peritoneum. It was discovered that the peritoneum itself formed the hernial sac. This was no sooner known than the fear of peritonitis, which dominated surgery in the decades before the discovery of antisepsis, paralyzed all thought of surgical remedies. The only aid for hernia patients henceforth became "taxis," cautious compression of the rupture, followed by application of a truss. In such desperate cases as strangulated hernia "forced taxis" was attempted. Preliminary injections of tobacco juice were supposed to expand the strangulating ring of tendons; then the physician endeavored to press the contents of the hernia back into the abdominal cavity by force. The English surgeon Hood performed his operations with the aid of muscular London longshoremen who would work away at the rupture for hours until they succeeded in pressing back the contents of the sac by sheer strength, either relieving the strangulation or inducing death by tearing of the intestines or nicotine poisoning. As late as 1876 two of my friends in London died of such therapy.

Since then antisepsis and asepsis had been developed into reliable techniques. Fear of peritonitis had been largely dispelled, and the groundwork thus laid for surgery to attack the problem of hernia under entirely new conditions. There had, of course, been no lack of experiments during the past fifteen years. Vincenz Czerny in Heidelberg, John Wood in London, August Socin in Basel had taken up Celsus's recommendation of eighteen hundred years before. They had opened the abdominal wall over the hernial sac, forced the contents of the sac back into the abdominal cavity, carefully separated the spermatic cord from the sac, then tied off the latter and extirpated it on the anterior side of the ligature. Finally they had sewed the inguinal canal below the rupture in order to close the groin tightly. Hundreds of such operations had been performed without complications or infections. But time after time the operation would be followed by fresh protrusions of the descended portions of the intestines.

At the time I set out for Padua no one ventured to speak of cure any longer. The honest surgeon would advise his patients to resort again to trusses after operation, in order to prevent recurrence. Surgical success, if it could be called that, consisted in achieving relief but not cure. That was the situation after thousands of years of experimenting.

Heat baked the ancient walls of Padua when I arrived there early in the afternoon of July 11, 1888. Gallmann seemed to be less enervated by the temperature than I. He met me at the station, and I was immediately struck by the change in him since I had last seen him in Berlin—he had become an enthusiast. Even as our fiacre rolled through the Barriera Mazzini he began talking about Bassini.

"This discovery should really interest you," he began eagerly. "Have you noticed that doctors are often led to new developments by personal crises or illnesses of their own?"

I had, as a matter of fact, and acknowledged it without grasping the point Gallmann wished to make. "It's a curious business," he continued. "During the past few days I have been wondering why Bassini, who has already dealt with so many pathological and surgical problems, should have been so interested in pursuing the cure of rupture."

"And you have found the answer to your question?" I asked.

"Yes. At least, I think I have."

"Do you mean that Bassini himself suffered from hernia, or is still suffering from it?"

"No," Gallmann said, "not that. . . ."

We turned into the Via Garibaldi, a rather narrow street winding between ancient houses and along low arcades. "The story is somewhat different," Gallmann continued. "Bassini studied in Pavia. At the time of his graduation in 1866 he was twenty-two years old, and a passionate Italian nationalist. When the Austro-Prussian War broke out and the Italians fought the Austrians on the Germans' side, Bassini joined Garibaldi's volunteers—who alone came through that war without a single defeat. When Garibaldi shortly afterwards marched against Rome to overthrow the so-called secular domination of the Popes over Rome and make Rome the capital of Italy, Bassini was again with him. As you know, the campaign failed. On October 20, 1867, Bassini took part in the battles around Villa Glori, and during a fight at close quarters with a zouave of the Papal army he received a bayonet wound in the groin. It was a broad, severe wound running from the ridge of the right hip down into the abdomen. Among other things, it slit open the vermiform appendix. Bassini was taken prisoner, but removed first of all to the old Santo Spirito Hospital. Later he was transferred to the still older and still more plague-stricken Sancta Orsola Hospital. There he came down with fecal phlegmon, complicated by septic peritonitis. He himself feels that he came out of it alive only by a miracle. The peritonitis fortunately localized itself. Still feverish, he was confined to the Castel Sant' Angelo, and finally released at the end of December. When he reached his parents' home in Pavia he was suffering from one of the most horrible afflictions of the human race—a fecal fistula in the groin which would not close. Despite all his teacher, Professor Porta, tried to do for him, Bassini suffered from this for a very long time. I need scarcely tell you more."

No, he certainly needed to say no more about that. It was fairly clear that Bassini, in his determination to master this horrible illness of his, must have devoted unusual attention to study of the inguinal region.

Gallmann continued: "During the time he was assistant to Professor Porta in Pavia, Bassini dealt almost exclusively with the groin. When you see tomorrow how simple his method of operating for inguinal hernia actually is, you will understand my astonishment that no one ever hit upon it before."

The bells of Padua were ringing the fifth hour of the afternoon next day when Gallmann and I arrived at the piazza in front of the Ospedale Civile, which still blazed from the sun.

"Today is visiting day," Gallmann remarked. No further explanations were necessary. In those days Italian hospitals presented an extraordinary sight to the eyes of northerners. Whole families, husbands and wives, grandfathers and grandmothers, and swarms of children, had come to Padua to visit their sick. The old folk, bowed by poverty and work; the mothers, prematurely faded; the adolescent girls in rags, but beautiful; the children half naked and covered with the grime of villages and highways—one group after the other straggled through the hospital portals.

Gallmann knew the way and led me down the ancient corridors of the building. "Imagine a German hospital under such an onslaught!" he groaned as we mounted the worn stone stairs. "They fill the wards and sit around the patients making a ferocious noise. They sing and pray, eat and feed the patients. The children crawl on and under the beds. They bring amulets and holy water with which to sprinkle the bandages. A German surgeon would go out of his mind with despair. Diet—antisepsis—good Lord! Even a man like Bassini cannot, apparently, alter age-old habits."

We entered an upper story into which the noise of the visitors penetrated only as a distant hum. Gallmann stopped in front of a door. Here Bassini worked and—if I remember rightly—here he also lived. For he did not yet own his 750-acre estate in Vigasio where he later played the role of progressive landowner, building roads and experimenting with modern methods of husbandry. "He has never made much money," Gallmann told me. "The only amusement that he allows himself is riding. Every morning at four you can find him at the riding school, or trotting along by the Bacchiglione or the Brenta. But he is back at the hospital at six on the dot."

We entered a plain, whitewashed room with a stone floor and a few simple pieces of furniture. A tall man seated behind a crude desk rose to his feet. He was lean, but well knit, and for an Italian surprisingly sparing with gestures. His face was deeply tanned, his hair and beard similarly dark, with a few scattered threads of gray. He spoke to me in fluent German.

"I am pleased that you are interested in my method of operation," he said with little preamble. "We are a young nation, and it is hard for many people in the outside world to take us seriously. Our young German colleague has informed you, I believe, that at the moment I have three patients with inguinal hernias in my department. I intend to operate on two of them tomorrow, on the third, the day after tomorrow. I shall be happy to have you witness the operations, as well as the antiseptic preparations of the patients, with which we shall be beginning shortly."

Involuntarily, I showed my surprise. Did he actually begin his preparations the day before the operation? "Oh yes," Bassini replied. "I know that this is unusual. But preparation of the groin demands a good deal of special work, in my experience. Let me explain this further while we go down to my patients."

He led the way to the corridor. "I have discovered," he went on, "that the groin is, of all regions of the body, the least favorable for the healing of wounds. The sinews around the inguinal canal possess scarcely any blood vessels. Tissues with poor blood supply are always good hosts for bacteria. We therefore practice exceptionally careful antisepsis before every operation in the groin. Before operation I place my patients in a small isolated room where visits are forbidden. In the wards they would be beset by visiting members of their families, and all our antiseptic measures would be undone. Family feeling is one of the finest qualities of our nation, but in hospitals it is unfortunately a drawback."

He opened the door and paused in surprise. In the utterly bare, prisonlike little room stood only three iron beds of the kind that Italy, a country poor in wood, was at that time producing by the hundreds of thousands. Over each bed hung a crucifix. The occupants of the beds were young men of no more than twenty. The nearest of these was sitting up in bed in violent agitation. In front of his bed, equally overwrought, eyes flashing scorn, stood a young woman, a slender, lithe beauty in a cheap, close-fitting red frock.

"Signorina," Bassini said as soon as he recovered from his surprise, "do you not know that it is forbidden to enter this room?" My spoken Italian was then not very good, but I understood enough to follow the scene.

The girl glared defiantly at Bassini. "Forbidden!" she exclaimed. "He sent word to me to come. And I came just to tell him to leave me in peace." She pointed contemptuously at a broad-shouldered, muscular young fellow who looked at her with meek, imploring despair. "I've told him time and again that it's all over between us. What do I want with a man who can't even dance because his guts are falling out of his belly? A nineteen-year-old cripple! Does he think I'm going to spend my life buckling on his truss?"

"Isabella!" the patient groaned. Then he turned his eyes to Bassini. "Professor, you'll make me well, won't you? You've helped so many. Promise me you'll make me well!"

It was a display of emotion of the kind you encounter only in the south. Bassini's expression was a curious compound of bitter experience, resignation, and kindness. "Arturo Malatesta," he said, "I intend to try. But only if you do not have this girl come here again. We cannot have our preparations ruined."

The girl ran past us and out the door. "Professor," the patient groaned, "she was my betrothed. Now she won't have me because this damned trouble has ruined me. I'm a blacksmith. Look at my arms, look at my body. But these ruptures have made me a cripple, and she laughs at me. Professor, you are the only one . . ."

Bassini went up to the bed and laid his hand on the man's forehead. "If she laughs at you because you have this trouble, my boy, she isn't worth marrying, and you'll find a better girl," he said. The big fellow did not reply. Bassini turned to me.

"Here you have my three patients," he said. He lifted the blanket from the young blacksmith. "As you have heard, this is Arturo Malatesta. Hernia on both sides, of medium size, complicated by adhesions of the mesentery."

A glance sufficed for me to see the protrusions of the hernias in the boy's groin. Bassini went over to the next bed. "Aloisi Marchiori," he said. "A day laborer from Bassano Veneto, twenty-six years old, inguinal rupture on the right side." And in the next bed: "Ernesto Calzavare, a storekeeper from Padua; twenty-two years old, likewise inguinal rupture on the right side. I intend to operate on these two patients tomorrow, and on Malatesta day after tomorrow."

Once more the young blacksmith heaved himself up. "Why not tomorrow?" he groaned. "She'll forsake me, she'll surely forsake me."

A few minutes later a small, plump, but agile nurse came waddling in. She placed two pails of hot water beside Calzavare's and

Marchiori's beds. Pietro, a male nurse, brought jugs of antiseptic solution and large rubber and linen sheets. Finally a Dr. Tansini appeared, a young man whom Bassini introduced to us as his pupil and assistant.

The two patients were placed naked on the big rubber sheets. Then Pietro and the nurse scrubbed their bodies from neck to knees with a strong soap solution. The doctors stood by, watching the work closely. The washing done, Pietro stropped a razor and shaved first the one and then the other patient over his whole body, from the back and armpits right down to the knees. In both cases the shaving of the groin took almost half an hour. But Bassini, who watched in silence, refused to be satisfied until not the slightest trace of hair remained on the groin of either patient. The patients protested, especially when the area of the ruptures was touched, but Bassini was obdurate.

When this was done, Dr. Tansini himself took up the first jug of antiseptic solution. He poured it over the patient, once again from neck to knees, soaked it up with sponges, and poured more of the solution over the groin. The patients cried out when the liquid touched nicked spots in the shaved areas. Finally Pietro and the nurse dipped the big cloth sheets into the solution, wrapped the patients in these, and finally swaddled them tightly in the rubber sheets. Only their necks and heads and their legs below the knees protruded from the wrappings.

Bassini left the nurse there to ensure that they did not escape from their wrappings.

"I am operating tomorrow morning at six o'clock," he explained to the patients. "It now depends on the two of you whether or not you want to get well. If you do not move, I can make you well; otherwise I cannot."

He turned again to Gallmann and me. "Now we have done what can be done," he said. He led the way to the door and closed it behind him. "If you care to follow me to the cellar, I shall demonstrate on a cadaver the method of operation I shall use tomorrow."

Tansini and the male nurse joined us.

A dense, heavy odor of decay assailed our nostrils as we descended a narrow, damp staircase into the vaulted cellar. All was darkness but for the ghostly light of the hurricane lantern the attendant had taken from a hook beside the door. Mold clung to the walls, spidery vermin scurried away, and it seemed to me that I heard the characteristic noises of startled rats. Bassini said not a word.

The attendant set the lantern down on a ledge and uncovered one of the cadavers. It was a middle-aged man who had died of pneumonia, a homeless indigent whose name no one knew. Tansini took two aprons from a wooden clothes rack. He handed one to Bassini and donned the other himself. Then he produced a bowl of instruments from a niche in the wall. I stepped to the left, closer to Bassini, and drew my light summer coat closer around me. From the black depths of a cavernous adjoining room came an icy current of air.

Bassini seemed unaware of the cold. He took a scalpel from the solution of sublimate in the bowl. "When I began concerning myself with surgery of inguinal hernia about five years ago," he said, "I operated according to the method of Czerny or Wood or Lucas-Championnière. In the course of this work I discovered that every third patient had a relapse after a short time. Simply sewing up the external portal of the hernia does not give sufficient firmness to the abdominal walls, even when a network of silver wires is inserted. And I agree with Bull of New York who has demonstrated statistically that all previous methods of hernial surgery do not produce reliable cures. Lucas-Championnière contends that a truss must be worn after operation as well as before. The question I asked myself for many years was: Why is this so? And I will now show you the answer I believe I have found. I think it is very simple, like so many solutions to apparently insoluble problems."

Wielding the scalpel in his small, sinewy hand, he sliced the skin over the right side of the cadaver's groin with a cut that ran diagonally from the direction of the hip to the innermost corner of the inguinal region. Tansini drew the yellowish edges of the incision apart.

Bassini said: "Here you have a healthy groin. I am now opening the aponeurosis of the obliquus externus above the inguinal canal and exposing the vas deferens."

He did so with a swift incision diagonally upward. It began at the external inguinal ring, the point of exit of the vas deferens from the inguinal canal. At once the tubelike vas deferens was exposed as far as the internal inguinal ring, where it entered the abdominal cavity. "And here you see a healthy canal," Bassini said. "Here the aponeurosis is strong enough to withstand the pressure of the viscera, in spite of the passage already made by the vas deferens. Nature has deliberately placed the inguinal canal obliquely, so that the pressure of the intestines is constantly tending to keep the canal compressed and the internal ring closed, thus preventing the penetration of any part of the viscera or peritoneum. But let some congenital or developmental flaw, or subsequent overstrain of the abdominal muscles and their aponeuroses, cause a displacement of the canal from an oblique to a straight position, and hernia occurs at the slightest provocation; parts of the intestines press the peritoneum outward until a more or less sizable sac has formed."

Bassini paused, then continued: "I know what I am telling you is all familiar. But I must repeat it so that you will understand the conclusions I arrived at. Once the hernia has formed, it is useless, as all experience has shown, simply to sew together weakened or displaced tissues. It is equally useless to attempt to strengthen these tissues by cicatrization or the insertion of foreign bodies. My teacher, Spencer Wells of London, who may certainly be termed the founder of abdominal surgery, has experimented with conducting galvanic currents through the inguinal canal in cases of hernia—in the hope of achieving improved tension in the tissues. These trials were all in vain. My own proposal is radical, but I am convinced of its efficacy."

His voice rang louder within these ancient walls. I forgot the icy draft that had been chilling me. "Genuine healing of the rupture," he said, "can come about only through the rebuilding of a strong posterior wall of the inguinal canal, the canal being at the same time restored to its oblique position. The wall must be such that it will never again yield to the pressure of the intestines. Logically, it should consist of the strongest possible muscular tissue."

He extended the incision in the aponeurosis beyond the internal inguinal ring, running his cut obliquely upwards to the point where the aponeurosis united with the anterior and posterior layers of the oblique abdominal muscle. Tansini then assisted him by plucking the elastic tube of the vas deferens out of the wound and holding it clear of the incision. "I found the new posterior wall for the inguinal canal," Bassini said, his cool, scientific tone betraying a slight trace of excitement, "in the posterior layers of the oblique abdominal muscle, the obliquus internus, together with the musculus transversus. This layer of muscle can easily be drawn down behind the spermatic cord far enough to be sewed to the edge of Poupart's ligament. If I then connect the new inner abdominal wall thus formed with the rectus abdominis muscle, a new wall of great firmness is created. The vas deferens is replaced, and above it the incision in the aponeurosis of the oblique externus is closed. Thus a new and strong inguinal canal is established."

He accompanied each sentence of description with corresponding actions. It was astonishing to see how easily he drew the inner edge of the oblique abdominal muscle up to Poupart's ligament; how he sutured it; how the deep sutures closed the opening, the vas deferens was laid against the new wall, and the aponeurosis closed above it.

There was nothing theatrical about Bassini's mode of working. Rather, he seemed deliberate and matter-of-fact.

"Now the skin suture follows," Bassini said. "With my first operation I provoked the patient to severe coughing and even vomiting during the operation, immediately after the muscle suture, to test the stamina of the new wall. Since then I have operated along these lines one hundred and twenty-three times, including cases of strangulated hernia. The youngest patient was thirteen months old, the oldest sixty-nine years. In two thirds of the cases healing took from nine to sixteen days. Only in a few cases in which the antisepsis was imperfect, for undetermined reasons, did convalescence require more than twenty days. Among these hundred and twenty-three cases I have had only two deaths from shock and pyemia, and only five cases in which the hernia recurred because of a faulty suture or marked weakness of the abdominal walls. Even in these cases a second operation produced a lasting cure. This statement may sound presumptuous to you, but it is justified, for I have now observed the majority of my patients for periods of from one to four years. Not a single one of them has ever worn a truss after the operation."

There was a moment's silence. Still filled with amazement, I watched as Bassini completed the skin suture and Tansini collected the instruments into a bowl and covered the unknown corpse once more. Both men began dipping their hands in various solutions, which stood ready in basins, and washing themselves with painstaking care. When they were almost finished, I said: "Dr. Gallmann tells me that you have reported on your work only once to the Italian Surgical Society. That was last year. No one in the rest of the world has heard about it. Why have you not spoken at some international congress in Berlin, London, or Paris, or published in one of the major international periodicals? Tens of thousands of patients are waiting for a real cure for hernia. Tens of thousands will hail you as their savior."

Bassini smiled with a touch of bitterness. "We Italians," he said, "have gained the reputation during the past century—in spite of our great medical tradition—of having failed to participate in the general progress of medical science, of being backward and superficial. I do not intend to publish my work until I have more than two hundred and fifty cures to my credit, so that no one in international medicine will be in a position to challenge my work. Only then shall I be serving not only the patients but my country as well."

He nodded to Tansini, who took up the lantern again and led us up the tortuous stone staircase. Everything in this building was old, dark, and decaying. But these conditions had not hindered the tall, gaunt man who ascended the stairs in front of me from making a discovery which would certainly shake the world of medicine as soon as it learned of it.

While we were in the cellar, the tide of visitors had apparently ebbed. The corridors seemed silent and deserted now. But suddenly a girl appeared from some embrasure and blocked Bassini's way. She seemed to be about fourteen, wore a pathetically skimpy black dress, and was barefooted. She started to kneel before Bassini and tried to kiss his hand. "*Signore Dottore!*" she exclaimed in a thin, childlike voice. "You will make him well. Please tell me you will make him well?"

Bassini laid his hand reassuringly on the carefully braided and oiled hair. "Whom do you mean?" he asked.

"Aloisi," the girl said. "Aloisi Marchiori of Bassano Veneto. They say you are going to cut him open tomorrow and they won't let me see him. *Signore Dottore*, he is my brother. We need him."

Bassini withdrew his hand. "Oh, Marchiori," he said. "You're his sister." He reached into his pocket and handed her a coin. "Go home now," he said, "and have no fear. He will be well. You can be sure of it. . . ."

After the girl had pattered off on her bare feet, Bassini stood for a moment with bowed head. "I cure them of rupture," he murmured, "and they die a few years later of tuberculosis or malaria or malnutrition." He straightened up in a gesture of either pride or rebellion against the world in which he lived and worked. "I will see you tomorrow," he said tersely, shaking hands briefly with Gallmann and me. "At six." Followed by Tansini, he strode off.

The clock read precisely six, the following morning, when Bassini entered the wooden amphitheater where he operated. His face was still flushed from his morning gallop.

The benches, creaking with age, were filled to the very last seat. That was noteworthy, for at that time the profession of physician offered little more to Italian youth, on the whole, than ill-paid places in some army hospital or village. A doctor was a poor man living among the poor, and seldom indeed did he rise to prosperity and fortune. The better situations in the large cities were few. Two thirds of the young people who attended the universities therefore chose the legal profession.

Gallmann and I had found seats in the lowest row, close to the operating table. While the first of the two patients, twenty-one-year-old Ernesto Calzavare, was carried in, still inside the antiseptic wrappings in which he had spent the night, Bassini asked Gallmann and me to step up to the operating table. Tansini assisted. Two young doctors administered the chloroform and regulated the spray. The carbolic mist was concentrated upon the patient's groin as two nurses unwound the rubber and linen wrappings. The patient sank into deep sleep almost immediately, and Bassini began the operation.

His procedure was exactly as he had demonstrated it to us on the cadaver. He incised the skin and hypodermic tissue below the protruding hernia. There was scarcely any bleeding. A new incision opened the inguinal canal and the aponeurosis of the obliquus externus to high above the inner inguinal ring. Once more there was scarcely any significant bleeding. The hernial sac bulged out, alongside the vas deferens, which had been forced to one side, out of its normal position. Cautiously, Bassini plucked the vas deferens away from the hernial sac and raised the latter. He opened it and found a loop of intestine. Carefully, he freed a few adhesions and pushed the intestine back through the ruptured wall into the abdominal cavity. Then he ligatured the sac close to the rupture, severed the empty sac, sewed the ligatured spot, and let it likewise drop back into the abdominal cavity.

This was what many surgeons before him had already done in the same or a similar manner. Now the crucial new phase of the operation began. Tansini lifted the vas deferens high above the incision. With extremely careful movements Bassini exposed the lower posterior edges of the oblique abdominal muscle. He drew it down, pushed it under the vas deferens, and brought it up to the lower edge of Poupart's ligament. Each phase of the operation made the futilities of earlier surgery seem altogether incredible. Already Bassini was beginning his suture. He used silk thread, and did one button stitch after the other. Close to the pubic bone he took two sutures in the rectus abdominis muscle. Immediately afterward the new abdominal wall lay before us, taut and visibly strong.

Bassini nodded to one of his assistants. The young doctor took a feather and introduced it into the patient's throat. Almost immediately the patient gagged and began to cough violently. His intestines and all the muscles of the abdomen convulsed. I stared at the sutures in the newly formed abdominal wall. Would they really resist such strain?

My concern was needless. The abdominal wall remained taut and tight until the coughing ceased. Bassini threw us a glance. Then Tansini allowed the vas deferens to slip back. He placed it on the new wall, and over it Bassini sewed the anterior surface of the aponeurosis. Then followed the skin sutures, and a light bandage.

Bassini straightened up as the students in the stand applauded wildly.

I stayed in Padua until the end of July, 1888, in order to watch the convalescence of Bassini's patients. At the end of the month Ernesto Calzavare, Arturo Malatesta, and Aloisi Marchiori left the hospital, completely recovered. On July 22 Bassini was already performing another hernia operation upon a thirty-eight-year-old domestic servant from Monfelice named Della Valle. This, too, had proceeded without complications.

During my stay in Padua I looked up, in the city and its environs, no less than forty persons upon whom Bassini had operated during the past several years. The sight of these patients swept away any last doubts I might have harbored. For years they had been going about their work without trusses. Among them were workers in the heaviest trades who could by no means spare themselves. They were every one of them completely restored to health and strength, something which in those days could not be said of any other hernia patients anywhere else in the world.

When I left Padua on August 1, I was convinced that hernia, that nightmare which had beset mankind for thousands of years, had finally lost its terrors and that after the usual slow acceptance which in those days befell every surgical innovation, Bassini's operation would spread beyond Italy and through the rest of the civilized world.

Two years later Edoardo Bassini reached his first large audience when he published an account of his method in the fortieth volume of the German *Archiv für Klinische Chirurgie*. By then he could record no less than 262 operations. It was as though a long-closed door were opening. Although Macewen in England and Halsted in the United States were likewise developing new methods around the same time—indeed, Halsted's bore a certain kinship to Bassini's—Padua became the mecca for numerous surgeons eager to follow the path Bassini had blazed. His method, in its original form or in variations and improvements, proved to be the pattern for successful hernia surgery in times to come.

The Second Battle
Against Pain

Sigmund Freud – Carl Koller
William Halsted – Paul Reclus
Carl Ludwig Schleich – August Bier
Leonard Corning – Heinrich Braun

I must return now to Paris and to that early morning of September 17, 1884, when I breakfasted with Paul Reclus and he called to my attention the newspaper report of the Ophthalmological Congress in Heidelberg at which a Viennese eye doctor named Carl Koller made known his discovery that the human eye could be rendered insensitive to pain by trickling into it a few drops of cocaine solution. That incident heralded the beginning of the second great battle against pain, the battle for a local anesthesia, whose need had been so greatly felt, for example, by the developers of the goiter operation.

After I left Reclus that day I considered where I might learn more about these developments, and recalled the American ophthalmologist from San Francisco, Dr. Ferrer, whom I had met in Paris the previous week. He had mentioned at the time that he was on his way to a congress in Heidelberg. I decided to telegraph Ferrer and ask him for a confirmation of the newspaper item and whatever details he could supply.

Since I myself knew virtually nothing about cocaine, I spent the intervening time boning up on the subject. The available information ran about as follows: In 1532, during the conquest of Peru, Pizarro had discovered that the natives chewed the leaves of a shrub they called *coca*, and that mastication of these leaves ap-

279

parently enabled them to perform remarkable physical feats. The matter received no further attention—at least not in Europe. In the middle of the nineteenth century, however, the globe-trotter and linguist J. J. von Tschudi once again became interested in the leaves, and especially in their faculty for increasing physical performance. In Paris a manufacturer named Mariani made an infusion of coca leaves with wine and put it on the market as a tonic. Here and there attempts were made to employ coca as a drug for syphilis and whooping cough, but these made no headway. In 1858, finally, a Dr. Scherzer, ship's doctor aboard the Austrian frigate *Novara*, brought dried coca leaves to Europe and turned them over to the German chemist Wöhler of Göttingen for analysis. Wöhler's pupil Niemann succeeded in extracting the effective component of the leaves, which he called cocaine.

Ferrer's wired reply informed me that the reports in the Paris newspapers were quite correct. The discovery seemed to him of enormous significance. He intended to be in Paris on September 19, for one day, and would gladly tell me more.

My interest had been so greatly stimulated that I met Ferrer at the station. From him I learned that Carl Koller was a minor assistant at the Vienna General Hospital, a man not yet thirty. His personal finances had not permitted him to make the trip to Heidelberg, and the manuscript in which he described his discovery had been read by an Austrian colleague, Dr. Brettauer. To put the matter to the test, several patients in the Heidelberg eye clinic had been operated on for cataract in the presence of the assembled opthalmologists. A few drops of cocaine trickled into the eye sufficed to produce complete anesthesia.

Ferrer was afire with what he had seen and in an extraordinary hurry to return to San Francisco, where he expected to cover himself with glory by making use of the new procedure. I myself left that very evening for Vienna. Surgery was fast reaching the point at which I was finding it difficult to keep abreast of its multiple developments. But the tale I traced to Vienna still stands out above the others. The first surprise for me was that it had not begun with Carl Koller, but with another as yet unknown young Viennese doctor. No one suspected at this time that he would later win world fame by his creation of a new and tremendously controversial kind of neurology and psychotherapy, namely psychoanalysis. His name was Sigmund Freud.

At this time Sigmund Freud was twenty-seven years old, a slight, dark-haired young man with sensitive, finely carved features. He was the son of an impoverished Jewish textile merchant who lived with his family of eight in a more than modest dwelling on Kaiser Josef Strasse. Sigmund Freud was a person of almost morbid sensitivity and great pride. In his childhood he had felt deeply the humiliations imposed upon his father, his brothers and sisters, and himself because of their Jewish origins. Never had he forgotten an incident he witnessed when he was twelve years old when some bullies ordered his father, "Jew, off the sidewalk," shoved him into the street, and knocked his cap from his head. And never had Sigmund forgiven his father for obeying the dictates of prudence, stooping silently and without a word picking his cap up out of the dirt. As a child Sigmund had had the burning desire to escape the narrowness and oppression of his world and to be in a position to command instead of being ordered and knocked about. He had dreamed of becoming a great soldier or statesman. But Austrian life had soon smothered these dreams, for the only careers open to Jews were those of businessman, lawyer, or physician. Out of no particular conviction, but because law and business left him indifferent, Freud had resolved upon the study of medicine. But he had in the course of time developed so profound a distaste for the practice of medicine that for years after passing his final examinations he worked in Professor Brücke's physiological institute and Professor Salomon Stricker's anatomical institute without making the slightest preparations for beginning a practice. Not until the spring of 1882 did he suddenly cease working for Brücke and apply for a post as subordinate physician at the General Hospital. No one knew the reasons for this sudden change of mind. They were of the most private nature, and I learned part of the story only after long years.

At the time Freud had fallen in love with a twenty-year-old girl named Martha Bernays, child of a Jewish businessman who had moved from Hamburg to Vienna and died of a heart attack some three years before. One evening in April, 1882, Martha Bernays and her sister had paid a visit to the Freud home; Freud's sisters were school friends of theirs. When Freud returned from work at Brücke's institute that day, he saw the slender, charming girl chatting gaily with his sisters and peeling an apple for his invalid mother. That single sight of Martha sufficed. Freud was so overcome that during the following days he spent all the money he could lay hands on to send Martha a rose, a card, and a letter every day. It was the end of May before he had his first opportunity to go for a walk with Martha, and the two went up to the Kahlenberg together. He returned from this outing convinced that she returned his love. On June 10 they kissed for the first time, and next day Freud made that sudden decision to go to work in the General Hospital in order to prepare for private practice. He was suddenly seized by the desire to achieve economic independence, so that he might marry Martha.

In the spring of 1884 Freud was on the verge of desperation. Two years had passed since his meeting Martha and he still saw no way for them to marry. Martha's mother, Emmeline Bernays, had from the beginning made it plain that she would not accept a son-in-law who could not offer a secure position. In the summer of 1882 she sent Martha to her relatives in Wandsbek, near Hamburg, in order to separate her from the undesirable suitor. Freud borrowed money to make clandestine trips to Wandsbek during his vacation. He wrote to Martha daily and suffered torments of jealousy when he so much as heard of her writing to anyone else. In June, 1883, Martha's mother moved to Hamburg, and kept a close watch over her daughter. Nevertheless letters flew back and forth. The high-strung Freud veered between hope, despair, love, and burning jealousy, between faith and fear. Not until the autumn holidays of 1884, as far as he could see, would he have another chance to go to Hamburg. The interval seemed to him unbearably long. He suffered from severe depressions which became linked with physical complaints: violent stomach upsets and attacks of sciatica. He believed he would inevitably die unless he could somehow shorten the time until his next meeting with Martha. Thus was born the desperate desire to make some unusual discovery which would enable him to earn money and sue for Martha's hand. While he worked at the General Hospital he hit upon the wildest ideas for novel and in his opinion sensational therapies. But each idea soon petered away to nothing.

Reality seemed more and more unendurable to him. At this time

Freud was working in the neurology section, the worst administered
of the entire hospital. So seldom was the floor swept that every
draft whirled up clouds of dust. There was little water and no
electric light. After nightfall the patients were left in darkness.
The doctors had to make late rounds with lanterns, and by the
light of such lanterns perform emergency surgery. It was a dreary
atmosphere, ill suited to alleviate the near-hysterical complexes of
a keyed-up young man.

In his days of deepest gloom, around the middle of April, 1884,
Freud chanced across an article in the *Deutsche Medizinische
Wochenschrift* of December 12, 1883. Written by a German army
doctor named Theodor Aschenbrandt, it was entitled "The Physiological Effect and Importance of Cocaine." Aschenbrandt had administered cocaine to a number of Bavarian soldiers during the
autumn maneuvers, and fancied that the drug had considerably
heightened their marching performances.

Freud had never heard of cocaine before. But, ever on the look-
out for some sensational discovery, he instantly speculated whether
this drug might not perhaps be useful in combating physical illness
and nervous diseases—might not, in short, be useful to him in winning fame and fortune. He pursued the matter and learned that
Merck, in Darmstadt, was the only drug firm which had hitherto
produced pure cocaine—in minute quantities. The price per gram
was prodigiously high, and more than Freud could afford. But in
his desperate mood he ordered a gram, with the vague hope that
he would be able to pay for it sooner or later. Immediately after
the drug arrived, he began experimenting on himself, and observed
a most remarkable effect. For the first time in many months he felt
capable of working. His depressions vanished, gave way to moods
of abounding confidence. Even his burning jealousy lost a good
deal of its painful keenness.

Already his hopes of making a sensational scientific discovery
were spurred, and he saw himself as the author of a major work on
the hitherto unknown curative properties of cocaine, a work that
would make a name for him throughout the world. Systematically,
he searched through the libraries of Vienna for possible older
studies of cocaine. In the course of this research he came upon a
paper which an American doctor named Bentley had published
some time before in the *Detroit Medical Gazette,* and which had

gone completely unnoticed. Bentley discussed morphine addiction, which had become widespread, especially among physicians, since the discovery that this drug could be injected. He suggested that morphine addicts could be cured if cocaine were substituted for the morphine, since the habit induced by cocaine was easier to break. Freud fell upon this proposal, which suggested still another effect of cocaine.

One of his older friends, Ernst von Fleischl, assistant in the physiological institute where he himself had worked, was a morphine addict. Thirty-eight years old, an attractive and handsome fellow and splendid scientist, Fleischl had incurred an infection in the course of anatomical work at the age of twenty-five. Only prompt amputation of his right thumb had saved his life. But subsequently neuromata (tumors due to enlargement of the ends of a nerve in the stump) had formed, necessitating further operations. His hand had become a focal point of fearful neuralgic pains. For thirteen years Fleischl had been taking morphine in steadily increasing doses. His chronic morphinism resulted in spells of unconsciousness and mental derangement.

At the time Freud went to him with the proposal that he try cocaine instead of morphine, Fleischl had just undergone a course of electric shocks administered to his hand under anesthesia, which, it was hoped, would help his condition. The treatment, however, had so intensified the pain that afterwards Fleischl was several times found unconscious on the floor of his room. Consequently, Fleischl leaped to the idea with the eagerness of a drowning man. Money being no problem for him, he assured Freud that he would pay for any quantity of cocaine that the firm of Merck could supply. After a short time he was taking a daily dose of a gram. He felt miraculous relief. The spells of mental derangement vanished; he ceased to be subject to bouts of fainting and delirium, and was filled with new vigor. Freud felt borne up by a wave of confidence. In order to accumulate evidence, he distributed cocaine to colleagues, friends, patients, and his own sisters. He himself was now taking the drug regularly. He even sent a sizable dose to Martha in order to "strengthen" her.

Once, in the course of his experiments, Freud observed that after he had taken cocaine his tongue and the mucous membrane of his mouth showed distinct insensitivity, so that the pain of an inflamed gum was alleviated. A few days after making this observation, he met two colleagues in the garden of the Vienna General Hospital. One of them was Dr. Koller of the section for diseases of the eye. Koller's companion complained about toothache. Freud trickled a few drops of cocaine solution on his gum, without explaining the nature of his panacea. Next day he again encountered Koller, who asked the nature of the medicine. Freud explained, and invited him, as he had done others, to participate in the experiments. Koller promptly acceded and for several weeks took cocaine along with Freud. Both men measured their physical strength and the degree to which it was increased by cocaine. They observed that cocaine induced warmth, deepened respiration, and increased the blood pressure. During this time, however, neither man commented on the local anesthetic effect of cocaine in the mouth. I have often wondered at this, and can only conclude that Freud's interests were already directed principally to problems of the nervous system. He lacked any concern with other aspects of medicine, and surgery was quite alien to him. So absorbed was he with the presumptive anti-addiction, antidepressive, and tonic effects of cocaine that any notion of analgesic effects for surgical purposes remained far from his thoughts.*

On June 18 Freud finished writing his paper in praise of cocaine. He stated that cocaine was a valuable medicine for overcoming all types of depression, for eliminating nervous stomach complaints, and for augmenting mental and physical efficiency. He declared that it had no habit-forming properties and no serious side-effects. It was therefore an excellent substitute for morphine and could be used to wean morphine addicts from their addiction. At the very end of this report Freud commented, in two casual sentences: "The ability of cocaine and its salts to render mucous membranes insensitive suggests possible future use especially in cases of local infection.

---

* Among the original letters of Freud published by Ernest Jones in his biography of Freud is a letter to Martha written at this time which suggests the extent of Freud's enthusiasm for the drug. He wrote: "Woe to you, my Princess, when I come. I will kiss you quite red and feed you till you are plump. And if you are forward you shall see who is the stronger, a gentle little girl who doesn't eat enough or a big wild man who has cocaine in his body. In my last severe depression I took coca again and a small dose lifted me to the heights in a wonderful fashion. I am just now busy collecting the literature for a song of praise to this magical substance." Jones, *Freud*, vol. I, p. 84.

Several further applications of cocaine, likewise deriving from its analgesic effect, may conceivably be developed some time in the future."

He had no more to say about the analgesic effect and never dreamed that he was passing over the truly significant aspect of cocaine, wherein lay hidden the discoverer's fame he so passionately desired. He did not suspect that he had applied himself exclusively to the menacing and diabolic aspects of cocaine, and that as the result of far too hasty experimentation, impelled by the craving for success, he was extolling the worst side of the drug, far more habit-forming than morphine. At the time Freud was sending his paper to Heitler's *Zentralblatt für die gesamte Therapie*, Fleischl was already showing the first signs of the terrible effects following from chronic use of cocaine. He suffered from deliriums reminiscent of the delirium tremens resulting from alcoholism. He imagined he saw white snakes crawling over his body. But these attacks passed. Larger doses of cocaine brought him fresh relief. Moreover, Freud's paper was already written, and it appeared in the July issue of the *Zentralblatt*.

The reverberations were disappointingly small. But by the time Freud fully realized this dismal fact, half of August was past. His vacation and the visit to Martha, to which he had looked forward with such longing for more than a year, now lay immediately before him. The experiments with cocaine had helped him to pass the seemingly unendurable wait through the summer. Cocaine itself had repeatedly helped him shake off his deepest moods of depression. He resolved to continue his experiments on a greater scale after his return from Hamburg, and with them to win the success still denied him.

For the present, however, his thoughts were upon the goal of his longings. On September 1 he bade goodbye to his close friends, among them Leopold von Königstein, a lecturer on opthalmology whom he had known when they were students together. The conversation turned casually upon cocaine once more, and at this time, just before his departure, Freud suggested that Königstein might try whether cocaine did not alleviate pain in such distressing eye diseases as trachoma and iritis. Once again he revealed that he himself lacked interest in this aspect of cocaine. He readily relinquished his claim to being a specialist. Königstein, as it happened, also accepted the suggestion in the most casual manner. Shortly afterwards Freud, filled with joyful anticipation, forgetting everything else, boarded the train that was to take him to Hamburg.

Carl Koller was a person of utterly different character from Freud's, far less sensitive and quite lacking Freud's lively imagination. In contrast to Freud, however, Koller had experienced hundreds of times what Freud had never seen, the suffering of patients with eye disease who had to be operated on without anesthetic. As an oculist, he knew what it meant to attempt, while struggling with a flinching, terrified patient, to perform an operation in which the tiniest slip could do irreparable damage. For years Koller had apprehended that discovery of a method for local anesthesia of the eye was one of the foremost problems of ophthalmology. The moment Freud demonstrated the effect of cocaine upon an inflamed gum, Koller had wondered whether the drug might not have the same effect upon the eye. But oddly enough, fear of disappointment had for weeks restrained him from making a simple test. Nevertheless, he had meanwhile read through the available older literature on cocaine. In doing so he came upon a sentence written by Niemann, the first to extract cocaine from the coca leaf, in 1859: "It tastes bitter and has a peculiar effect upon the nerves of the tongue, namely that the place of contact becomes temporarily numbed, almost entirely without feeling." Koller found other allusions to the numbing effect of cocaine, especially in a report by a surgeon-general in the Peruvian army, one Moreno y Maiz. In Maiz's paper, which had been published in French as long ago as 1868, and strangely enough had been completely ignored, the direct question was raised: "Can cocaine be used as a drug for local analgesia? The future will show if it can."

While Freud's train chugged northward, Koller made up his mind to try the effect of cocaine on the eye. A few days later Koller went to Stricker's laboratory again. He found Stricker's assistant, Dr. Gärtner, and showed him a small bottle containing a white powder. Did he have something new? Gärtner asked. Koller explained that it was cocaine, and asked his help in preparing a strong solution. Gärtner had heard some rumors about Freud's experiments and was highly skeptical, but he did not refuse to help. When the solution was ready he produced a frog from a glass tank and held the creature tightly while Koller sucked up some of the cocaine solution in a pipette and held the pipette, with a single drop forming at the end of it, over the frog's left eye. The pipette quivered slightly, and then the drop fell into the eye.

A minute passed in utter silence. Koller laid the pipette aside. His hand was trained in eye operations. It was fine and steady in its movements, as an oculist's hand must be. But at that moment he was unable to hold that small tube of glass without betraying to Gärtner how tense he was. So, at any rate, Gärtner later described the scene to me.

Koller waited a full minute. Then he took up a sharp probe. He braced his hand on the table, in order to conquer its trembling, and moved the point of the probe to within a fraction of an inch of the eye. Ordinarily, any such movement sufficed to make an eye blink defensively, to make the whole head jerk back.

But now the response was entirely different. The frog's eye did not move or show the slightest reaction. Koller brought the tip of the probe still closer, until it had met the eye. The point was now resting directly on the cornea. Once again there was no reaction. Koller pressed the point into the cornea at various spots. Still no reaction.

Swiftly, then, Koller moved the probe over to the frog's other eye, which had not been treated with cocaine. The frog's head instantly jerked back, before the probe could touch the eye. Koller stimulated the numbed eye with heat, with cold, with a mild acid— still there were no signs of feeling. Again and yet again he repeated his test, seeking to be absolutely sure, to resolve all doubts. But the miracle held true: the cocaine had utterly benumbed the surface of the eye. In the future, painless cataract operations would be possible without general anesthesia.

At that triumphant moment Koller had not the slightest suspicion that Dr. Leopold Königstein was simultaneously experimenting with cocaine. For Königstein had taken up Freud's parting suggestion and proceeded to treat several cases of trachoma with cocaine. He observed that the pain seemed to disappear for a time after introduction of cocaine into the eye. Oddly enough, although Königstein was an oculist, like Koller, this discovery did not prompt him to try cocaine as a local anesthetic. He slavishly followed Freud's suggestion in regard to the drug's possible therapeutic effects upon diseases of the eye. Moreover, he was diffident in his approach and quite content to suspend judgment until he had more cases of trachoma.

By one of the quirks of fate and medical history, Koller was not among the friends to whom Freud bade goodbye. He therefore did not hear the suggestion that Freud had made to Königstein. And yet it was he and not Königstein who actually discovered the anesthetic effect of cocaine upon the eye. In later years Koller lived in New York, so that I saw him frequently, and I discussed this matter with him a number of times.

The day after his discovery Koller treated a dozen frogs in succession. The results were always the same—anesthesia of the eye treated with cocaine. Gärtner then provided a dozen rabbits for Koller. Once again the different stimuli were tried—heat and cold, electricity and instruments. The anesthesia was complete. Even deep incisions were stoically endured by the animals.

Koller performed his next experiments on dogs. Lastly, he made himself the subject. He enlisted the reluctant Gärtner to treat his eyes with cocaine and subject them to the probings of various instruments. When he himself felt not the slightest pain, his last hidden doubt was removed. Buoyantly, he went to the eye clinic, quietly persuaded one of his patients to submit to an experiment, and once again achieved complete anesthesia. This same patient thereupon declared his willingness to undergo a cataract operation from which he had hitherto shrunk. Koller performed the operation in secrecy, without witnesses, and experienced a miracle; for the first time an eye patient lay perfectly still without general anesthesia, so that the oculist was able to operate at his ease, without constant injunctions, without fear of sudden jerks.

Koller's joy was now tempered by the fear that someone might anticipate him—although he still knew nothing of Königstein's experiments. His first successful cataract operation had taken place on September 11. The congress of ophthalmologists in Heidelberg was due to convene on September 15. Here was his chance to publicize this discovery so that no one could contest his priority. But Koller, wholly unknown, could scarcely hope to be accepted as a speaker on such short notice. Moreover, he could not afford the trip.

At the last moment he chanced to make the acquaintance of a Trieste oculist, Dr. Brettauer, who was stopping briefly in Vienna on his way to the Heidelberg congress. Koller demonstrated his findings to Brettauer, who, deeply impressed, immediately agreed to announce Koller's results in Heidelberg and to repeat his experiments before the assembled oculists.

So Koller remained behind in a state of almost unbearable suspense. He assured himself that his discovery could not possibly fail of recognition. But he knew only too well the fate of many great discoveries which the medical profession had scorned for decades. Three days passed. Then, at last, Koller received news of the at first stunned and then jubilant reception of his report in Heidelberg. Despite his lack of imagination, Koller could foresee that local anesthesia with cocaine would not remain limited to ophthalmology, but would exert a revolutionary influence upon the whole further development of surgery.

In Hamburg, meanwhile, Freud heard nothing about Koller's discovery and the sensational demonstrations in Heidelberg, although I heard of them in Paris almost immediately. Freud had quite forgotten Vienna. Since the morning of September 3 when he saw Martha at the railroad station in Wandsbek and took her into his arms, all his thoughts had been focused on her and on the glorious weeks that stretched before them. During the next days, when he saw Martha almost constantly, he became calmer and far more composed. Martha even persuaded him to call upon her mother, whom he thought he hated for having snatched his sweetheart away. For the first time the ice was broken here, too. Filled with a rare sense of happiness, Freud returned to Vienna early in October, resolved to continue his investigations of cocaine, win success at last, and marry Martha in 1885 at the latest.

The first news he heard upon arrival in Vienna was of Koller's discovery. Curiously enough, he was not in the least shaken by it. Once again there is only one explanation for this. His complete indifference to surgery prevented him even now from recognizing the tremendous importance of cocaine for that branch of medicine. To him cocaine was still a miraculous drug whose uses in neurology must be investigated; to his mind, Koller had merely discovered a small subsidiary effect. Regarding cocaine as his discovery, his own possession, he thought of Koller's work as a helpful contribution to his major, long-range cocaine project. Neither did it disturb him when Königstein came to him with the revelation that he, too, quite independently of Koller, had learned that cocaine could make the whole eye insensitive to pain—unfortunately, Koller had stolen the march on him. He made Freud come to the eye clinic where he demonstrated the painless removal of a dog's eye. Upon this occasion Freud also learned that on October 17 Koller intended to appear personally before the Vienna Medical Society and lecture on his discovery.

Freud, meanwhile, resumed his experiments on the effectiveness of cocaine as an internal medicine. He was encouraged by a letter from the firm of Merck, whose interest had been aroused by his report on cocaine and who now sent him a newly isolated component of the drug for experimentation. And improbable as it may seem, he drew encouragement from the example of Fleischl, who concealed his more and more terrible bouts of hallucination in order not to have to confess that cocaine, his last great hope of cure from morphine addiction, was in fact completing his destruction.

During the early weeks of October, Freud experimented with diabetics. He hoped that the effect of cocaine upon the nervous system would help these then hopeless unfortunates. But these experiments proved vain. From his sister Rosa and a ship's doctor who was her friend, he heard that cocaine had once proved of value in seasickness. He tried this effect upon himself by swinging back and forth in a swing at the Prater amusement park until he induced a kind of artificial seasickness. But here, too, cocaine brought no relief. Then, on October 15, two days before the meeting of the Vienna Medical Society, his eyes were opened in ghastly fashion.

He was called to Fleischl. His friend had locked himself into his room. He was writhing on the floor, delirious, screaming in frightful torment, and fending off imaginary monsters. The door of the room had to be forced open. Dimly, at that moment, Freud began to realize that he had been pursuing a will-o'-the-wisp, and that perhaps Koller had found not a subsidiary effect of cocaine but its only positive medical application.

In deep gloom, Freud went to the medical meeting on October 17. He saw Koller at the height of his glory, heard the address, and listened to the resounding applause. He heard also Koller's dutiful sentence: "A careful and interesting paper by my colleague Dr.

Sigmund Freud introduced cocaine to the physicians of Vienna." But was that to be all? Was he only to have sowed the seed from which another reaped the fruits of fame? Freud was still lost in these painful thoughts when Leopold Königstein stepped upon the platform. Königstein began to speak of his own application of cocaine to anesthesia of the eye, of his experiments, his operations, his discoveries. He did not so much as mention Koller's name. He gave the impression that he was trying, with stubborn defiance and in utter blindness to reality, to wrest for himself the fame that fate had withheld. The assemblage greeted his talk with dead silence. A sense of embarrassment pervaded the whole hall when the audience finally rose.

Somewhat dazed, Freud stood up. In him, too, the feeling rankled that he had been cheated by fate. He could not altogether bring himself to admit this, but inwardly he already knew it.* He smarted also from the slight administered him by Königstein, who after all had also been indebted to him for the initial suggestion. Suddenly he found at his side young Dr. Wagner-Jauregg, who like himself had worked in the neurological section of the Vienna General Hospital and who in time to come was to receive the Nobel Prize for his method of treating paralysis by artificial fever. Wagner-Jauregg's face was flushed with anger. He asked Freud to go with him to speak to Königstein. Together, the two men came down hard on the wretched Königstein, whose bitterness and frustration had temporarily robbed him of his judgment. Finally Königstein agreed to write a letter to one of the well-known medical journals in which he would present the facts correctly and frankly admit Koller's priority. In reasoning thus with Königstein, however, Freud was tacitly renouncing all claim to priority for himself.

Freud's disappointment was profound. Within a few days he was taking cocaine to overcome his depression. Today, when the habit-forming properties of cocaine are so generally known, it seems a miracle that he did not become an addict for life. Gamely, he resumed his experiments with the drug. He treated a great variety of nervous diseases with cocaine, even hydrophobia. But all his attempts failed, and gradually his hopes perished. In January, 1885,

* In the above-mentioned biography of Freud by Jones there is an extract from a letter which Freud wrote at this time to Martha's sister. He said: "Cocaine has brought me a great deal of credit, but the lion's share has gone elsewhere."

he attempted to still the fearful pain of trigeminus neuralgia in one of his patients by injecting a solution of cocaine directly into the nerve. He did not guess that at this moment he was grazing the edge of another great success, and that for the second time he was passing it by—namely, the discovery of the method by which cocaine could be used to anesthetize whole areas of the body, the method later to be known as conduction or regional anesthesia. Alas, his injection did not take effect; he had so little surgical experience that in all probability he missed the nerve.

After further struggles to achieve a modest livelihood as a neurologist in Vienna, Freud at last married Martha Bernays on September 13, 1886. He had by then turned away from all the physical aspects of medicine and was devoting himself to that interpretation of the most deeply buried layers of the psychic life which was ultimately to win him international fame—and notoriety. Nevertheless, the cocaine episode remained a thorn in the psyche which in later life repeatedly reappeared in his own dreams and his interpretations of them.

In May, 1888, Koller emigrated to the United States. He settled in New York, where he was attached to the Mount Sinai Hospital and Montefiore Home. Although he had great success as an oculist, his character became more and more withdrawn. Avid for more glory than had been vouchsafed him, he was more and more inclined to drop Freud's name entirely from interviews and papers. Perhaps also his disappointment arose from the fact that other men took up and advanced the idea he had initiated. These men brought local anesthesia with cocaine out of the restricted field of ophthalmology and applied it to all parts of the human body. I am referring to William Halsted, Paul Reclus, Carl Ludwig Schleich, August Bier, Leonard Corning, and Heinrich Braun.

I continued to remember Halsted as a passionately active young man determined to introduce asepsis into New York hospitals, which were still largely hotbeds of infection. You had only to see him, with his broad athlete's shoulders and his self-willed, irregular, energetic features, to be convinced that he would reach his goal. How he returned to New York after his student years in Germany to become a leader among the surgeons of New York, practicing asepsis in a tent in the hospital yard rather than yield to the backwardness of pigheaded surgeons; how he operated in six big hospitals, rushing from one to the other; how he taught a growing band of enthusiastic pupils the principles of European pathological anatomy and asepsis and nevertheless found time to give big parties and play the man of the world—all this is well known.

However, I knew nothing as yet of the important role Halsted had been playing in continuing Koller's work on local anesthesia, and it was in all innocence, by sheer chance, that I strolled past the handsome house on 25th Street one fine June day in 1886 where Halsted practiced, evidently in partnership with a colleague, Dr. Thomas McBride. Noticing Halsted's shingle, I decided on the spur of the moment that I wanted to see this young, dynamic doctor again.

A tall servant opened the massive door. He apparently assumed that I wished to consult Dr. McBride, and gave me a dignified but inviting smile. However, the moment I asked after Halsted his expression underwent a peculiar change. In an almost hostile manner he declared that Dr. Halsted was not there. My questions as to whether Halsted was away on a journey, or where he was staying, netted me no answer, and I was on the point of giving up the attempt and leaving my card when a younger man entered the vestibule. This was Dr. McBride. When the servant explained that I wished to see Halsted, I observed the same slightly nervous and mistrustful expression pass over his face that I had already seen in the servant. He asked whether I knew Halsted well. I said I did.

McBride hesitated for a moment. Then he invited me to his study. "Dr. Halsted has left for some time," he said. "It is not certain whether he will ever return to New York." He gave me a penetrating glance, then asked abruptly whether I really did not know why Halsted had left the city.

His obvious mistrust astonished me all the more. I felt that something unusual must have happened to Halsted, something that perhaps called for concealment. I explained that I had just returned from Europe and that I knew nothing whatsoever about Halsted's recent affairs.

McBride continued to hesitate. Finally, however, he said: "Well, since you appear to be a good friend of his and genuinely interested, I shall tell you where he is. . . ." He broke off, and then continued in a strangely gloomy tone: "At the moment he is in Providence. To put it bluntly, he is in a mental institution. . . . No," he added quickly, "he is not mentally ill. But he is suffering from an addiction which necessitates a long cure, and the outcome . . ." He shrugged, seeing in my expression my inability to grasp the meaning of what he had just said. It was difficult for me to imagine that Halsted, with his boundless energy and vitality, should at the moment be in a madhouse. Nor could I conceive what his addiction might be. Abuse of morphine? Of alcohol? What in God's name had happened that a man of no more than thirty-three . . .

"I suppose you are familiar with the discovery of cocaine as a local anesthetic," McBride said.

"Why, of course," I replied. "I have studied the matter very closely; in fact I spent a considerable time in Vienna for that very purpose."

"Well," McBride said, "this drug has produced nothing but misfortune for Halsted and several of his friends and students. Ever since the first accounts of Koller's discovery were received here in New York, Halsted has been concerned with ways and means of extending local anesthesia with cocaine to other parts of the body besides the eye. To that end he has experimented on himself and on friends and students. In the course of his work he has actually found a method for anesthetizing parts of the body by injecting solutions of cocaine into the pain-conducting nerves. He has called this method conduction anesthesia and made it public. But before he could really devote himself to perfecting the method, his own breakdown came. I take it you have not yet heard of the new method?"

I said I had not. For if I had heard or read so much as a hint concerning it, I would have made a point of calling on Halsted and not have left another meeting to chance.

"Undoubtedly, however," McBride continued, "you must have read the recent reports from various parts of the world warning that cocaine has exceptional habit-forming properties. These reports are, alas, only too correct. Protracted intake of cocaine makes for addiction far more dangerous than that of morphine. Once accustomed to its stimulus, one can no longer do without it. It undermines normal vitality, saps the will, and makes wrecks out of strong men."

Of course I had read of the various cases which only too monotonously repeated the story of Fleischl. Letters from Vienna gave me to understand that Freud was now under attack for having initiated the abuse of cocaine. But how could one explain that a powerful and robust chap like Halsted should have fallen victim to a drug which had left the feeble-bodied unscathed? There seemed no rhyme or reason to it. But McBride was continuing:

"We had to take Halsted to Providence virtually by force. There at the sanatorium they have had considerable experience with morphine addiction, and perhaps they will be able to save him. Withdrawal of cocaine has frightful effects—but even without that you would scarcely recognize the man."

I spent the rest of the afternoon with McBride and learned the chief details of Halsted's discovery, and the developments that had led to his breakdown. The following day I was told a good deal more by William Welch, the great New York master of pathological anatomy, in whose dissection rooms Halsted had frequently worked.

During that same September of 1884 when I heard about Koller's discovery the first sensationalized reports had reached New York. Halsted, currently working at Roosevelt Hospital with his assistants Richard J. Hall and Frank Hartley, had instantly taken up the matter, for here was something after his own heart. His conclusions were swift and simple: If cocaine would eliminate sensitivity to pain in mucous membranes when dropped or painted on the membrane, why should it not be effective in the interior of the body as well, if only it were possible to direct solutions of cocaine to the desired area? It should then be possible to anesthetize whole layers of tissue, perhaps entire internal organs, and consequently to operate without the necessity of putting the patient to sleep.

Penetration of cocaine into the interior of tissues could be accomplished only by injection—that appeared obvious. Even before the end of September, 1884, Halsted and his two assistants began experimenting on themselves at their laboratory in Roosevelt Hospital. They injected fairly strong cocaine solutions—concentrations of 5 to 15 per cent—first into their skins, then under the skin. They soon observed that such injections produced fairly long-lasting analgesia.

Even while these experiments were in progress there were curious developments. No one in Halsted's group had read Freud's reports on the enormously stimulating effect of cocaine. Quite independently Halsted, Hall, and Hartley discovered that after every experiment they were endowed with tremendous vigor. They had the feeling that they could work day and night without the slightest trace of weariness. Never before had their minds functioned so brilliantly, so reliably, so readily. They knew no precedent for such keenness of thought and such flights of the imagination.

Their eyes seemed to see with uncommon clarity. They felt like gods who had cast off all earthly burdens. Halsted's day's work was more hectic than ever before. To his friends and colleagues he seemed to be working simultaneously in a number of places. His speech was easier, more fluent, more relaxed. Writing papers seemed to him child's play. During operations his hands moved with trance-like sureness of touch.

Friends and students who asked Halsted, Hall, and Hartley for the secret of these remarkable performances were magnanimously given a dose of cocaine, and felt their own abilities miraculously enhanced. Efficiency dropped as soon as the effect of the dose wore off, but then they had only to take another tiny morsel in order to fly once more to the same heights. Hartley, suffering from a severe cold, tried cocaine powder. He inhaled it, and almost instantly his clogged respiratory passages cleared; moreover, he felt a peculiar animation and sense of happiness. From now on, whenever they felt the slightest weariness, Halsted, his friends, associates, and students snuffed a little cocaine powder and promptly felt fresh and vigorous. Along with his labors as surgeon, anatomist, and teacher, Halsted now undertook an enormous reading program for the purpose of tracking down every reference to the wondrous coca leaf. Early in January, 1885, he came upon the now seventeen-year-old paper by the Peruvian doctor Moreno y Maiz, *Chemical and Physiological Studies of the Coco Plant of Peru and of Cocaine*—the same essay that Koller had read. Halsted read with special attention Moreno y Maiz's conclusion: "It is a curious fact which seems to us worthy of attention that in all cases of cocaine injection motor ability is never destroyed, whereas the capacity for feeling vanishes." And then: "Can cocaine be used as a drug for local analgesia? The future will show if it can."

After reading this passage Halsted had the most fruitful idea of all those stormy months. If Moreno y Maiz had injected cocaine into a thigh and the whole leg, including the foot, had thereupon become insensitive to pain, there could be only one explanation of this phenomenon. By chance or intention the Peruvian physician must have introduced the cocaine solution into the pain-conducting nerves which united all the sensory nerves of the leg via the spinal cord with the pain-center in the brain. What a tremendous conception! Far simpler than the previous method of numbing zones of the body by a whole series of injections side by side. The path formed by the sensory nerves between parts of the body and the brain must be interrupted by injecting the cocaine solution directly into the nerves.

In a fever of excitement, Halsted entered his laboratory. He exposed the sciatic nerve of an animal and injected a dose of cocaine into it. Shortly afterward the entire leg was insensitive. Subsequently, Halsted, his assistants, and students engaged in a great variety of anatomical studies to determine the places at which the pain-conducting nerves to the various extremities and organs could most surely be blocked. And far off in Vienna, Sigmund Freud tried once to make the trigeminal nerve insensitive by injecting cocaine into it and, failing this, wrote off the whole idea. Halstead, meanwhile, evolved a whole system for producing local analgesia in the simplest way. When Hall, at the end of 1886, was attacked by severe toothache, Halsted for the first time injected cocaine into the inferior alveolar nerve. A whole segment of Hall's jaw became insensitive for almost twenty-five minutes, in which time the tooth was painlessly extracted. Thus Halsted became the discoverer of that type of local anesthesia which was to conquer the world and utterly revolutionize dentistry.

At the time these findings were published, in the spring of 1885, Halsted and his friends had long since made it a habit to snuff cocaine even when attending the theater, since it heightened for them the colorfulness of the spectacle on the stage. For a while Halsted did not notice that several of his students had become unpunctual, talkative, and irresponsible. But when he himself happened not to take cocaine for several days he suddenly discovered that he suffered from dizziness, pallor, trembling, and respiratory difficulties. The following day he began to have severe stomach cramps, and insomnia. Struck by a vague but terrible premonition, he asked Hall to discontinue his own doses. A few days of abstinence, and Hall collapsed completely. He was ridden by unbearable pain and panic terror of some miserable death. Only a large dose could restore him.

Was cocaine, then, not the wonder drug they had supposed it to be? Was it habit-forming just like morphine? And might it exact a far more terrible price from its credulous victim? Once more Halsted attempted to stop taking cocaine. This time the consequences were even more frightful than they had been before. Altogether gone were the feelings of vigor and efficiency, of godlike superiority and strength. He could no longer think, no longer concentrate. Fainting spells alternated with intense pain, insomnia with hallucinations. If he hoped to continue his work, to go on operating and teaching, he needed cocaine.

With a last spark of his old intelligence Halsted was cognizant that an even more terrible change was taking place within him. At times he no longer lived in the world of reality at all. The over-stimulated world of cocaine had become his true world. For spans of time that grew longer and longer he did not feel any genuine desire to return to reality. Suddenly old friendships, old ties, meant nothing to him; the affairs of daily life no longer interested him. In a few passing moments of clarity he once more spoke with Hall and Hartley, and learned that they were undergoing the same deteriora-tion. By March they were all drifting along without will, conscious only of their craving for cocaine, scarcely aware of their own rapid decline.

Those among Halsted's New York friends who had not taken part in the cocaine experiments—such as McBride—were only too well aware of the tremendous degeneration in all three men. They realized that cocaine contained not only the blessing of liberation from pain but also the curse of an addiction whose effects were far more baneful than those of all other known narcotics.

At the end of March they were still helpless spectators of this ter-rible drama when the first of those scattered reports came in, some from Vienna and some from other medical centers, on the severe addictions produced by cocaine. But it was already too late. Several of Halsted's students sank out of sight in the slums of New York. Hall was forced to give up his New York career. He went out west and some time afterwards began again as a surgeon in Santa Barbara, California. But his life had been shattered.

In the endeavor to keep Halsted from deteriorating completely, two of his friends, Dr. Monroe and Dr. van der Poel, sent him to the institution in Providence, which accepted morphine addicts and alcoholics in addition to the mentally ill. Halsted, the brilliant, successful, promising young doctor, disappeared behind the walls of an institution.

Halsted was gone for an entire year. No one ever learned what was done to him at the institution, what torments he suffered, what infernos he went through. All my own later efforts to find out something about the regimen within those walls met with defeat. It was a place which kept its secrets well. According to Welch, who later told me about it, when Halsted returned to New York at the end of the year he was a changed man. Where he had once been gay, he was now glum; where he had once loved friends and society, he was now shy and incapable of forming ties with others. Where he had once been lively, energetic, quick to act, he was now slow and painfully careful. Where he had once been the picture of health and strength, he was now emaciated and feeble. But the worst of all was that he had by no means recovered from his addiction to cocaine.

He avoided seeing his former friends. In a morbid desire for solitude, he engaged a cabin aboard a ship that was sailing in the winter of 1886 for the Windward Islands. He took with him a supply of cocaine. But in a strange and fitful impulse, he took care that the supply was too small to last for the entire voyage. He would be on the high seas, with absolutely no access to cocaine, and here if anywhere he must force himself to live without it. On the return voyage the moment came when his stock gave out. Half insane with the craving for the drug, he who little more than a year ago had been one of the foremost surgeons in New York, a perfect gentleman, the discoverer of a vital principle of anesthesia which in days to come would be a blessing for hundreds of thousands of human beings, broke into the captain's locked cabin. He forced open the pharmaceutical cabinet and stole the supply of cocaine. After the landing in New York, Halsted had to be taken to Providence for the second time.

He did not return until the following December. Once again no one ever learned what had happened to him at the institution. Welch, for example, to whom I owe all these details, could say nothing about it. In the interval, however, the physicians at the hospital seemed to have acquired some experience in the wholly new field of breaking habituation to cocaine. The worst excesses of Halsted's addiction seemed to have been overcome. But he still needed cocaine. While he sought in vain, back in New York, to take up some kind of research work again, and while his old friends could in all prudence offer him nothing but sympathy, a single one of them dared to have faith in Halsted. That was man was William Welch.

Welch had just moved from New York to Baltimore, where the new medical school of Johns Hopkins University was to be built up on European principals. Welch, appointed professor at the new medical school, took Halsted with him to Baltimore. He put him up at his own house, and kept close guard on the secret of the young man's addiction. He had Halsted work in his pathological laboratory and watched how Halsted slowly regained interest. Some of Halsted's old strength of will seemed to return as he studied problems of intestinal suture. After a while Halsted of his own accord expressed the desire to go back to Providence and undergo still another cure. Welch began to believe that his friend might be saved after all when he learned from the institution that this time Halsted had voluntarily abrogated the right to receive any money, by which he might have secured cocaine behind the doctors' backs.

After several months Halsted returned, for the first time in a fit condition to work concentratedly. He remained, however, a different person, compared with his former self; he was shy, permanently on the defensive, and friendless, with the one exception of Welch. In his work he was slow, exaggeratedly careful, entirely lacking in audacity, proceeding only in the most cautious manner and after endless preliminary work. Even his new-found tendency to over-refined elegance, his fad for wearing only French shirts and sending these to Paris to be washed, was, in Welch's opinion, a consequence of his years of cocaine addiction. For Welch had observed that cocaine addicts suffered from the feeling of being constantly unclean, and therefore were apt to devote exaggerated attention to clothing and the care of the body. Halsted actually wore many of his clothes only once. He took to writing with an old-fashioned goose quill, and spent hours cleaning it.

But in spite of these peculiarities, his one-time intellectual brilliance reasserted itself, and a good measure of his old capacity for work. Cocaine, however, was something he never discussed, and he completely eschewed all experiments with local anesthesia. Henceforth only general narcosis existed, as far as he was concerned. But in the slowness and care with which he now worked, he developed a type of scientific surgery quite new in America. Whereas he himself had formerly required an hour to excise a cancer of the breast, he now took four hours. But in those four hours there were no untoward incidents, no infections, no hemorrhages. He applied no method of operation without preparing for it by endless anatomical studies. There would not be a single capillary that Halsted had not studied before the operation. He treated tissue with a circumspection hitherto unknown. Years of investigation of the behavior of bacteria in wounds, microscopic examinations after the operations, led him to an infallible system of asepsis, treatment of wounds, and bandaging.

Welch was the first to understand that this restless man of action had been transformed into a master pedant who could bring to American surgery—still colored by the devil-may-care attitudes of pioneering days—a foolproof system of instruction. In 1889, with Welch's backing, Halsted was appointed professor of surgery at Johns Hopkins University. There I myself saw him nine years later; I observed the alteration in the man and heard from Welch his recent history. But in all my conversations with Halsted I never found an opportunity to inquire into his discovery of local conduction anesthesia. As soon as I made the slightest allusion to the subject, his expression reproved me, and he became evasive. With his slow, imperturbable deliberation he continued to develop the most important school of surgery in the United States. But to the end of his life he never shook off the characterological changes which had followed in the wake of his addiction to cocaine.

Meanwhile, however, others continued the development of local anesthesia—amid storms, setbacks, and disappointments.

Following on Halsted's discovery, the years 1886 to 1888 saw a world-wide application of cocaine for local anesthesia, and a general enthusiasm for cocaine, especially among young surgeons. Operations on the teeth and jaw, tumor operations of the most varied kinds, operations on hands, arms, feet, legs, operations for hernia, and operations on the lowest segment of the intestines were carried out under local anesthesia, cocaine being injected into the relevant nerves, tissues, and mucous membranes. American, French, and Russian surgeons in particular undertook the task of classifying the nervous system and discovering what nerves governed what bodily zones. Definitive techniques were developed, and I took great satisfaction in following the rapid progress of local anesthesia in spite of stubborn resistance on the part of the older generation of surgeons. As always, it was a problem of generations, and in the end the victory of the newer men seemed to be assured.

I had become quite certain of this victory. Then, in the summer of 1888, the technical journals began to carry reports of sudden deaths after cocaine injections, deaths which could only be attributed to severe shock from cocaine poisoning. And then, early in September, 1888, I received a letter from Professor Rauchfuss in St. Petersburg. Rauchfuss, who was later to treat Czar Nicholas's son for hemophilia, was one of the doctors with whom I maintained a steady correspondence and who kept me abreast of developments in his part of the world.

"Something quite ghastly has happened," he wrote. "You recall Professor Kolomnin, one of the pillars of surgical science here in Russia. A week ago he left his work and his family behind, and died by his own hand. Along with others here, Kolomnin had for several years been experimenting with local anesthesia by injection of cocaine. A female patient suffering from intestinal tuberculosis applied to him for operation. He injected somewhat more than a gram of cocaine into the mucous membrane of the rectum. The desired analgesia was produced, and the operation performed. Very soon, however, such severe symptoms of poisoning ensued that all antidotes were ineffective. The patient died two hours after the operation. Overwhelmed by guilt to the extent of losing his mental balance, Professor Kolomnin ended his own life with a revolver. I imagine that his suicide will have far-reaching repercussions. It sharply underlines a point that has been advanced more than once recently—that cocaine is not entirely an unmixed blessing. This toxic effect is all the more disturbing because it is so completely unpredictable. I am most anxious to learn whether there have been any similar deaths in American surgical practice. Please write me promptly about this. If the powerful toxic side-effects of cocaine are con-firmed elsewhere, then, I am afraid, the hopeful prospect of local anesthesia with this drug will have to be abandoned."

The shock of Rauchfuss's letter was all the stronger because the very next day I heard from Paul Reclus in Paris. Reclus, who had called my attention to the first reports on the analgesic effect of cocaine, and who had hailed the innovation so heartily, now dis-played a pessimism as alarming to me as Rauchfuss's.

The situation in local anesthesia, Reclus wrote, was rapidly reach-ing a critical phase. Injections of such minor areas as the hands, or the nerves of teeth, were resulting in sudden deaths. In less dire cases, the reaction was limited to anything from an increase in pulse rate, sensation of anxiety, and difficulty with respiration, to cold sweats, fainting fits, and attacks resembling epileptic seizures. The number of unfavorable reports were now all coming in so fast, it would seem, because surgeons had at first hesitated to publicize their fail-ures. He had recently received from Dr. Brouardel in Paris a list of thirty deaths due entirely to cocaine injections. This news had pro-duced a tremendous stir in Paris and virtually paralyzed all further work on local anesthesia. If these were the consequences, this method offered no hopeful alternative to the dangers of general anesthesia. Knowing of his own unhappy experiences with general anesthesia, I would surely understand what a blow this latest de-velopment was to him. He simply could not resign himself to the situation, and had decided to look more closely into Brouardel's mortality list. He must discover the precise manner in which co-caine caused death; perhaps, then, it would be possible to avoid this fatal effect. On the other hand, all his experiments might prove in vain. But he was determined to continue them until he made certain, one way or the other.

I soon found out for myself that all that Reclus had written was by no means exaggerated. In answer to my inquiries, from New York, Boston, Philadelphia, and Chicago came data on deaths result-ing from cocaine injections. Dr. Simmes in Philadelphia cited the case of a strong young patient who had died twenty minutes after injection of eight-tenths of a gram of cocaine into the urethra. Dr. Belfield in Chicago told of the case of a young actress who had fallen dead after a cocaine injection into her ear. Dr. Abadie of Paris reported that a cocaine injection into a patient's eyelid had sufficed to kill her. Dr. Mattison in Brooklyn showed me a still unpublished list of one hundred and twenty cases of cocaine poisoning, four of which had ended fatally. The method Halstead had proposed, the blockage of nerves by cocaine injection, proved to be particularly dangerous in the case of the larger nerves inasmuch as heavy doses of cocaine were needed to check the conductivity of a big nerve. Dentists, who had taken up cocaine injection, reported severe fainting spells and long-lasting symptoms of poisoning. Local anesthesia by injection of cocaine into the tissues showed fewer fatalities and fewer toxic symptoms. But even with this method the statistics were alarming enough. Only in operations on the eyeball, where cocaine was dropped according to Koller's method upon minute areas of mucous membrane, did there appear to be no dangerous results, aside from occasional slight inflammations. Wherever a deep injection was required to achieve the local anesthesia, severe toxicity might occur. As always in such situations, the initial bad news released a veritable tide of disaster reports.

Dr. Ferrer of San Francisco, who four years before had come from Heidelberg with the first enthusiastic account of Koller's discovery, wrote me that he felt compelled to abandon cocaine injection and return either to general anesthesia or to working without anesthesia. With the exception of its original form, the trickling of cocaine into the eye, the method seemed thoroughly discredited, and likely to remain so even if improved techniques should be discovered. A certain Dr. Oberst working at Professor Volkmann's clinic in Halle, Germany, seemed to have developed a method for local anesthesia of the finger which sounded promising. He made a tight bandage around the finger where it joined the hand, thus preventing the cocaine injected into the finger from entering the blood stream and flowing swiftly into the rest of the body, where it could cause poisoning. But this was a meager triumph, considering the high hopes that had been held only a short time before.

I wrote to Volkmann hoping to hear, amid all the discouraging accounts, at least one positive development.

I was still waiting for Volkmann's reply—this was during May, 1889—when I fell from a horse while riding in the vicinity of Pleasantville, N. Y. With my leg fractured in three places and a break in my right wrist also, I was taken to my home in New York City. Dr.

Hibbs of the Orthopedic Hospital did what could be done for such injuries in those days when X-rays were unknown. There was no need for him to tell me that at best I would have to stay in bed for several months. I was therefore laid up and in a dismal state of mind when Volkmann's answer arrived. He confirmed the success of Dr. Oberst, who had evidently transferred Halsted's method of numbing the dental nerve to the nerves of the finger, with the added refinement of checking the blood supply. But, Volkmann observed, this method was good only for fingers and perhaps for toes. For the rest, he added, there was such widespread doubt regarding cocaine in Germany that the future looked black for the development of local anesthesia. If Volkmann, an innovator who had never hesitated to accept revolutionary ideas, and who had been one of the first to introduce Lister's antisepsis into Germany—if Volkmann took this attitude, the case looked bad indeed.

Volkmann's letter intensified my general gloom. Probably for that reason I failed to notice a note he had penned on the back of the last page of his letter, and chanced upon it only a few weeks later. It ran as follows: "One of my students who has been off working in Paris told me a few days ago that a Paris colleague of ours whom I believe you know, Dr. Reclus, is engrossed in a study of methods for eliminating the toxic effects of cocaine. He is said to have had considerable success with several hundred patients, but this is as much as I yet know."

Since Reclus's pessimistic letter of last year I had heard nothing more from him. If Volkmann's information were correct, the reason was now clear. It had never been Reclus's habit to write until he had reached some final results in any new research he was pursuing.

I cabled at once to Reclus—and received no answer. I cabled again, and again there was no answer. Had my accident not condemned me to immobility, I would have been inclined to set out for Paris at once. But as it was I could not even sit up in bed, wash, or shave without help, and so I lay raging inwardly against my accursed fate.

I dictated a letter to Aristide Verneuil, chief surgeon of the Pitié Hospital and Reclus's teacher and superior, who like myself had a burning interest in the history of medicine and with whom I used to discuss current problems. Verneuil replied that Reclus was not opening telegrams or letters these days, that he was completely wrapped up in his experiments. If I hoped to reach him with any message, it might best be done through his wife. As I read these lines I could see Reclus before me—that puny little man with conscientious eyes. Perhaps the fate of local anesthesia lay upon those narrow shoulders.

I dictated a letter to Madame Reclus and waited impatiently, alternating between hope and bitterness. Still no answer. I wrote a second time. And then, on June 20, there at last arrived a letter from Reclus himself.

I was still confined to my bed, and my ill-humor had only grown during the interval. But Reclus's letter swiftly put my black mood to rout. He wrote that his determination to rescue the cause of local anesthesia was now firmer than ever. He had investigated Brouardel's list of fatalities and discovered that of the thirty names on the list, only nine persons had actually died of cocaine poisoning. The others had succumbed to various illnesses or to infections resulting from inadequate asepsis in the preparation of the cocaine solution. Of the nine fatalities, six were due to overdoses of cocaine. Certain clear conclusions followed. Not only was it an imperative matter to make up fresh solutions each time cocaine was used, but a table of the correct dosage must be established. He defined correct dosage as that which would produce no toxic effects but would suffice exactly to induce analgesia. Hitherto cocaine solutions of up to 30 per cent had been the rule. He had discovered, however, that 3 per cent solutions were sufficient to produce lack of sensation in conduction anesthesia. For anesthetizing tissues which were not susceptible to neural block, the procedure had to be much more careful. No longer should the surgeon aim to induce complete anesthesia before the beginning of an operation by injecting large quantities of cocaine into all the tissue to be operated upon. Rather, anesthesia must be extended along with the progress of the operation. A small quantity of cocaine must be injected into each layer of tissue before incising it, and the surgeon must proceed from layer to layer, anesthetizing as he went, until the operation was finished. In this way the body was spared the sudden shock of a large influx of cocaine, and tiny quantities of the drug sufficed. Tissue anesthesia was to be preferred to conduction anesthesia, he believed, for even with the dilute solutions he would recommend, the latter still involved the larger doses of cocaine. As yet he could not give me any final results, for he was still in the midst of his studies. But he firmly believed that he was on the right track. As soon as he had more conclusive data, he would write again.

Reclus knew me well enough to know that I would not wait patiently until the spirit moved him to communicate with me again in the years to come. But while my hand and two of the breaks in my leg were healing with comparative rapidity, the healing of the third fracture went so poorly, owing to an error in therapy, that the leg had to be broken and splinted anew. Never in my life had I felt so cabined and cribbed, and now I was worse off than before. The operation took a great toll of my strength, so much so that I experienced in my own person the dangers of chloroform anesthesia. My heart gave out, and only artificial respiration brought me back to life. In November I was sent to Warm Springs to take the waters and to learn how to walk again.

While recuperating there, I received a second letter from Reclus. He reported that he had now treated two hundred patients and had operated for tumors on fingers, hands, and feet, for cancer of the breast and benign tumors of the breast, under local anesthesia—that is to say, after the injection of 3 and at times 2 per cent solutions of cocaine into the connective tissue and in and around the operating fields. He had performed numerous tooth extractions, jaw and lip operations, and even hernia operations, and was now about to attempt abdominal operations under local anesthesia. In all his work he had encountered no distinct instances of poisoning, but only several temporary and comparatively mild disturbances. He now knew that in addition to the use of diluted and always fresh solutions it was necessary to observe a number of other precautions. Every patient must be well nourished before operation, and must not be allowed to sit or stand during or for some time after. Local anesthesia should not be used at all on children. Major operations, to which he was turning his attention now, presented special difficulties because of the constant alternation between surgery and cocaine injection. This called for more than normal aseptic measures. But he had already treated with complete success a large number of patients suffering from severe circulatory disturbances who would not have survived conventional anesthesia. However, Reclus continued, he needed several thousand cases before he would be absolutely certain of his thesis and be ready for general publication. He wanted to try reducing the dosage still further, in order to exclude the danger of even slight poisoning. This would be a tricky affair. It might mean that in some circumstances he would be administering too low a dosage, thus causing pain which would again defeat the whole method.

As ill luck would have it, I was compelled to spend the entire winter in Warm Springs. At last, in March, 1890, I was able to return to New York. In the heap of medical journals awaiting my perusal, I came upon numerous articles which condemned the application of cocaine even in dentistry. The writers recommended returning to cholorform or ether anesthesia for dental extractions. And wonder of wonders, there was a letter from Reclus waiting for me! He wrote that he had now treated eight hundred patients. But he had not yet clarified the question of whether it would be possible to dilute cocaine solutions down to less than 1 per cent. He was now tackling this problem. Reclus's cautious, methodical slowness was maddening to me. On March 28 I discarded my crutches without more ado and set sail for Europe. In the middle of April I arrived in Paris.

Reclus lived on the Rue Bonaparte in a big but modest house that suited his quiet, unaffected character. It was already late afternoon when my train pulled in. I assumed that my friend was at home, and accordingly drove directly to his house. His daughter, Marie, opened the door and gave me a startled look. Immediately afterwards Reclus's wife appeared. From her pale, flustered expression I could see that something unusual and alarming must have happened. It was immediately evident to me that she was terrified, and that her terror concerned Reclus.

I knew well how deep and close was her relationship with her husband. Early in their marriage she had discovered what tenacious will inhabited his slight frame and hid behind his outward sensitivity. She, and later on the children, had helped sustain Reclus in those unavoidable times when his surgical or anesthetist's skill failed him. She knew his superstitious fear of certain numbers, certain unlucky days, and I had seen her, for example, go to vast trouble to obtain a cab whose number was not one of those he regarded as unlucky. For she had learned that otherwise he would rather walk in rain and snow, overstraining his frail physique. She and the children made it their task to preserve their father's eternally threatened health.

Marie Reclus told me that her husband was at the Pitié, and that she and the children were gravely worried about him. For the past week he had been suffering from an abscess on his right index finger, which had now spread to the hand. "He would not say how he had come by it. But Professor Verneuil has confided to me that several weeks ago Paul scratched himself on a bone splinter while removing a tubercular rib. This must be what caused the infection. Professor Verneuil is afraid that the infection will spread and endanger Paul's life unless the finger is amputated. In fact, I am supposed to persuade Paul to go through with the amputation and sacrifice the finger—which he so terribly needs in his work." She gave me a look of anguish. "Rather than burden anyone else with the responsibility, he anesthetized himself yesterday, using the cocaine method he is working on, and opened and cleansed the abscess himself. He hopes that in this way he can keep the finger. The main thing now is for him to husband all his strength to defeat the infection. But he refuses to stay still. He will not listen to any of us, or to his brothers. Today he went straight back to the hospital. . . ."

I realized the gravity of the situation. If Verneuil, an excessively cautious, almost too conservative surgeon, insisted on amputation of the finger, then the danger must be formidable. The infection could spread so quickly that even amputation of the entire arm would not save him. I therefore wasted no time, but drove directly to the hospital to talk with him.

It was approaching seven o'clock when I entered the old Pitié building. On the stairs I met a nurse and asked for Reclus. She replied that he was in his office. I went on up, knocked, and pressed the latch. But I found the door fastened. I knocked again. This time the key was turned in the lock and an unknown young man opened the door slightly and asked what I wished. I gave my name and at once heard Reclus's voice. The young man opened the door, and I saw Reclus, looking meager in a tattered and oversized surgeon's gown, sitting at his desk under a lamp. I was taken aback by the weariness of his smile and the resignation of his large, gentle eyes. His right hand was bandaged. His left hand lay among papers which he had evidently just been leafing through. Apparently he had been dictating to the assistant, for the latter's pen lay on a pad.

"Come closer, my friend," he said, and then he added with his characteristic quiet, melancholy irony: "You find me taking inventory. I have come to the conclusion that my work to redeem cocaine anesthesia is the happiest scientific effort of my life." He hesitated, then went on: "Perhaps I should say was. For that reason I am setting down all the results."

I understood that he was reckoning on the possibility of death and did not wish to leave this world without putting into conclusive form all his research on local anesthesia. I made haste, of course, to reassure him, to banish his thoughts of death. But with an urbane smile and a wave of his translucent hand he stopped me, and signed to his young secretary to leave us. He then gave me a precise account of his recent feat, the operation he had performed upon himself. He had first injected cocaine into his right hand, ringing the abscess and blocking the pain-conducting nerves. Since he could not operate with his left hand, he had clamped the scalpel in a vise and drawn the affected part of his right hand in various directions over the scalpel until the abscess was opened. Then he had inserted a sharp spatula into the vise and by moving the hand scraped out the bed of the wound. Yet he spoke as though the operation in itself had no emotional meaning for him. He was concerned only with the experience he himself had had with cocaine.

"There is no better experiment for a scientist," he said, "than the experiment in which he himself is the subject. I used only a half-percent solution, which cannot possibly have any side-effects. And this solution was quite sufficient to eliminate all pain. I can absolutely vouch for this. I felt nothing at all. Not even the scraping of the bone caused pain. If I still doubted the validity of my method of using very dilute solutions, this test would have removed all doubts."

I tried to make him see that he ought to rest in order to give himself a fighting chance against the infection. But all my arguments were vain. He insisted that his "taking inventory" came before everything else. I can still see Reclus sitting there before me, his pitiable physique seeming no match for anything so dread as general infection. But in that same physique lay such reserves of courage that I have never forgotten the picture that he made.

Destiny did not yet desire Reclus's death. He was, indeed, granted another twenty-five years of life, more than enough time to redeem the cause of local anesthesia. In fact, he gave himself a little too much time. For it was not until 1895, after administering local anesthesia almost seven thousand times, that he at last got around to publishing his "inventory" under the title of *L'Anesthésie localisée par la co-caïne*. He earned great applause in France, but he had forfeited the chance to be the first to proclaim the creed. One year earlier a work had appeared in Germany which went far beyond Reclus's. With that dash characteristic of new discoveries, it opened up altogether new and inspiring perspectives for nontoxic local anesthesia. Its title was *Schmerzlose Operationen* (Painless Operations) and the author a young Berlin surgeon named Carl Ludwig Schleich. With its appearance there began—after the acts in which Koller, Halsted, and Reclus had played the leading roles—the fourth act of the drama which had the development of local anesthesia as its theme. And once again it was an act full of involvements, dreams, disillusionments, human trials, and human weaknesses.

I spent Christmas of 1890 in Germany, and saw the New Year in there. During the latter part of January, 1891, I was in Berlin. One day I called on Ernst von Bergmann in his new private clinic on Schwarzkopfstrasse. Bergmann had just finished an operation performed with all his characteristic skill, and we were once more discussing the great concern of his life, the affair of Emperor Friedrich's cancer. Later, toward nine o'clock, Bergmann invited me to accompany him to the Hotel Prinz Albrecht, where in those days many of the dances given by Berlin society were held.

Bergmann's wife Pauline was waiting for her husband in the ballroom, accompanied, if I remember rightly, by her eldest daughter. Next to the Bergmann ladies sat a strikingly pretty young woman. Bergmann greeted her with that gallantry of his which was a compound of Baltic, Russian, and Prussian elements, and introduced her as Frau Hedwig Schleich, the wife of the surgeon Carl Ludwig Schleich. Her husband, it seemed, was still working at his hospital and would be along later. For this reason she was rather pleased with the stranger whom chance cast her way.

It turned out that she was not only pretty but intelligent and cultivated. I learned that her husband had worked as assistant to Virchow, Langenbeck, and Bergmann, and that for the past two years he had been director of a private surgical clinic on Belle Alliance Platz in Berlin.

After an hour passed and Schleich had not yet appeared, his wife felt obliged to explain his absence to me. She remarked that for the past year he had been engaged in work which was literally consuming him.

Chiefly from politeness I asked the nature of the work. Oh, she replied—and revealed a wider knowledge of the situation in medicine than most doctors' wives—no doubt I was aware of the attempts to introduce local anesthesia, and of the severe toxic symptoms that were apt to follow the use of cocaine. Her husband had found a way to avoid all danger of toxicity. For many months he had been perfecting his new method, which he called infiltration anesthesia, and he was now literally besieged by patients who were afraid of general anesthesia and would have no one else but him for surgeon.

The whole story took me so by surprise and sounded so fabulous that for the moment I fancied my charming companion was spinning me a tale such as doting wives are prone to concoct, all the more so since Schleich's name was totally unknown to me at this time. Nevertheless, I listened with sharpened attention. I thought of Reclus. Was this another instance of that phenomenon so common in the history of medicine: the simultaneous solution of the same problem by two scientists working independently? I asked Frau Schleich what method she was referring to.

"The infiltration method," she repeated, and then explained that naturally I had never heard of it, since her husband had not yet published any account of it. But she did know that he had found incredibly weak solutions of cocaine, from .1 to .01 per cent, sufficient. If I were interested in the matter I ought to talk with her husband himself; it was his discovery and he could explain it to me more scientifically.

My curiosity was aroused, for the weakest cocaine solution Reclus had used was enormously stronger than the dilutions Frau Schleich spoke of with such authority. This surely must be looked into, I thought. Since Dr. Schleich did not appear in the course of the next hour, I gladly accepted his charming wife's invitation to drop in for coffee the following afternoon.

Carl Ludwig Schleich was thirty-one years old when I first met him, and a distinctly odd bird. He was middle-sized and had a dandy's mustache, thick, close-cropped hair, and a rather soft but handsome face whose florid cast suggested that he was fond of wine. He had ardent, imaginative eyes and dressed with bohemian negligence.

Schleich was the son of a physician who was himself a controversial figure, though on the whole highly respected. The son had not made life easy for the father. Even as a child he had manifested an unusually active intellect, a wild imagination, and very little inclination to devote himself to work requiring scientific precision. The circus and the theater were his passions. While still a schoolboy he wrote hundreds of poems, dramas, and epics, and persisted in reading them aloud to his unhappy father. He wanted to be a poet, actor, or musician. His father gave his dreams short shrift and sent him off to study medicine in Zürich. Inwardly, Schleich clung to his resolve to be a poet. In his first two years in Zürich he scarcely applied himself to his proper studies, but espoused a pseudo-artistic idler's life, dabbling in music and poetic romanticism, squandering the money his father sent, playing patron of the arts, and piling up fantastic debts. He once dashed off to Milan and sent a telegram saying: "Am in Milan, going to be singer. Faithfully, your son." His father had to go to Italy to fetch him back. By this time the young man was on the verge of physical collapse, exhausted from drinking bouts and endless pranks. With infinite patience his father persuaded him to work for his natural-science examination, this time at the University of Greifswald.

Henceforth the father worked with his son every day, and Schleich's extraordinary intelligence enabled him to accomplish in weeks what others needed months to learn. Perhaps his new motivations sprang from his recent closer acquaintance with his future wife, whom he had known as a schoolgirl. At any rate, he passed his examination in the natural sciences at Greifswald and went on to Berlin to resume his medical studies. Old acquaintances of his father's helped him, and he worked with Langenbeck, Bergmann, and Virchow. As he slowly began to grasp the miracle of human life, to become deeply immersed in the study of anatomy, for the first time he came to accept medicine as a profession. The still mysterious functions of the nervous system attracted his interest. For months he studied the finest neural structures, in particular the ganglial cells of the brain. He conceived the first of those rampantly imaginative theories of neural function which were later to figure greatly in his life. But after some time he once more fell into the roistering artistic life of the *fin de siècle*. He drank a great deal, appeared as an actor in minor theaters and as a cabaret singer in dingy cafés, took part in hole-in-the-corner orchestras for a pittance, desperately anxious to make his way by such employment, so that he could be independent of his father. But it was all in vain. He was nursing thoughts of suicide when his father came from his home in Stettin and once more rescued him from the lower depths into which he had sunk. The father abandoned his own practice for six months in order to work again with his son, this time to help him pass the state medical examination. The best way to appeal to the young man was to invoke the name of Hedwig, who was waiting for Schleich and who, like his father, was willing to forgive all his errors. Day after day the father sat with the son, teaching and tutoring. With enormous patience and great psychological adroitness, he kept young Carl at work. And, against all odds, he was victorious. Schleich passed the state examination and began working as an intern in the fields of general medicine, gynecology, and surgery. After some time his father once more came to his aid; he lent his son the money to establish a private surgery clinic. This was the clinic on Belle Alliance Platz.

In 1889 Schleich married Hedwig Oelschlaeger—this was about two years before I first met the two—and began his career as a surgeon. He who had rebelled so furiously against the prospect of medical work, who had yearned to be an artist at all costs, never forgot his poetic and musical inclinations. But he had discovered that great achievements in surgery demanded an artistry that went far beyond mere craftsmanship. And since he possessed that artistry in his very fingertips, he soon achieved remarkable successes.

At bottom he was not a man to study scientific publications with great care. Intuition and imagination were his guiding impulses. Nevertheless, of the multitude of papers on experiments with cocaine anesthesia, some had not escaped his notice. He was likewise aware of the phenomenon of cocaine toxicity. Of Reclus, Schleich knew nothing; he had not even heard his name. Basically it was chance alone that led him into the field of local anesthesia. Even after passing his medical examination he had never entirely broken off relations with artistic circles in Berlin. One evening in the summer of 1890, barely half a year before our first meeting, Schleich met, in a group of young bohemians, a medical student who like himself dabbled in poetry and music. Over wine and the piano keyboard—the student played Chopin brilliantly—Schleich glanced at the young man's lecture notebooks. The music ringing in his ears, he saw in these notebooks exquisite drawings of the fine neural structure of the body, drawings of a precision and delicacy he had never encountered before. And abruptly the music and the drawings combined into a single inspiration. His imagination soaring in an intoxication compounded of wine and music, Schleich spontaneously exclaimed: "Neurology is a piano damper, a soft pedal. . . ."

The idea that struck Schleich at this moment can be reduced to a simple formula, although at the risk of oversimplification: Just as the strings of a piano could be muted by pressure, so, Schleich reasoned, it should be possible to check the pain-transmitting vibrations of the finely branched nerves if pressure were exerted by the surrounding tissues. This pressure he thought to achieve by injections of salt solutions.

Schleich rushed over to his clinic and routed out his assistant, David Wittkowsky. Within the next half hour, by making numerous injections into his own left arm, he had come to the conclusion that saturating the tissue with sodium chloride solution did indeed dampen the conductivity of pain. Logic next counselled that nerves whose conductivity was already dampened in this manner would need only a very tiny quantity of cocaine to have their pain-conducting function completely blocked. Schleich tried a .2 per cent solution of cocaine. He made an incision into his arm—and felt no pain.

Schleich was now seized by a veritable frenzy of inventiveness. He lost no time before he made his first experiments on patients, confining himself at first to minor operations on the surface of the body, and on hands and arms. Fundamentally, his method of injection was not too unlike that already being practiced by Reclus. Schleich, however, did not use direct conduction anesthesia. He worked by layers into the depths of tissue, preceding each incision by an injection. It was no longer necessary to keep careful check upon the number of injections. He could inject large quantities of his solution, all the more so since he later lowered the percentage of cocaine to .1 and then to .01. In one respect, however, his procedure differed from that of Reclus. In order to eliminate even the pain of the needle prick which accompanied every injection into the still unanesthetized next layer, Schleich revived the cold-spray method invented by the London surgeon Benjamin Richardson. This was an attempt to produce local anesthesia by spraying ether or ethyl chloride upon a surface. Richardson had observed that highly volatile substances like ether produced a chilling effect when sprayed upon the skin, and along with the cold a brief insensibility. Ever since, dentists had occasionally employed the Richardson ether spray for extractions. Now Schleich applied the spray constantly during the whole course of his operation, and observed that its application increased the pain-deadening effect of his highly dilute cocaine solutions. As yet Schleich was far from realizing the crucial importance of this spray for the actual success of his technique.

Schleich had already performed a large number of such operations by the afternoon of January 31, 1891, when he invited me to witness three demonstrations of his method. Of his patients, the first was a woman with a cardiac condition, and the others were elderly men with severe bronchial affections who would scarcely have survived general anesthesia with ether or chloroform. In the first case he removed a mammary gland, in the second he amputated a gangrenous foot, and in the third he dealt with a case of inguinal hernia. The operational procedure was in itself somewhat more involved than Reclus's because of the additional use of ethyl chloride spray. Moreover, the swelling of the tissues produced certain anatomical changes. But Schleich mastered all the difficulties with admirable adroitness. Moreover, he had no need of the meticulous precautions Reclus applied, or his series of pre-operative and postoperative constitutional checkups. Toxic effects were virtually eliminated by Schleich's system.

In the course of a lifetime I had learned to curb my early tendency to upsurges of emotion. But at the moment Schleich successfully completed his third operation I felt the urge to embrace this young man who before my eyes was realizing an ancient dream of surgery.

I remained in Berlin for three weeks and spent several days

watching operations at Schleich's small clinic. During this time younger surgeons from Munich, Frankfurt, Paris, and New York presented themselves as his disciples. I met several of them. They, too, had no failures to report. Many, however, were deterred by the intricacy of the procedure and the demands it placed upon the surgeon's skill. On the last day I spent with Schleich he operated on an abdominal cyst under local anesthesia, a virtuoso feat which brilliantly displayed the effectiveness of his method. When I bade him goodbye I urged him, as I had Reclus, to publish his work as soon as possible. He replied that he intended to do so either next year or the year after at the congress of the German Society for Surgery in Berlin.

A year passed. From various surgeons who had been in Berlin I heard of the scale on which Schleich was working. He had already performed several thousand successful operations. Once again my old restlessness seized me. Each time I heard of a death under anesthesia I thought of how it could have been prevented by application of Schleich's method. The congress of the German Society for Surgery for the year 1892 approached. At the time, I was in London. If Schleich was not to let another year pass by, he must submit his name to the committee in charge of drawing up the agenda. At last, some time before the congress, the list of speakers reached me. I skimmed through it—and sure enough, there was the name of Dr. Carl Ludwig Schleich. The announced subject of his paper was "Painless Operations by Local Infiltration Anesthesia."

The congress had already begun when I arrived in Berlin somewhat belatedly in April, 1892. I was just in time to attend the session at which Schleich was speaking, and had no opportunity to see him beforehand. He stepped into the big, white-and-gold hall accompanied by a lion-maned old gentleman of perhaps seventy. For the occasion, Schleich was wearing a formal dark suit which gave him quite another air from that of the impulsive young man I remembered. Nevertheless, his face was deeply flushed with excitement, his eyes shining as though he could already envision the triumph that was to be his this day. But the eyes in the deeply wrinkled face of the old gentleman at his side were shining even more brightly. I was informed that this was Schleich's father, who had come to Berlin to witness his son's triumph. This, then, was the remarkable man who had guided a ne'er-do-well son to such heights of achievement.

The hall was jammed by the time Schleich stepped onto the platform. Some seven hundred physicians, under the chairmanship of the director of the Charité Hospital, Professor von Bardeleben, were assembled. Bardeleben was fundamentally a kindly soul, but easily incensed and in anger given to obstinacy. He had moved from the small town of Greifswald to Berlin. In Greifswald he had enjoyed the position of absolute ruler among the surgeons. In Berlin he stood in Bergmann's shadow. This had increased his tendency to irritable outbursts and fits of stubbornness.

Schleich's excitement had mounted to fever pitch by the time he began to speak. Later it was frequently asserted that he had sought courage in the bottle before his address. I do not believe this, however. He began in a voice that trembled slightly. But then he settled down to his task and set forth the results of his work in language that was, for all its figurativeness and vigor, objective and convincing. It seemed beyond question that at the end of his address he would be applauded tempestuously. So confident was I of this that I forgot the strange reception accorded to Lister, Semmelweis, Wells, and so many others. All those experiences vanished from my memory, even when I looked about and observed uncomprehending expressions on the faces of Bardeleben, Esmarch, and other German celebrities of the medical world.

Toward the end of his speech Schleich's tone grew even livelier and for me even more persuasive. Carried away by the sense of the historic importance of his own discovery, he concluded with the triumphant statement: "In view of the state of anesthesia as described here, I no longer consider myself justified in employing chloroform anesthesia or any other inhalation procedure in operations unless the method of infiltration anesthesia has been previously tried. Only if this should prove insufficient in individual cases, or not appropriate for the particular operation, can general anesthesia be considered especially indicated. But given the present status of infiltration anesthesia, operating under narcosis when this or some similar form of local anesthesia could be used must be regarded—and I say this from the standpoint of humanity and of the moral as well as legal responsibility of the surgeon—must be regarded as a crime."

Even I was jolted by the word "crime" which suddenly fell from Schleich's lips. But after all, though the term was a strong one, what did it mean? It was only a manner of speaking, a rashness to which I myself had so often succumbed, a bit of rhetoric springing from that revolutionary desire to stride ahead which had produced so much vital progress. I still expected to hear any second the clamor of applause for Schleich.

Instead, all around me there began a low grumbling that certainly did not express approval. Indignation, rather. Suddenly Bardeleben was on his feet, his face flushed with anger. He called out in a voice that rang through the hall: "Gentlemen, our society does not in general take votes. But when a charge such as that contained in the speaker's last sentences is hurled into our faces, we may certainly express our opinion, for this is a public assembly. I ask those who agree with that charge to raise their hands. . . ."

Everything that followed took place so swiftly that I sat numbed with surprise. There was a storm of applause, but for Bardeleben, not for Schleich. Not a hand was raised. I saw the hot flush upon Schleich's face change abruptly to a gray pallor. Dumfounded, quivering, Schleich begged for the floor. He could prove that everything he had said was true, he stammered. But Bardeleben exclaimed: "No." And he thundered: "I note that no hands have been raised." Another wave of applause greeted this statement. "Is discussion desired?" he asked, without looking at Schleich. "Will those who wish a discussion kindly raise their hands." This was followed immediately by: "No hand has been raised; there will be no discussion."

Still I sat numbed, watching Schleich desert the platform and march down the hall toward the exit, perplexed, humiliated, plunged from the heights of joyous anticipation, and no doubt failing to understand that the single word "crime" had been the cause of this inexplicable uproar. Perhaps he was not even aware of the word he had used in his excitement. I saw his father's gray head and bowed shoulders as the old man followed his son. Good Lord, I thought, is all this possible—because of a single word? Was it possible that so extraordinary a discovery should be denied the public recognition it merited because of a single breach of form? Was it possible that because of a slip of the tongue thousands of persons ill adapted for general anesthesia were to lose their lives? Was this to be another of those dramas of unrecognized achievement which had so often darkened the past?

I pulled myself together and amid the general commotion tried to make my way to the door, to overtake Schleich and speak a few consoling words to him. But by the time I reached the exit, he and his father had already disappeared. I did not see him until the following day, and found him embittered by his reception and filled with a hatred and contempt for the bigwigs of surgery which were to remain with him forever. His father, however, whom I had imagined would have been utterly felled by the terrible disappointment, proved to be the one who had rallied his son in this hour of despair. "Carl, the bunch of them are out of their minds," he said. "Come on, let's go to Hiller's and drink a bottle of champagne. You'll prove right in the end."

The repudiation of Carl Ludwig Schleich at the surgeon's congress of 1892 grew into a legend in Germany, and became a favorite subject of writers who were pleased to contrast the achievements of genius with the stupidity of academic medicine. Schleich's own lively fancy soon blurred the true story, in which he bore a certain trace of blame for his incautious word. What is more, he lost no time presenting himself to the public in the role of a martyr of science, whereas men like Semmelweis and Lister had spent years and even decades in lonely struggle for recognition. Schleich was aided by his personal acquaintance with artists and journalists, who made his cause their own. Thus he had the vindication which his inflammable and easily offended nature required, but in winning the recognition which his colleagues could not long deny him he also placed himself for good and all in the position of an outsider who never really belonged to the close-knit group of leading German surgeons. The resentment on both sides created a gulf which was never bridged. As for myself, after the scene at the congress I remained unconditionally on Schleich's side.

In a mood of bitter doggedness, Schleich continued to pursue his method, and it was Bergmann who first gave him support.

During the Berlin surgeons' congress of 1894 he invited Schleich to give a demonstration at his clinic on Ziegelstrasse, and asked the guests at the congress to be present as observers. The test project was a hemorrhoid operation. The scene had its garish humor, for after Schleich had done the anesthetizing, Bergmann thrust his entire hand into the patient's anus, observed not the slightest sign of pain, and exclaimed: "I'll be hanged if the aperture is not pain-free." But, significantly enough, of the seven hundred guests of the congress not thirty found their way to this demonstration. It was Bergmann, again, who the following day stood up before the congress to declare: "I can accordingly recommend application of Schleich's infiltration anesthesia for operations which are not too extensive, and must acknowledge that Herr Schleich deserves the highest credit for the development of this method." This was the first official recognition, but it was scarcely heeded by the majority of the audience. After this occurrence I fully understood Schleich's bitter mockery of the "caste who will not admit their mistakes," and of the "conceited dignitaries" of medicine, although in his resentment he sometimes went too far. At this time I frequently visited Schleich's clinic, and when I saw patients come through operations which under general anesthesia would have been their death, I was more than ever convinced that the situation was scandalous. To my friends and acquaintances, such as Esmarch, Mikulicz, and Bergmann, I expressed my attitude candidly.

Despite the urgent need for an alternative to general anesthesia, Schleich's method was making no great headway. Its chief practioner was Schleich himself. According to numerous visitors to his clinic, this could be attributed to the fact that the method was too complicated for the average surgeon who did not possess Schleich's extraordinary skill.

In the spring of 1894 Schleich finished the manuscript of a large book which discussed in detail the application of his method to many kinds of operation. It bore the title *Schmerzlose Operationen, örtliche Betäubung mit indifferenten Flüssigkeiten* (Painless Operations. Local Anesthesia with Indifferent Fluids). Undoubtedly the manuscript contained a number of exaggerations, such as the assertion: "My method of local anesthesia, once it is universally

employed, can obviate at least 90 per cent of all general anesthesia."
But in other respects the book was a work of art. It created a
sensation and made Schleich an international celebrity. He became,
in fact, so celebrated that this book of his proved to be the salvation
of local anesthesia—before Reclus's book on the same subject
appeared. Even if Reclus had been first to publish the results of
his patient, tenacious work, Schleich's volume would have put
his out of the running everywhere except for France, not only
because Schleich's method more convincingly abolished the toxic
effects of cocaine, but also because of the energy of Schleich's
presentation.

With the publication of Schleich's book, the usefulness of cocaine was once more vindicated. Schleich himself demonstrated
even more conclusively than Reclus its remarkable properties. He
stimulated surgeons to be open-minded with regard to new types
of anesthesia. From the moment his book succeeded, the prejudice
and calumny that had followed in the wake of his speech at the
congress died away and the attacks upon his method ceased.
Although it soon was plain that its technical complexity did indeed
put it beyond the scope of the average surgeon, and thus restricted
its general application, Schleich deserved praise for having overcome the widespread defeatism among surgeons. This remained
true even after Schleich and faithful adherents like myself were
struck by a second blow, which shook Schleich to the roots of
his being. The German surgeon Heinrich Braun—a new figure
in the arena and the man who brought local anesthesia to its
peak development—showed that Schleich's procedure was based
upon an erroneous conception. To be sure, what Schleich did was
effective and successful. The theory underlying infiltration anesthesia, however, especially that initial "piano damper" inspiration
which had been at the root of the whole thing—that theory was
wrong.

But this story constituted the last act in the long struggle to
achieve local anesthesia. Before it began, there was a highly remarkable intermezzo.

At the beginning of August I was staying in Vichy to take
the waters for a stubborn bladder complaint. Even then I harbored

the gloomy suspicion that my trouble was hypertrophy of the prostate in its earliest stages.*

About a week after my arrival I found in my forwarded mail a letter which was already several weeks old. It came from Kiel. The sender was Friedrich von Esmarch.

Esmarch at this time was more than seventy, but he continued to hold his post as chief of the surgical clinic of the University of Kiel. He was, however, tiring, he wrote, and could consider himself fortunate in having found in Dr. August Bier a capable and energetic deputy, who could take over for him for long spells at a time. Unfortunately, he foresaw that Kiel would soon become too narrow a sphere of activity for a person of Bier's qualifications and personality. For some time Bier had been concerning himself with the problem of local anesthesia. He was turning over an idea which he, Esmarch, could not endorse but did not wish to obstruct. Bier's thought was to inject cocaine solutions directly into the spinal canal, in order to block the pain-conducting nerves between the brain and the lower part of the body. In other words, he wanted to produce extensive local anesthesia of the lower part of the body. "You will recall," Esmarch continued, "that my colleague for internal medicine here at Kiel, Professor Heinrich Quincke, some eight years ago discovered that the spinal canal could be punctured with a hollow needle. He called this procedure lumbar puncture. In treating a child less than two years old with clear symptoms of high cerebral pressure, Quincke ventured to penetrate the spinal canal with a fine syringe. He permitted the spinal fluid to flow out, thus diminishing the morbid pressure on

---

* In 1913, almost at the same time as the famous French statesman Clemenceau, Henry Steven Hartmann was freed by operation of this complaint, which afflicts about a third of all men over fifty. It is characterized by an enlargement of the prostate gland, located at the neck of the bladder, which swelling leads to displacement of the urethra. For many years beyond the turn of the century this disease continued to be regarded as fatal, an irremediable condition of old age. Only introduction of catheters through the urethra, that is to say, the creation of an artificial duct for the urine, brought temporary relief. In extreme emergencies a trocar was thrust through the abdominal wall into the bladder to prevent the bladder's distention and tearing. In any case, death inevitably ensued. This disease took an enormous number of lives. Here again Hartmann was fortunate in that his disease developed slowly enough for him to take advantage of the advance of surgery into this branch of urology. Research by men like Belfield, McGill, Fuller, Freyer, von Dittel, and Young led to a successful operative technique. Partial or complete removal of the prostate produced a radical cure.

the brain. From this Bier concluded that it should be possible not only to withdraw spinal fluid but to inject cocaine in solution."

After reading Esmarch's letter I naturally included a visit to Kiel and a talk with Bier on the program of my next visit to Germany. But since the matter seemed by no means urgent, I decided to finish my cure and then go on to Rome, as I had already planned. I did not guess that the deliberate spirit which I was for once displaying was going to cheat me of an extraordinary experience. Not a week after I received Esmarch's letter there began in Kiel a wholly new act in the battle centering around local anesthesia. Before long Bier's name had sped around the world.

On the morning of August 15, 1898, Dr. August Bier sat at the bedside of a thirty-four-year-old workingman with a hopeless case of tuberculosis. The unfortunate patient had undergone several operations, and each time had suffered severely from the aftereffects of the anesthesia. He felt acute terror of more general anesthesia. At the same time he complained of unbearable pain in one ankle, the bone of which was gravely tubercular. Conservative treatment of the ankle was hopeless. Only resection could provide the feverish patient with relief. Since the joint was inflamed and purulent, Schleich's infiltration anesthesia would not do. In these circumstances Bier was strongly tempted to try his idea of central neural block on this patient. He told the patient that he knew of a possible way to perform a painless operation without narcosis, but that this technique had not yet been tested and might fail.

The young man declared without hesitation that he would be glad to submit to the new method. Bier felt the heavy responsibility imposed upon him by such trustfulness, for he had so little to offer in return: no promise of success, not even the certainty that some slip or some unknown factor might not lead to a fatal outcome.

On the morning of August 16, 1898, the patient lay on the operating table. His emaciated body had been arranged on its side, the back somewhat bent, so that the individual vertebrae were plainly visible. Bier, aided by his assistant, August Hildebrandt, used Schleich's method for anesthetizing the thin superficial layer of tissue above the spinal column which he must penetrate in order to reach the spinal canal. Then he applied a longish hollow needle, closed with a stopper at the upper end, between two of the lumbar vertebrae, and with a swift push thrust it into the spinal canal. The end of the needle, trembling almost imperceptibly, protruded from the patient's skin. The questions Bier had to ask himself at this moment were these: Had the point of the needle penetrated correctly to the interior of the spinal canal? Had it caused any injury which might have unknown consequences, such as paralysis? Cautiously, he removed the stopper from the needle. Next moment a few drops of spinal fluid trickled out the end. So he had hit the right spot. Bier kept his finger pressed against the needle to prevent the outflow of too much spinal fluid. Hildebrandt handed him a syringe which fitted the needle. The syringe contained three cubic centimeters of .5 per cent cocaine solution. As the syringe was screwed to the head of the needle, a few more drops of spinal fluid ran out. Then Bier slowly pressed down the barrel until the syringe was empty. Only the rapid, feverish breathing of the patient could be heard. Hildebrandt took the man's pulse. But nothing unforeseen happened. Bier waited two full minutes, so that the cocaine would not, as the result of freeing the aperture in the dura mater, trickle back into the surrounding tissues. Next, he removed syringe and needle and closed the tiny hole with collodion. Then Bier and Hildebrandt sat down beside the operating table and waited.

After twenty minutes Bier touched the patient's leg. First he pinched the skin—and the patient made no sign of pain. He pricked the patient's thigh with a needle—still no reaction. Small incisions with the scalpel also produced no sensations of pain. The patient only mentioned feeling a vague pressure. The venture seemed to be succeeding.

The moment Bier made his first incision a wailing sound came from the patient's lips. The affected leg, however, lay perfectly still. Bier stopped. But there seemed to be no connection between the cry and the imperviousness of the leg. He continued the operation. He began scraping out the ankle-bone, and again the patient groaned, but his leg did not so much as twitch. Thereupon Bier completed the operation without regarding these mysterious moans. He cut out the capsule of degenerated tubercular bone.

Then he left the bandaging to Hildebrandt, and waited until the patient had been carried to his bed.

At the patient's bedside again, Bier asked the reason for the moans. The patient stated that he had not felt any actual pain. But he had had the feeling that something drastic was being done to his leg. After an hour the lower part of the patient's body was still without sensation. It was not paralyzed, but it could feel nothing. Not until two hours after the operation did slight pain begin in the back and then in the leg. Shortly afterwards he began to feel pain at the site of the operation. Then the sensitivity of the entire lower part of the body was restored. The experiment had succeeded.

Bier, however, refused to jump to conclusions. He feared complications that still remained obscure. And it was well that he did so, for shortly after sensivitity to pain returned, the patient was seized by raging headaches and violent fits of vomiting. Both symptoms soon exceeded anything the patient had previously experienced under general anesthesia. Bier suspected that the cause was irritation of the meninges by the cocaine. The vomiting responded to treatment, but the headaches lasted throughout the night and the following day, resisting all medicaments. Then, on the evening of the next day, they vanished as quickly as they had come.

Now Bier was plunged into a conflict between doubt and confidence. It seemed evident that anesthesia of the entire lower part of the body could be achieved by a single injection of cocaine into the spinal canal. But how high was the price that had to be paid for such anesthesia? Was not the patient's very life in danger if the cocaine rose as far as the sinuses of the brain? If these perils were greater than, or even as great as, the perils of general anesthesia, what sense was there in continuing the work? And yet, Bier argued with himself, the first patient might have been a singular case. What did a single experiment prove? Much more experience must be amassed. But could he take the responsibility of subjecting other patients to the same aftereffects? Bier fought out the very struggle with his conscience that had been the lot of so many innovators before him. But the hope that he was on the right track was a consuming flame. He could not abandon his efforts now.

On August 29, 1898, there lay on his operating table a fourteen-year-old child suffering from a tubercular knee joint which had to be resected. Bier successfully injected two syringes of .5 per cent cocaine solution into the spinal canal. After the waiting period, he performed the resection of the stiffened joint and riveted the ends of the bone. The terrified child complained of pain, but submitted to every operative procedure without the slightest twinge. Bier was forced to assume that the outcries, as in the case of his first patient, were due not to actual pain but to the fear of pain, and he had the child carried to bed.

About three quarters of an hour later he injected cocaine into the spinal canal of a seventeen-year-old baker's apprentice afflicted with necrosis of the tibia. Each of the injections consisted of half a cubic centimeter of 1 per cent cocaine solution. Within five minutes sensitivity to pain disappeared entirely from the lower part of the body. Almost the whole tibia was chiselled open and several parts were removed. The patient testified that he had felt not the slightest pain. After the operation, sensation slowly returned. But then the same disturbing symptoms, vomiting and headaches, occurred once more.

On August 22 Bier made a fourth attempt, this time on an eleven-year-old child whose ischium had to be removed. Again spinal anesthesia produced painlessness—but this time there was no postoperative vomiting or headache. Were children, then, immune to the aftereffects of cocaine?

Two days later Bier once again injected a 1 per cent cocaine solution into the spinal canal of a thirty-year-old patient with a suppurating complex fracture of the right thigh-bone. The operation was very extensive: exposure of the ends of the fracture, sawing, opening of various abscesses. But again the patient said that he had felt not the slightest pain. Moreover, hour after hour passed without any signs of vomiting or headache. Evidently, then, there was no law that children were immune from aftereffects and that adults would necessarily suffer them. When did the aftereffects ensue, when not? To determine this it was essential to know more about the inner mechanism of the injections. More precise data were needed than patients could supply.

Bier spent the afternoon of August 24 alone in his room. After some time he sent for Hildebrandt. The patients' statements seemed to him unreliable, he explained; the time had come when only self-observation could provide the data for further conclusions. He therefore requested Hildebrandt to inject a 1 per cent cocaine solution into his, Bier's, spinal canal.

Hildebrandt agreed at once. Bier undressed and lay down on the examining table. The needle and several syringes lay ready from the previous experiment that morning. Hildebrandt injected Schleich's solution into the tissues and waited for it to take effect. Then he jabbed the needle through to the spinal cord, as he had done five times before on children and adults since August 16. With the alertness of the scientist Bier took note of every sensation. He was concerned with the slightest nuances. He had felt no pain when the needle was jabbed in, except for a slight, rapid, stabbing sensation in one leg. Then he waited for his own spinal fluid to flow out. It did so at once, and painlessly. At this point the syringe with the cocaine solution should be mounted on the needle. Bier felt a slight tugging sensation. The cocaine-filled syringe which Hildebrandt was attempting to use did not fit the socket of the needle. In vain Hildebrandt worked. Meanwhile, more and more spinal fluid ran out.

When Hildebrandt at last began injecting the cocaine, the syringe was still not tightly inserted into the needle. The greater part of the cocaine solution was wasted. Bier could feel the wetness spreading out on the skin of his back. When Hildebrandt, hands now nervous, withdrew syringe and needle and closed the puncture, he knew that only a small part of the cocaine solution had actually entered the spinal canal.

Bier waited, without much hope, for ten minutes. Then he pricked his thigh with needles and asked Hildebrandt to make cuts in the calf of his leg. Every needle prick and cut was painful. There could be no question of anesthesia. The experiment had failed through clumsiness and haste.

In his report Bier contented himself with the laconic statement: "Dr. Hildebrandt then volunteered to try the same experiment upon himself." Bier accepted the offer. He now carefully matched his needle to his syringe, drew half a cubic centimeter of 1 per cent cocaine solution into the syringe, anesthetized the puncture area, and applied his needle.

Hildebrandt stated that he felt only slight pressure. This time only a few drops of spinal fluid ran out before Bier screwed the

syringe onto the needle and injected the cocaine solution. Hildebrandt declared that he felt a sense of warmth in both legs. Bier
waited seven minutes. He then tickled the soles of Hildebrandt's
feet. Hildebrandt showed no reaction. He stabbed needles into
Hildebrandt's thigh. Hildebrandt felt only slight pressure. One
minute later Bier drew a large curved needle through the flesh of
Hildebrandt's thigh. There was no pain. Again Bier waited two
minutes. Then he jabbed a large needle all the way in to the thigh-
bone. And once more Hildebrandt declared that he felt no
pain.

Bier lit a cigar. After the thirteenth minute he touched Hildebrandt's legs with the glowing tip. Hildebrandt spoke of a sensation of warmth again, but no pain. Two minutes later Bier pinched
first Hildebrandt's legs and then various parts of his skin on his
chest. The chest felt pain, the legs did not. After twenty-three
minutes Hildebrandt did not even feel hard blows of a hammer
against his shin. After forty minutes he felt the blows, but not as
painful. Sensitivity to pain did not return until forty-five minutes
after the injection. It required another quarter hour before the
numbness in the lower part of Hildebrandt's body vanished and
normal sensitivity was restored.

If there had been the slightest doubt as to the effectiveness of
the procedure, it now vanished. Bier's idea of anesthetizing the
lower part of the body by blocking the pain nerves in the spinal
cord was correct. But there still remained the far more difficult
question of aftereffects.

Bier invited Hildebrandt to dine with him. Both men ate well
and heartily. They drank wine and smoked several cigars. Perhaps
they were aware that they were behaving unreasonably. Indeed,
it is possible that Bier intended to burden their systems with alcohol
and nicotine in order to create favorable conditions for possible
aftereffects.

Both men went to bed about eleven o'clock. Bier slept soundly
and awoke in the morning feeling perfectly refreshed. He took
his usual morning stroll. Toward the end of it, however, he
became aware of a slight headache. Nevertheless he went to his
clinic. There he found Hildebrandt looking very wan, and keeping
on his feet only by great effort. Hildebrandt had been unable to

sleep during the night. By midnight he had been attacked by a frightful headache, and around one o'clock in the morning he had begun to throw up. The headache still oppressed him; he was barely able to change a few dressings. Bier felt comparatively well, but at three o'clock in the afternoon his pulse suddenly began to flutter. He was overcome by dizziness, had to lie down, and then found that he was no longer able to get up. Around the same time Hildebrandt, too, was forced to take to his bed. His tenacious will brought him to his feet again the following day, although he still felt wretched and continued to suffer from headache. Bier, however, had to remain in bed for nine days before he was again capable of working. For three weeks Hildebrandt continued to be plagued by feelings of weakness, not to speak of the severe bruises on his legs from the tests.

But such injuries were of no consequence to either of the men. Their interest was entirely focused on the aftereffects of the cocaine. There could no longer be any doubt that these were severe. If on the one hand it was plain that spinal anesthesia was effective, on the other hand it was equally plain that without further research this simple method of local anesthesia could not replace general anesthesia. Here was a grave disappointment, but neither Hildebrandt nor Bier was inclined to give up. Had not Reclus and Schleich continued to overcome the toxicity of cocaine by their rather complicated procedures? It should be possible to do the same thing for spinal, or lumbar, anesthesia, as Bier called it.

During that August of 1898 when Bier and Hildebrandt were performing these crucial experiments, I was still at Vichy. I went on to Rome in early September without the slightest inkling of these developments in Kiel. Shortly afterwards I learned that my deceased mother's only sister, an old lady of eighty-nine, had suffered a stroke, was paralyzed on one side, and was insistently asking for me. She lived in Richmond, Virginia. Since Aunt Elsie had always shown me great kindness and displayed rare understanding of my restless life, I decided to return to America. Aunt Elsie lived for another seven months. Since I had promised her not to leave the country again before she closed her eyes forever, I was tied down to Richmond or New York until the spring of 1899. After she died, I myself was in such poor health as the result of recurrent bladder disturbances that I could not think of undertaking any prolonged journey in the near future. Amid all these events, I quite forgot the letter from Esmarch with its provocative references to Bier.

Consequently, it was with considerable surprise that I read— in New York in the autumn of 1900—an article by the French surgeon Théodore Tuffier, of the Hôpital de la Cité du Midi in Paris, describing the events of two years previously in Kiel. In 1899 Bier had published, in the *Deutsche Zeitschrift für Chirurgie*, a cautious account of his experiments with spinal anesthesia. Tuffier had taken up Bier's suggestions and in spite of a large crop of aftereffects had performed more than one hundred operations under spinal anesthesia.

A few days later I learned from the New York surgeon Fowler that he too was engaged in extensive experiments on lumbar anesthesia. Nor was he, he informed me, the sole American surgeon using the new method. It was particularly effective for abdominal operations, he declared, and the unpleasant side-effects simply had to be accepted—after all, every method had its unpleasant side. At the moment he was engaged in a whole series of experiments. He readily granted that he had received his initial inspiration from Bier in Germany. But, he stated, it appeared that this new type of anesthesia had been developed fourteen years earlier by an American colleague named James Leonard Corning. At that time, however, no attention had been paid to the matter. Probably, Fowler thought, Bier had only appropriated the results of Corning's publications.

Barely three weeks later, at the beginning of November, the *Philadelphia Medical Journal* carried a series of articles indicating that spinal anesthesia was conquering the operating rooms of the United States. Many of the foremost American surgeons sang its praises, although they had to admit to the frequency of severe aftereffects. At the same time they contended, with an amazing unanimity, that lumbar anesthesia was definitely an American discovery. Again Dr. Leonard Corning was cited as the originator of the technique. Fowler sent me an article of Corning's in which the man himself claimed priority and declared that Bier was a mere imitator.

By then I had been occupying myself with the history of surgery for more than fifty years, and I had long since learned that it was a rare discovery for which the priority was not contested. In my state of health at that time I might not have pursued the matter had I not received, early in December, 1900, a letter from Greifswald, Germany. The sender was none other than August Bier himself.

I read the letter with rapidly growing excitement. Bier informed me that he had meanwhile moved from Kiel to Greifswald, where he had taken the post of professor of surgery. Esmarch had spoken of me to him and given him my New York address. In a tone all the more convincing for its restraint and modesty, Bier described his idea and his work, and enclosed an offprint of his first German publication. He wrote that he could scarcely condone the uncritical application of his method which had already begun in France and in the United States. The technique would no doubt someday constitute an important alternative to general anesthesia for abdominal operations. At present, however, the foremost task was to overcome or at least to diminish the toxicity of cocaine. Various chemists were now busy transforming cocaine so that it would no longer be so dangerously toxic. The first new drugs, eucaine and tropacocaine, had been produced and were now at his disposal for study. His assistant, Dr. Eden, was at present testing their effectiveness on animals. The unrestricted application of his method in France and America deeply troubled him, for he feared that the end result would be to cast discredit on the technique before its development was complete.

Furthermore, he wrote, he was concerned about the claims to priority in the discovery of lumbar anesthesia which were being made by a certain Dr. Corning of New York. Such disputes always proved harmful to the cause itself. He had never heard of Corning's name before this matter came up, nor read anywhere of proposals by Corning in regard to lumbar anesthesia. I would surely understand his wondering how it was that the method of spinal anesthesia was suddenly being taken up in America after his publication, and not fourteen years ago, when Corning had allegedly discovered it and published his findings. Nevertheless, he certainly would not desire to deprive any other person of his rights to a discovery. That was the reason for his letter to me. In Germany he was unable to obtain Corning's original publications. Perhaps I could locate them and send either the originals or copies to Greifswald. He wished to study all the sources before coming to a conclusion. Unfortunately, it was a trait of Germans to sneer at members of their own nation and admire foreigners, so that Corning was already finding supporters in Germany. If these supporters were right in their contention, he was willing to bow to the fate of having rediscovered someone else's discovery. If not, he must be in a position to defend himself. He would therefore be greatly obliged to me if I could help him to clarify the situation. . . .

Bier's letter so roused my curiosity that I at once began searching for all the scientific papers James Leonard Corning had ever published. Meanwhile I learned by inquiry that the man himself was thirty-eight years old, had studied medicine in New York and in Würzburg, Germany, and that he was on the staff of the St. Francis and St. Mary's Hospitals as a neurologist. My search for publications turned up three papers by Corning which had appeared in New York and Philadelphia in 1885, 1888, and 1894.

As soon as I saw the title of the first essay, I started. It was *Spinal Anesthesia and Local Medication of the Cord*, and had been published in the *New York Medical Journal* in 1885. Was Corning in the right after all? Had he actually discovered the technique fourteen years before Bier? I studied the report. Corning described how he had treated first a dog and then a patient suffering from "spinal weakness" (a favorite diagnosis of the period for unknown diseases) by injecting a 2 and then 3 per cent cocaine solution between the thoracic vertebrae. He hoped in this way to eliminate the "weakness" of the spinal cord. But Corning had not, like Bier, introduced his needle into the spinal canal; he had placed his cocaine solution outside it, in the vicinity of the vertebra. His hope was that the "stimulating" cocaine (this was the period in which Halsted, too, had been deceived by the supposed miraculous effects of the wonder drug) would travel through the blood vessels into the spinal cord. Evidently he had not thought of anesthesia, only of a therapeutic effect. Quite by the by he remarked that sensivity in the legs of his dog and his patient had been diminished, and expressed the thought that only experience would show whether this method would ever find application for surgery of the abdomen.

If Corning's claim to be the discoverer of lumbar anesthesia were based upon this paper, it was certainly unjustified. I read the second article, which had appeared in the *Medical Record* for March 17, 1888. This "further contribution" contained nothing new. Once again Corning had injected medicaments, not only cocaine but a number of different acids, in the vicinity of the spinal column. Powerless to combat certain nervous diseases, he had experimented rather indiscriminately, and asserted that some of the diseases could be helped by such injections. But he said not a word about local anesthesia or injection into the spinal canal.

I opened Corning's last paper: *Pain in Its Neuro-pathological, Diagnostic, Medico-legal and Neuro-therapeutic Relations.* It contained a section on "Local Medication of the Spinal Column." I imagined that Corning would repeat his earlier statements. But I then discovered that between 1888 and 1894 he had actually moved on to direct injection into the spinal canal. I read on with that sense of suspense and excitement that always overcame me when I was on the track of anything new. But my final feeling was disappointment. It was evident from the paper that Corning had continued his aimless experimentation. Nowhere did he suggest local anesthesia. In addition to cocaine, Corning had injected antipyrine, caffeine, and even strychnine, practicing dubious treatments for undiagnosed diseases. Once again he remarked casually that one patient had become insensitive in parts of his thighs and feet after a cocaine injection. But he drew no conclusions.

That was all, then. It was difficult to see how anyone could deduce from these vague and ultimately pointless experiments that Corning had anticipated Bier's deliberate efforts to achieve spinal anesthesia. But, without knowing Corning, I felt a profound pity for him. Clearly he had been the first person to inject cocaine into the spinal canal. But it was equally clear that he had missed his opportunity to make the one discovery in connection with this procedure which now seemed worth while. He had pursued the cure of dubious spinal diseases and, like Freud, had come within an inch of fame, and passed it by. It was understandable that he was now rebelling against his fate and fighting to recapture what he had lost. I decided in any case not to let the matter rest here, but to call on Corning himself. It was, after all, quite possible that since 1894 he had performed further experiments which entitled him to claim priority.

Three days later I stood before the door of a house over which hung Corning's shingle.

I found Corning a man of medium height, with rather set features and hard, flashing eyes. My chief concern was to discover whether he had carried out any further experiments since 1894, and above all whether he had ever suggested to a surgeon that cocaine injection into the spinal canal be used instead of general anesthesia. So firm was Corning's denial that it was evident he had not understood the significance of my questions. I therefore repeated them.

He gave me an odd look. Then he said: "I am not a surgeon, I am a neurologist. The surgical application of cocaine injection is a subsidiary aspect of my procedure, and still a highly controversial one. The decisive aspect is the cure of nervous diseases by injection. And this I have discovered, no one else."

At that moment I felt as if I were talking to Freud rather than Corning. For here was the situation precisely repeated. Had not Freud, too, clung to the idea that Koller's discovery concerned only a minor and subsidiary aspect of the use of cocaine? Had he not, with obsessive stubbornness, clung to the notion of cocaine as a superlative treatment for internal diseases—when in reality this was to prove to be one of medicine's more dreadful errors?

I hastened to take my leave. The following day I sent Bier the papers, and a note on my conclusions.

Several months passed during which the rumblings over the problem of lumbar anesthesia and the priority of its discovery somewhat died down, at least in print. Meanwhile the method was more and more put into practice, in spite of all the unpleasant postanesthetic effects. The campaign in Corning's favor grew more heated. A wave of nationalism among American doctors tended to becloud the issue. But I had seen more than once that such waves were generally of short duration. Americans are realists and tend, sooner or later, to prefer an objective view of the facts. Bier sent me the text of an address he had delivered before the German Society for Surgery in which he stressed the necessity for cautious development of spinal anesthesia; he had also discussed Corning's claims, and in the calmest and fairest manner had dismissed them. I assumed that this would end the matter, at least in Germany and Europe, and that all efforts would henceforth be concentrated upon perfecting spinal anesthesia so that its side-effects might be overcome and it could replace general anesthesia for all operations on the lower parts of the body. Several weeks later I encountered Fowler, and noted that he was already beginning to discount Corning's claims. This made me all the more certain that the matter would by now have been completely clarified in Germany, and that no one would continue to challenge Bier's priority. Deluding myself, I did not guess that the battle was far from ended, and indeed would rage for some time to come.

Bier labored for six years, first in Greifswald and then as professor of surgery in Bonn, exploring various aspects of his method. His aim remained the elimination of the side-effects. He worked with Schleich's solution, with cocaine solutions of the type devised by Reclus, with eucaine and tropacocaine. The results did not satisfy him. Finally he began experimenting with methods for blocking the flow of cocaine to the brain by mechanical aids. He knew that increase in pressure within the brain resulted in cerebral fluid being vented into the spinal canal. This, then, would stop the injected cocaine from penetrating from the canal into the cerebral sinuses. In order to achieve increased pressure in the brain, he placed tourniquets around his patients' necks to lessen the flow of blood away from the brain. Such measures did in fact modify the side-effects of lumbar anesthesia. But the procedure was so troublesome that Bier himself scarcely expected it to yield fruitful results. Then, a year later—in 1905—came the discovery which at one blow wiped out all the difficulties and established a permanent and valid basis not only for lumbar anesthesia but for all forms of local anesthesia. This was the discovery of novocaine by the German chemist Einhorn. Bier was among the first surgeons to try the new drug, and it worked like magic. Novocaine had virtually no toxic effects. With its advent, spinal anesthesia was established overnight as one of the stable and major forms of local anesthesia.

Henceforth, Bier's lumbar anesthesia remained, together with conduction anesthesia, which was restricted to smaller zones, and infiltration anesthesia, one of the three chief pillars of local anesthesia at the end of a century of research, high hopes, failures, and achievements. At the last minute, however, one more great pioneer figure appeared on the stage to perfect, by an ingenious stroke, the simplification which had been lacking in the technique that bore the name of Schleich. This last great pioneer was Heinrich Braun.

When I met Braun in 1904, he was working as head physician at the Sisters of Charity Hospital in Leipzig. He was at that time in his forties. As Volkmann's assistant he had witnessed so many mishaps with general anesthesia that he, too, had early begun a systematic study of local anesthesia. He had devoted years to working out the foundations of Schleich's infiltration anesthesia. From the start Braun had questioned Schleich's contention that the extremely dilute solutions of cocaine used in his system took effect because swelling of the tissues dampened the conductivity of the nerves. In the spring of 1900 Braun chanced to come across an article in a periodical dealing with an extract from the suprarenal glands of animals. It was stated that this extract, called adrenalin, caused constriction of blood vessels when injected locally, and tended to lower the blood supply to the tissues.

Early experiences with cocaine injection had shown that the anesthetizing effect was most lasting where the circulation of the blood was interrupted, thus hindering the removal of the cocaine through the blood stream. In Volkmann's clinic Braun had witnessed Oberst's experiments in anesthetizing fingers and toes by cutting off the circulation. He now wondered whether adrenalin might not produce the same effect in any part of the body. Suppose cocaine were mixed with adrenalin—perhaps this would keep the cocaine at the site where it was needed. Braun made his first injections on his own forearm, and found a hitherto unknown intensity of anesthesia at the inoculated sites. In the course of several years he worked out a cocaine-adrenalin formula of extreme effectiveness—and at the same time demonstrated that the secret of Schleich's local anesthesia was due largely to the effect of the same principle. The ethyl chloride spray which Schleich had consistently applied during his operations in order to make the needle puncture at the next site of injection painless had, to some extent, fulfilled the same function as adrenalin. That is to say, the cold produced by the spray had temporarily checked the blood circulation in the tissues.

When Braun began publishing the details of his procedure, from 1903 on, he encountered a great deal of opposition, especially on the part of Schleich, who hated to abandon his own explanations for the effectiveness of his technique. But in the end Schleich had to accept these newest advances, which, like his own a decade earlier, rendered the old order obsolete.

Adrenalin-cocaine anesthesia soon assumed the role that had been assigned to infiltration anesthesia. The appearance of novocaine removed the last flaws from this method, as it did for conduction anesthesia and lumbar anesthesia. Henceforth local anesthesia was no longer a dream, but a reality, a new basis upon which surgery could steadily build. It lent tremendous impetus to thyroid gland operations. Now many operations were feasible which before had been ruled out because of the perils of general anesthesia. New vistas were now opened for surgical exploration.

Moments of Destiny

Chicago

On the morning of June 9, 1898, John B. Murphy of Chicago delivered an address, *Surgery of the Lung*, before the forty-ninth congress of the American Medical Association, being held in Denver. His speech was greeted with more than usual applause. At this time I was confined to my bed in New York. An attack of sciatica had prevented me from attending the congress. According to the scanty accounts in the New York newspapers, Murphy had introduced two surgical methods for combating diseases of the lung which fully merited the epithet "revolutionary." I knew only too well how easily such a word fell from the pens of newspapermen. But the acclaim Murphy had received from that scientific gathering suggested that he had indeed made a great discovery, perhaps one which would put the still-forbidden field of diseases of the lungs within the province of surgery. Ever since I had known Murphy he had been, for most of his colleagues, the object of uneasy suspicion and often of undisguised dislike. That the congress had hailed him would seem to mean that he had presented acomplishments of so remarkable a nature that all their antagonism for the man was forgotten in their admiration for the surgeon.

My attention had first been called to Murphy some eight years before. At that time barely thirty-two, he had created a stir at Cook County Hospital in Chicago. With outrageous vehemence the red-haired Irishman had insisted upon early operation of appendicitis, thereby violating the time-honored rule that the disease should be treated by specialists in internal medicine. "The old fossils," as Murphy publicly called the older generation of doctors, had risen to oppose him as one man. But he would have his way, and soon he had proved by some two hundred operations (largely rush affairs, performed on kitchen and dining-room tables in the homes of his patients so that no time should be wasted) that removal of the appendix at the first signs of inflammation was the way to a permanent cure. Newspapers began writing up his work, and making much of Murphy. It appeared that his personality, so utterly unlike the conventional image of the medical man, exerted an enormous attraction upon newspapermen, and that he himself had an extraordinary gift for publicity.

I myself had gone to look him up in Chicago, but he was not to be seen either at his hospital or in his home on Throop Street. After some initial difficulty I had learned from his assistant—who happened to be named Hartmann, like myself—that Murphy suffered from pulmonary tuberculosis and had repaired to Nevada, whose desert climate was supposed to have curative properties. There, in the rising gamblers' paradise of Las Vegas, where the original spirit of the Wild West prevailed and Colts were still drawn rather readily, I finally met Murphy—already recovered, rather dubious about the diagnosis of his disease, and full of a restless urge to get on to new work. Almost at once I had become deeply interested in the man.

Murphy was the son of Irish immigrants, driven from the Old Sod by want and hunger, who had settled on a farm near Appleton, Wisconsin. The youngest of five children, he grew up in poverty. His mother, who saw the boy's gifts, had impressed him with one principal goal in life: to make money and to leave misery so far behind him that it would never again catch up with him. Murphy had taken that doctrine to heart. For a time he worked as a helper in Lewis's drugstore in Appleton, then by chance he became an apprentice to Dr. Reilly, the town physician. He quickly realized that medicine and surgery represented virgin territory awaiting its explorers, and that fame and wealth as well as the joy of discovery were in store for the successful adventurer. Attendance at Rush Medical College in Chicago was expensive; it would cost all of sixty-five dollars a year. His mother raised this sum for him. With his mother's injunctions always in mind, he developed a tremendous capacity for work and drank in all available knowledge. Attending the lectures of my friend Christian Fenger, who had brought back from Europe the theories of pathological anatomy, with all their consequences for the development of diagnosis and surgical treatment, Murphy realized that he must go to Europe in order to learn the fundamentals which alone would equip him for sensational feats in medicine. Once again his mother produced a leather sack of coins from a hiding place in the wretched little house in Appleton, and donated all her savings to her son. Murphy went to study under Billroth in Vienna, Schröder in Berlin, Arnold in Heidelberg. His life consisted of nothing but work and sleep; of pleasures, he had none. He converted his limited dollars into the maximum of attainable knowledge. He suffered from renal hemorrhages, which Billroth held to be the consequence of tuberculosis of the kidneys. Murphy proved to be stronger than his disease, and in 1884 he was back in Chicago and opening a practice. He was almost penniless and had no well-to-do patients. But he could boast a European education, which counted for a great deal in those early days of American surgery. Moreover, he had an extraordinarily skilled hand and a brilliant grasp of those areas of surgery in which sensational innovations were possible. And, as I have mentioned, he had his flair for publicity. When I first met him in Las Vegas after his reputation had already been made for operations on the appendix, I found a passionate, middle-sized man with red hair and a red beard in whom ability, profound knowledge, and a feeling that he was a man of destiny in surgery were combined with an abnormal craving for fame and wealth. He fitted into no category with which I was familiar, and I understood why his colleagues feared him, or hated and opposed him. He himself was utterly perplexed by this hostility. He simply could not understand why his fellow physicians took umbrage at his making headlines in the newspapers. What he longed for above all was recognition from his medical colleagues and scientific societies. A few years later the newspapers carried new headlines about him, this time for his invention of the "Murphy button," which greatly facilitated the stitching of the severed gut after intestinal operations, and was soon afterwards to be adopted in all the important operating rooms of the world. Murphy was invited to address the Eleventh International Medical Congress at Rome, and was elected an honorary president of the congress along with Bergmann, Koch, Macewen, and Mikulicz. Afterwards he was invited to Berlin by the Deutsche Gesellschaft für Chirurgie and made an honorary member of that society. The result was only a fresh volley of criticism from his colleagues regarding his "mania for publicity." Since then, there had been no signs of diminishing hostility toward him. Hence my conclusion that the reception Murphy had received in Denver constituted virtually a guarantee of some truly remarkable scientific achievement.

Incapacitated as I was, there was nothing for me to do but await the return of a number of New York doctors who had attended the meeting in Denver. From them I would be able to obtain precise accounts of what had actually taken place. Nevertheless it was already clear to me that Murphy had selected for his new exploration a realm hitherto completely closed to surgery. Surgical treatment of diseases of the chest and lungs was an absolute innovation. Whatever had been done in that regard up to 1898 was certainly anything but encouraging.

It was not until the beginning of the nineteenth century that the physical laws of respiration had been discovered by the British anatomist Hewson. He had recognized that the two lobes of the lungs, separated by a median partition called the mediastinum, lie loose and elastic in the pleural cavity. Nevertheless, the expanding and contracting movements of the chest are transmitted to the lobes of the lung, causing it to expand for inhaling and contract for exhaling. Between the outer surface of the lung and the inner surface of the thorax, Hewson declared, there existed a vacuum, or at any rate an area of lower pressure than that of the air which the lung inhaled. As a result of this difference in pressure the lung was forced against the interior of the pleural cavity and followed its movements. The moment an opening in the chest destroyed this vacuum by permitting the outside air, with its higher pressure, to rush in, the adhesion between chest and lung was destroyed. On the injured side the lung collapsed. It stopped breathing.

Hewson's discovery explained why chest wounds led to hampered respiration and asphyxiation. It made clear, too, why the collapse of the lung—which Hewson called "pneumothorax"—did not take place if the lung were inflamed and had become adhered to the wall of the thorax so that it could not fall away and collapse. These insights, however, had not led to the development of surgery of the lungs. Quite the contrary; they had paralyzed all attempts at lung surgery. Since opening the pleural cavity involved, in the overwhelming majority of cases, fatal pneumothorax, and since no method was known to forestall pneumothorax, surgical interference with the whole thorax was obviously hopeless, no matter whether lung or esophagus was attacked. The discoveries of anesthesia and antisepsis had therefore left this realm unaffected. It was useless to open the pleural cavity under the most beautiful conditions of antisepsis if certain death by asphyxiation were to follow.

Only in the past few years had surgeons once more begun hesitantly to risk draining accumulations of pus in the pleural region. Since such accumulations were often accompanied by inflammation and consequent adhesion, the body was protected against fatal pneumothorax. For cases in which there were no such adhesions, a Hamburg doctor named Gotthard Bülau had devised a closed-drainage system which prevented the introduction of air from outside. He introduced into the suppurating cavity a trocar connected with a tube whose lower end was held under the surface in a closed vessel of antiseptic solution. Siphon action removed the pus from the cavity without danger of admitting outside air.

Aside from these makeshifts there was little or nothing which could be done in the way of pleural surgery. The wars of the nineteenth century had produced many chest wounds which should have inspired new studies of the problem. But the wounded men had been left to nature, and only occasionally were efforts made to prevent collapse of the lungs by immediate stitching of the wound, or by shifting the patient so that he lay on his abdomen. As late as 1871 surgical infections in the thorax were still being recklessly combated by phlebotomy. Hemorrhages in the pleural cavity could also paralyze respiration by pressure of blood upon the lungs. In France, where duelling was still in fashion and chest wounds were common, a new profession had arisen, that of *suceur*. The "sucker" attempted to forestall internal hemorrhages by sucking the blood out with his mouth. But serious affections of the pleural cavity, which required surgical intervention, were left untouched. No one believed in the possibility of excising tumors of the esophagus which were concealed out of reach under the sternum. Victims of such tumors simply died of starvation. Nor did there seem to be any way to operate for tumors of the lungs. Even more hopeless was the situation in that most widespread and murderous of the diseases of the lungs, tuberculosis. Beholding the ravages of the disease upon the lungs, anatomists literally cried out their demand that the original foci of infection be removed in time by operation. The German anatomists Gluck, Schmid, and Block had attempted to determine by experiments upon animals whether it would be possible to remove parts of the lungs, or entire lobes of the lung, without ensuing fatality. After removing a number of ribs they had either completely excised one lobe of the lung or tied it off at the bronchiae and thus caused it to atrophy. In large animals such as pigs and cows it often happened that the animals survived the collapse of a single lobe of the lung, and even its extirpation, as long as the other lobe functioned. Block had therefore begun to wonder whether the perils of opening the human thorax and the dangers of pneumothorax had not been over-estimated. Should not the same operation which had succeeded in animals be possible for man? Perhaps tubercular portions of the lung could be extirpated in their initial stages; perhaps by this means consumptives condemned to death could be rescued. In 1883 Block made the attempt with a human patient.

But the disastrous outcome of this experiment put a dire terminus to all subsequent efforts along this line. The patient, a young woman related to Block and to Block's mind severely ill with pulmonary tuberculosis, had entrusted herself to Block with full faith in the doctor's theories. He had exposed the lung and attempted to remove the infected portions. But the patient had died under his hands, and Block, tormented and rendered desperate by guilt, had committed suicide. His fate hung like a great warning sign over the very thought of surgical intervention in diseases of the lung, and particularly tuberculosis. Only two years before, Paget had written in his *Surgery of the Chest* that any further development beyond the limited results hitherto achieved was out of the question.

It is understandable, therefore, that Murphy's announcement in Denver that he had found methods for surgically curing pulmonary diseases should create enormous excitement. But none of the reports I received specified the types of lung diseases that he had in mind. My knowledge of doctors, however, whose own illnesses frequently provided the impetus to their developing new therapies, suggested that Murphy might well have found new ways for combating pulmonary tuberculosis.

On the evening of June 11 my manservant surprisingly announced that Christian Fenger of Chicago was calling. Fenger had
come to New York for an urgent consultation, had heard of my
illness, and was paying me a sick call. No visitor could have been
more welcome. I knew that whether or not he himself had been
present in Denver, he would be well informed about Murphy's
most recent work.

Fenger was a Dane by birth, and had lived the kind of knock-
about life that is seldom the lot of physicians nowadays. He had
studied in Copenhagen, Germany, and Austria, served as a surgeon
during the Franco-Prussian War, and devoted himself passionately
to the study of pathological anatomy. His speech, unfortunately,
was very poor, often a clumsy mumbling spiced with oaths drawn
from half a dozen languages. This handicap had prevented him
from pursuing a career at the University of Copenhagen. He had
emigrated to Egypt, practiced there as a surgeon, and by his remarkable diagnoses had won so large a following that his only
European rival in the country, concluding that there was no room
for more than one medical man in the region, decided he would
leave. Fenger's innate generosity, however, prompted him to suggest to his colleague that they draw lots to decide who should stay
and who leave. Fenger lost, and without complaint moved on to
the United States. In Chicago he obtained, by borrowing a thousand dollars, a place on the medical staff of Cook County Hospital.
This position guaranteed him nothing beyond the opportunity to
observe patients and to dissect the large numbers of unfortunates
who died in the hospital. But the courses in microscopy which he
gave in his apartment every Thursday evening were overcrowded,
and his reputation as a teacher and diagnostician was still growing.
As a surgeon he had never been anything but average, and it was
a joke among his students that each patient who entered Fenger's
operating room was very much like a small dog about to be sacri-
ficed on the experimenter's bench. Therein lay the secret of
Fenger's strength and weakness. Patients interested him only to the
point of his diagnosis of their illness. Therapy was purely inci-
dental. Years ago in Chicago he had been called to a woman's bedside. He had declared an immediate operation necessary. Dr. Albert
Ochsner, who was in charge of the case, had asked dubiously
whether the operation would save the patient. Fenger had replied,

with perfect composure, that no, of course she would die. "I will then advise the relatives against any operation," Ochsner concluded. Fenger stared at him uncomprehendingly and demanded how he could confirm his diagnosis without operation. For diagnosis was everything to him; it was even said that as soon as he had removed morbid tissue in the course of an operation he would rush off to the microscope, and have to be reminded by his assistants that the patient still lay with gaping incision upon the operating table. Perhaps this was an exaggeration, but it characterized the man. His passion was research; he was on fire to learn, to diagnose, at all costs. During that period he was not alone in his monomania. And dubious though his therapeutic achievements were, as scientist and teacher he had furnished hosts of the younger physicians in Chicago with the foundations on which their future work was to be built. In this lay his importance, then and later.

Puffing, Fenger sat down beside my bed. I at once asked him about Murphy. To my surprise, his only reply was an incoherent growl. Then he reached into one of his enormous coat pockets, took out a folded newspaper, and dropped it onto my blanket. It proved to be the previous day's *Chicago Tribune*. My eye was immediately caught by a headline: "Says he cures Consumption. Dr. J. B. Murphy of Chicago addressed The American Medical Association in Denver." The article described further details of Murphy's treatment, as he had outlined it to the American Medical Association meeting in Denver. Murphy, it seemed, introduced nitrogen under pressure, by means of a hollow needle, into the pleural cavity, thereby compressing the lung, forcing it to assume a position of rest. Murphy had hit upon this idea by observing that nature often helped herself in cases of tubercular lungs and simultaneous pleurisy by pouring secretions into the pleural region, forcing one of the lungs to rest and thus promoting healing.

The brief summary was supplemented by a long article on an inside page featuring a two-column picture of Murphy. The character of the man emerged clearly from the photograph's aggressive, action-hungry eyes and all too resolute lips.

It almost seemed as if the Spanish-American War, which otherwise filled the front pages, was being overshadowed by the Murphy story. The newspaper quoted at length from Murphy's lecture and referred to the experiments he had conducted for many years in a laboratory above the mews of his house on Michigan Avenue in Chicago, as well as in St. Joseph's and Mercy Hospitals. It ended with references to the prevailing helplessness of medical science in its fight against any severe pulmonary disease and a brief survey of the unsuccessful attempts in the past to deal with such diseases.

Evidently my guess had been a good one. Murphy had taken up the challenge of pulmonary tuberculosis. I looked up at Fenger and once more asked him what he knew about it all. Fenger lifted his knobby head with its big, prominent ears. "What do I know about it?" he growled. "At present, no more than this." He waved his hand in an angry gesture at the *Chicago Tribune.* "They made him wait a long time before they gave him his turn to speak at Denver. And then, yesterday, they applauded him for the first time. And now what does he do?" Fenger picked up the newspaper and rapped it angrily against my bed. "What does he do but make his old mistake. He rushes the story to the newspapers before the *Medical Journal* has published his report. Wait till you see the reactions. The good doctors will all pounce on him, forgetting that he has discovered something new, something whose importance we cannot even begin to estimate at present."

"So it is a genuine discovery," I said.

Fenger glared furiously at me. "What else? I thought you were one of the few persons who don't think him a charlatan. What he has developed here may be even more important than his appendectomies. And then he ruins things for himself by this damnable craze for publicity. His enemies were on the point of coming over to his side. But now they will fight him harder than ever. He will retreat, embittered, and leave the greatest discovery he has ever made incomplete, as he has left so many other things unfinished. . . ."

I skimmed rapidly through the account in the *Tribune* again. Of course Fenger was right. If this story were true, if Murphy had succeeded in healing or even causing improvement in severe cases of pulmonary tuberculosis by the method described, he would deserve lasting fame for that work alone.

I asked Fenger whether Murphy had returned to Chicago yet. Fenger shook his head. "He and his wife were planning to go from Denver to Colorado Springs for a rest. You know as well as I that in attacking this disease he had his own fate in mind as much as anything."

"The tuberculosis had not cleared up entirely, then?" I asked.

"Apparently not," Fenger replied. "Nettie Murphy told me that he coughs and has nocturnal sweating. Did you know that his brothers and his sister died of consumption within a single year?"

Although I could not stir as yet, I wired next morning to Nettie Murphy in Colorado Springs, asking where and when I could see her husband. I received a reply that same day. She informed me that as a result of the publication in the *Chicago Tribune*, her husband was in a state of great agitation. He had not been responsible for the story. On the contrary, he had long been avoiding newspapermen, to deprive his colleagues of any pretext for attacking his scientific achievements. He was downcast, perplexed, and in despair. She was trying to keep him in Colorado Springs, since he urgently needed a rest, but she did not know how long she would succeed in doing so if there were any further attacks upon him by fellow members of the medical profession. She would let me know when he planned to return to Chicago.

I had met Nettie Murphy, too, on that occasion eight years before in Las Vegas. She was the daughter of one of the richest families in Chicago. Murphy had treated her when he was a young doctor, deputized to the case by his superior, and the lovely, dark-haired girl had fallen passionately in love with him. She was an ardent promoter of his work, ready to make any sacrifice whatsoever to further his career.

Shortly after this news from Colorado Springs reached me, Fenger paid me another call. His consultation in New York was finished, and he intended to return to Chicago next day. He informed me that the dogs were already yapping at Murphy's heels. Almost all his Chicago colleagues were nettled by the newspaper reports, and in fact most of the members of the American Medical Association had taken offense. Fenger asked me: "Do you recall when he invented the button? At that time certain persons had nothing better to do than to charge him with having stolen the idea from a Frenchman named Denans. The *Chicago Tribune* has already received letters asserting that Murphy has stolen his operation for pulmonary tuberculosis from someone else."

I asked who the originator was supposed to be.

"They mention an Italian doctor named Forlanini who worked in Pavia. He is said to have published on the subject in 1882. Have you ever heard of him?"

I said I had not.

Fenger shrugged. As he was leaving he mumbled that it was at least fortunate that Nicholas Senn was not in Chicago. Senn was quite intemperate in his hatred for Murphy. If Senn had not been busy in military medicine at the moment he would undoubtedly have thrown the considerable weight of his influence into keeping Murphy from even obtaining a hearing at Denver.

Nicholas Senn had been another of Fenger's pupils and was now professor of surgery at Rush College in Chicago, although at the moment he was serving as Surgeon-General of the Navy. Senn was only too well known as a ferocious opponent of Murphy's. For example, in the course of some of his lectures, he was known to have taken a Murphy's button and hurled it to the floor to express his contempt for the contraption. Swiss by birth, humorless and dogmatic, he was a person who could abide little competition. He was himself famous for his studies of the pancreas, but he hated Murphy for his ingenuity and his success in surgery, which far outshone his own. The letters to the newspaper about Forlanini, Fenger commented, might very well be Senn's work. But even without Senn's presence in Chicago there would be plenty of others to campaign against Murphy. We would see!

After Fenger's departure I heard nothing new about Murphy for four days. During this time, however, my condition improved enough so that I could get about again. On June 16 I received a telegram from Colorado Springs. Nettie Murphy informed me that she and her husband would be in Chicago on the eighteenth; Murphy could no longer remain outside the fray. She would be very happy to see me in Chicago. Perhaps, as an outsider, I might be able to help Murphy recover his equanimity.

That same day I ventured to take a carriage ride. Since it did not produce unbearable discomfort, I left for Chicago the next day.

Late in the morning of June 18 I was driving down Michigan Avenue. It was not then the impressive boulevard it is today, but it was still one of the most elegant streets in the city which had

arisen anew out of the ashes of the terrible fire of 1871. South of
Thirty-fifth Street I found the mansion which Murphy had been
occupying for two years. I was received by Mrs. Murphy. Poised
as always, she nevertheless betrayed her inner stress by the uneasy
flickering of her brilliant eyes.

"I don't know whether I ought to let you see J. B. now," she
murmured.

For many years she had been in the habit of speaking of her husband as "J. B." At that moment Murphy's high-pitched voice was
heard. He strode into the vestibule, pale, his flaming red hair and
red beard looking unkempt, a sheaf of newspapers and letters in
his hand. He did not even notice me as he rushed toward his wife,
barely avoiding the pieces of luggage scattered everywhere. "Who
did this thing?" he cried out. "Why do these men resort to such
methods to discredit me? Can't they understand, I'm only con-
scientiously doing my bit for medical science? Oh, Nettie, who
is behind all this?"

I saw how his wife attempted to soothe him. "You know, J. B.,"
she said earnestly, laying her hand on his arm, "it has always been
so. Look at other great doctors. Pasteur had injustices by the dozens
heaped upon his head. And you yourself have often told me how
Joseph Lister was at first the laughingstock of his own countrymen. . . ."

Even before she had finished speaking, Murphy had rushed out
of the vestibule again. His wife looked at me. "I know quite well
what people in the medical profession are thinking," she said.
"They assume that J. B. himself placed the article. But he did not.
He has been much criticized for giving stories to the newspapers,
and he has learned his lesson." It was touching to see how she de-
fended him. "He appeared at the convention only to ask for the
scientific recognition he deserves. The big article in the *Tribune*
must have been planted there by his enemies—unless it is a cruel
coincidence. Don't you believe me?"

In her devotion to Murphy she was so convincing that I did
believe every word she said. "Yes," I replied, "I certainly believe
you."

"Thank you," she said, listening with one ear to Murphy, who
was ranting somewhere in the house. "My husband has made mistakes, made them for many years. But before condemning him,

people should remember that shack where J. B. was born, the farm where he spent his boyhood, and how only twenty-five years ago he worked in Lewis's drugstore for fifty cents a week to earn the money for his first anatomy book. I was not born in a shack; my mother did not have to give up the last penny of her savings, as his mother did so that he could study medicine. I never had to go hungry in Europe and to work without pause, without pleasures. When I first saw him here in Chicago I was the daughter of the wealthy Plamondons of Throop Street, and he was an indigent doctor who had more talent in his little finger than a hundred others in their whole bodies. But I understood him. A man who comes from his background, and has his ability and his determination to rise and to do remarkable things in this world, may not be fastidious. He may be hungry for recognition and take it wherever he can get it, even from the newspapers which those who envy him despise. He needs self-assurance and reassurance so that he can forget his past."

She had more to say, in her love for this difficult man who was her husband, but she stopped short and smiled half apologetically for her outburst. "But you wanted to talk with him about his discovery," she said. "Perhaps talking will divert him—work has always been the only diversion he knows. He will never relax, never let himself rest. . . ."

Nettie Murphy opened the doors leading to the library, and I saw a richly appointed room filled with books and magazines. But what caught my attention was the floor, which was entirely covered with letters, among which Murphy strode nervously back and forth.

"Nettie," he called, "look at these letters. So many letters in three days from pulmonary patients all over the country who have read about my lecture in Denver and want to be cured."

"We will manage to answer them all," his wife replied. "We'll find a way. But I think you ought to see Dr. Hartmann now. He would like to hear about your method for fighting consumption, and has come specially from New York to see you."

Murphy looked absently at me, and shook hands just as absently. "This is the second time they have called me a plagiarist," he ranted. "I have never heard of this man named Forlanini. They say he spoke to the International Medical Congress in Rome about his method, and that it is the same as my method. And now they noise it about that I was at that congress. Nettie, do you recall ever having heard mention of Forlanini?"

Nettie had gone up to him. "No," she said, "I don't remember at all. But the matter will be cleared up. Dr. Hartmann is waiting. And your students and patients at Mercy Hospital have already heard of your return. They are all anxious to congratulate you."

She made a tiny sign to me, and left the room.

Murphy led me to the laboratory which had been mentioned in the *Chicago Tribune*. As soon as we entered the room above the mews, Murphy seemed to grow calmer. "Nettie fixed this place up," he said, "so that I would not have to spend my nights at the hospital, and would at least be near her."

In the back of the room a young assistant was working. Murphy introduced him to me as August Lemke. He was of German birth. "Mr. Lemke has worked with me for seven years," Murphy said. "Ever since I returned from Las Vegas and first turned my mind to the possibility of treatment for tuberculosis."

He fell silent for the moment, but he was still overwrought, as was apparent from his way of pacing back and forth. "So you want to hear the story of the method I have called 'artificial pneumothorax,'" he proceeded. "In the winter of 1891, just seven years ago, I was called to a new patient, a young girl of an Irish family. They live in one of the worst parts of the city. The girl had tuberculosis of the right lung. For more than a year she had had fever; several loci of infection could be distinctly determined. To make matters worse, as a result of the dampness of their dwelling she had developed pleurisy, with heavy secretion into the right pleural cavity. The case seemed utterly hopeless. I don't know how well acquainted you are with conditions in Chicago. This child had a straw pallet for a bed. The family had a one-room shanty to live in. Into this they managed to fit six children of various ages."

Murphy faced me squarely. "You've surely heard all those nice stories about my unscrupulous and grasping character," he said. "It's quite true that I wanted to be rich, and I'll attest to that to anyone. I have tasted poverty, and believe me, the taste is bitter. I swore to my mother that I would become rich and famous, and

she is still living in Appleton. It will be the greatest happiness to
her when I reach my goal. But when my enemies say that I have
squeezed fees out of the poor at the beds of their children, and
would not treat the children otherwise, they are lying as shame-
lessly as it is possible to lie. The parents of this child did not have
a cent they could have offered me. And I could never have suspected when I first saw the girl that she would prove more valuable
to me than the highest fee. . . ."

He resumed his pacing. "I don't know how many members of
the family were tubercular," he said. "Probably all of them. One
infected the other. The child was delirious, running a raging fever,
when I was called in. She was struggling for breath and clearly in
mortal danger. I was working at Cook County Hospital at the
time, but had no way to provide the child with a bed there. But
what was I going to do? Did I dare to take her to our own house
on Throop Street? As you know, I myself had just been through
a siege of tuberculosis. Finally we found a place for her with a
healthy Irish family that happened to have a spare room. The
child was so weak that I did not dare to attempt puncturing the
pleural cavity and releasing the secretions. There was nothing we
could give her but good nursing, compresses, camphor, febrifuges.

"To make a long story short, we pulled the girl through the
acute stage. The fever dropped. But the child remained so weak
that I still did not dare to drain the discharge, which was not
being resorbed. One could tell by the sound that there was a
great deal of it filling the chest. The tubercular right lobe of the
lung must be seriously compressed, I realized. Her respiration
was extremely hampered. Day after day I sat in perplexity beside
her little bed, until it suddenly struck me that my patient was
coughing less frequently, in spite of her weakness. One day she
herself told me that she had almost entirely ceased to feel the
irritation that produced coughing. Nocturnal sweating and os-
cillations of temperature diminished steadily, to my amazement,
although the pleural discharge remained. The whole clinical picture
had changed. The child acquired an appetite. After five months
she was strong enough so that I could have risked puncture and
draining without hesitation. She complained only of slight short-
ness of breath. But at that time it first occurred to me that there
must be some connection between the pleuritic discharge and the

amazing improvement in her pulmonary tuberculosis. I therefore did not attempt the puncture. During the sixth month she was able to get out of bed. She had no fever at all, and her only complaint was of a feeling of heaviness on the right side of her chest."

A shadow passed over Murphy's face. "A few days afterward," he said, "while the child was taking her first walk, she was killed in a traffic accident. Her poor mother was standing helplessly by as a heavy van went over her. I have never been squeamish about autopsies—they are, after all, the source of much of our knowledge. But in this case I hesitated. It took me two days before I could get up my courage to perform the autopsy, together with Mr. Lemke." He looked over at his assistant, who had meanwhile been quietly attending to his work. "August," he said, "tell Dr. Hartmann what we found."

Lemke came over to us. Such was his subordination to Murphy that he did not venture to use the word "we." "Dr. Murphy," he said, "exposed the entire right lobe of the lung. Four of the seven tubercular cavities had shrunk, cicatrized, and healed. The most curious feature, as Dr. Murphy observed, was that the healed cavities were situated exclusively in those parts of the lung which had been affected by the serous discharge and had been so extensively compressed that they could no longer participate in the respiratory movements."

Lemke had spoken dryly and unemotionally, with a strong German accent. Now Murphy interrupted passionately. "Do you understand now?" he asked me. "Everything I said in Denver, the idea of artificially forcing the lung to rest, that is, of using artificial pneumothorax to heal the loci of tuberculosis, was born in the course of this autopsy. As I examined this child's pleural cavity I realized that the enforced rest imposed upon the lung by an accidental serous discharge had led to extensive healing, to what amounted to recovery from tuberculosis. From that point it was only a brief step to the conclusion that in order to attain similar therapeutic results we must induce artificial compression of the affected parts of the lungs. Apparently, we must seek to avoid that tugging of the lung tissues which takes place with every breath; we must seek also to check the movement of the lymph, and to secure in general a state of rest which will give the body a chance to heal the lesions. The question was: How could we place affected lungs under moderate pressure without invading the pleural region and thus incurring the danger of ordinary pneumothorax? For we must not have a sudden pressure and sudden collapse of the lung, with all those dangers following from chest wounds. Now, I have always been a great reader. Whenever a new idea has occurred to me, I have searched the literature to see whether anyone else has dealt with it, whether I can perhaps benefit by past experience. And so Mr. Lemke and I ransacked the libraries. And what do you think we found?"

Years ago, in Las Vegas, I had noticed that Murphy, in moments of emotion, would practice this peculiar form of dialogue, a succession of questions and answers addressed to himself with increasing intensity.

"What do you think we found?" he repeated. "Not a word about any Signor Forlanini. August, have you ever read or heard the name Forlanini?"

Lemke shook his head.

"What did we find instead?" Murphy asked. "We found a reference to an old Scottish practitioner, Dr. James Carson, who was active in Liverpool around 1820. He wrote a paper on the elasticity of the lungs. In experiments on rabbits he determined, independently of Hewson, that the lung collapsed when the pleural cavity was opened, and that loci of infection which had previously been kept under tension were thereby relieved of the tension and the concomitant constant irritations. He therefore proposed that in cases of human pulmonary diseases the chest be opened in order to cause the collapse of the affected lung. Carson therefore had the right idea, at bottom. But his proposal led directly to fatal open pneumothorax. Carson is the only physician who to my knowledge ever published anything remotely akin to my idea. But we could not use his suggestion. In Cook County Hospital Mr. Lemke and I have done an autopsy on every tubercular patient who died of pleurisy with serous discharge. And what did we find? In every case we found the same phenomenon: cicatrization and more or less distinct evidence of healing where parts of the lungs containing cavities had been immobilized by discharges into the pleural cavity.

"In my laboratory, which at that time was still small and ill-equipped, we performed many experiments on animals. My object was to learn whether it was possible to open the pleural cavity with great care, so that the air entered slowly, without causing a sudden collapse of the lung. We discovered that this was occasionally possible, and that the deadliness of open pneumothorax came about primarily from sudden displacement of the mediastinum between the lobes of the lung. The mediastinum shifted and involved the other as yet unaffected lobe in the paralysis of lung functioning. But did this knowledge bring us any further? No. The open pneumothorax continued to represent a deadly peril. We had still to arrive at some method for slow, cautious compression of the lung without incision. Taking our cue from the morbid discharge in cases of pleurisy, we had to introduce into the pleural cavity a fluid or other material which would produce compression of the lung. It would have to be a substance not susceptible to resorption, or at any rate resorbed very slowly, so that the pressure would hold for a long time.

"What did we do? We undertook a new series of experiments on animals. In dogs and rabbits we incised the skin between the ribs, inserted a trocar through the pleura, and introduced at first oily fluids into the pleural cavity. We discovered that these fluids not only compressed the lungs but also frequently displaced the heart, diaphragm, and intestines. If we proceeded very slowly, however, the animals survived this procedure without difficulties. We then substituted air for the fluid. It was far easier to introduce air under slight pressure, and the effect was the same. The difficulty was that air was resorbed relatively quickly. The compressive effect therefore did not last long. Finally we replaced air by nitrogen. What was the result? Nitrogen proved to be the best of all these substances. Last year we were ready to take the next step. What was possible in animals ought to be possible in human beings, we reasoned. However, shortly before our first human experiment, something happened that made us hesitate once more."

Murphy was so out of breath from his restless pacing and rapid monologue that he had to pause. With fluttering fingers he searched among the books and papers on his desk, but could not find what he was looking for. Lemke composedly reached to a bookshelf and handed Murphy an offprint from some journal. "Here it is, Dr. Murphy," he said.

Murphy glanced at the title page, and then held the offprint out to me. "Édouard de Cérenville," he said. "Professor in Lausanne. This is the article I came across just last year. It was written in 1886, is now twelve years old. I have no idea why it has passed unnoticed for so long. There was also the German specialist in internal medicine, Heinrich Quincke, who dealt with rib resection in 1888, and likewise Carl Spengler, the Swiss specialist on tuberculosis. But the work of none of these men attracted general attention. In any case, the Lausanne professor had developed an idea which approached very closely to my goal. He, however, had chosen another method for achieving compression of the diseased portions of the lungs. Above the tubercular part of one lung he removed several ribs without opening the pleural cavity. Do you understand why? He could thereby make the wall of the chest yield, collapse into the pleural cavity, and thus bring about a collapse of the diseased lung. A brilliant idea.

"What did we do? We tried out the method. That was last January. It was our first attempt to produce closed, artificial pneumothorax in man. I first chose this Swiss method, which had been consigned to virtual oblivion, because it limited the surgery to the chest and required no filling of the pleural cavity. On January 9 I operated on a British patient at Cook County Hospital. He had a large tubercular cavity in the right lung, between the first and third ribs. Without difficulty I removed three inches of the second rib, precisely above the cavity. By January 24 the chest above the cavity showed indications of deep collapse. And what happened from then on? What do you think happened? The symptoms of tuberculosis, in particular the coughing and the fever, vanished bit by bit—as in the case of the Irish child. Does it make sense to you that Cérenville's idea has not been taken up in Switzerland or in all of Europe, that to this day it has yielded so few results? Does it make sense when year after year thousands upon thousands die of tuberculosis? Does it make sense that sheer chance sent that dusty article my way, and that here in Chicago I carried out his inspired suggestion?"

Murphy was momentarily carried away by his oratory, by his sense of the dramatic. Then he continued more calmly: "Very well, I took up the matter. But it was not my idea. It only gave me the courage to carry out my own idea. Cérenville's method required a bloody operation. If it yielded the desired result, how much more practical my own idea ought to be—requiring no major operation, scarcely involving more than a drop of blood. Last April I made my first attempt at artificial pneumothorax. Four more followed, the last on May 12. Twice I failed because the lung had adhered to the wall of the chest, owing to inflammation, so that it could not yield to the pressure of the entering nitrogen. In the other, more usual cases, the operation succeeded without the slightest difficulty. What was my procedure? I used a local anesthetic on the pectoral wall. Then I made a tiny incision through the skin between two ribs. The trocar, connected by a tube with a container of nitrogen, was introduced into the incision. Carefully, I forced it through the pleura. As soon as the tip of the trocar entered the pleural cavity, the nitrogen poured in.

"One essential is that the trocar must not be advanced any further, for injury to the lungs must be avoided. Possible side-effects on the heart and intestines must be carefully observed, and watch kept for any signs of increased respiratory difficulty. The amount of nitrogen admitted is governed by these criteria. In my successful cases I have not observed the slightest distress as a result of the operation. On the contrary, all my previous observations have been confirmed: subjective improvement, diminution of the fever, disappearance of the cough, appetite, swift gain in weight. The patients are able to leave the hospital immediately after the operation. All are today in a condition which their doctors had regarded beforehand as not to be dreamed of. They are free of fever, of discharges, in fact they are even without demonstrable tubercle bacilli."

Suddenly Murphy's tone changed from that of quiet exposition to one of indignation. "And in gratitude for all this my colleagues say that I am a thief, a plagiarist who has to steal his ideas from others. Who is Forlanini?" He repeated the question: "Who is Forlanini? I do not know him, nor does August. You do not know him. Who except my enemies does know him? If they have not invented him to slander me, if he really exists and has had the same idea before I did, I want to know it."

His eyes fixed upon me. "When are you going back to Europe?" he asked in a tight voice.

"At the end of July," I replied.

"Will you be going to Italy?"

"Probably in August."

Murphy's breathing came fast. He said: "Please look up Forlanini. Find out what the truth is in this case, the living truth, not the printed paper. And write me what you find out in Italy. Let me have the exact truth. But no matter what truths you write me, there is one truth that remains, and will always remain: I knew nothing whatsoever about this Italian professor."

Naturally, I carried out Murphy's request—all the more eagerly since I myself wanted to clarify the matter. Early in August I wrote a letter of inquiry from Paris to an old friend in Pavia. I received the reply that Carlo Forlanini was in Rome at present and could be reached at the Ospedale degli Incurabili, between the Via del Corso, the Via di Ripetta, and the Via San Giacomo. There, in that rather macabre atmosphere, I met him. I always felt a distinctly unpleasant shudder when I saw the blood-red institutional dress worn by the patients in this hospital, a place remarkable for its hopeless hygienic conditions.

We walked together through the corridors of the hospital, our footsteps echoing through dreary, empty halls. Hardly any visitors came here. Most of the patients, whose lives ebbed hopelessly toward a certain end, had been given up by their families. Among them were numerous consumptives.

Forlanini had heard nothing of Murphy's work. He proved to me, however, that as early as 1882 he had publicly stated his early theories on pneumothorax and pulmonary tuberculosis. They had passed unnoticed, however. At the medical congress in Rome in 1894 he had delivered a lecture in the section for internal medicine —not in the section for surgery, which Murphy attended—on the favorable effects of pneumothorax on tuberculosis of the lung. The title was *First Experiments in Artificial Pneumothorax in Pulmonary Tuberculosis*. Since the 1894 congress in Rome, Forlanini had also carried out his first pragmatic test of artificial pneumothorax on a girl of seventeen with a severe case of tuberculosis of the lungs. During the period from October 16, 1894, to October, 1895, he had achieved his first cure with her. On October 31, 1895 —three years before Murphy's appearance in Denver—he had reported on this case before the Sixth Congress for Internal Medicine in Rome. Once again little attention had been paid to him. Such was Forlanini's story up to the present moment.

The day of my meeting with Forlanini I wrote to Murphy and Fenger that Forlanini actually deserved the palm for having first developed the new method. Nevertheless, Murphy would remain the man who had established pneumothorax as a technique, not only by nitrogen injection but by rib resection as well. In both cases it was his misfortune not to have hit upon the idea first— an idea that for the first time offered surgery the prospect of combating diseases of the lung.

Murphy did not reply. In fact, three months passed before I received a letter from Fenger, sent to me in Germany, informing me of the further developments in Chicago. Murphy had abandoned his work on perfecting the method of artificial pneumothorax. He had referred the hordes of patients who requested his aid to his assistant. August Lemke, the mild, unassertive, awkward, but conscientious and industrious young man, had won a name for himself by numerous successful treatments.

Indeed Murphy never again published any work on artificial pneumothorax. Nevertheless, his name will always be connected with that historic achievement, since it was through him that the first methods for surgical treatment of pulmonary tuberculosis became widely known and struck root in medical practice. In 1906 Professor Ludolph Brauer took up the idea and established it firmly in medical practice. Brauer's case paralleled that of Murphy to the extent that his own pulmonary disease led him to the problems of surgical treatment of tuberculosis. Contracting the disease during his student days, he had been forced to go to Davos for a cure in the mountain air. After a while, the Davos doctors had advised his father to have him return home to North Germany, since his disease had reached a hopeless stage. Brauer happened to see the letter containing this intelligence, and the knowledge roused his extraordinary vital forces. As if by a miracle, he recovered from the disease. Later, as director of the Medical Polyclinic in Marburg, he worked both as physician and surgeon to introduce the practice of artificial pneumothorax. He drew inspiration for his efforts from the work of Murphy. Brauer did not hear of Forlanini until long after he had begun.

The second form of producing artificial pneumothorax, which Murphy had so strongly emphasized at Denver, was also disseminated throughout the civilized world. Rib resection above affected parts of the lungs was likewise developed by Brauer into a major, effective method, and extended by Paul Leopold Friedrich, director of the surgical clinics at the Universites of Greifswald, Marburg, and Königsberg, to the point of "complete deboning" of the chest.

When John B. Murphy died on August 11, 1916, of an arterial disease caused by his fiery nature and perhaps also by a hidden, lingering tubercular infection, no doubt remained that he had been one of the foremost pioneers of lung surgery.

Sauerbruch

I first heard the name of Sauerbruch in the spring of 1903, when this pathfinder in surgery was still an utterly unknown young assistant physician at a hospital in Erfurt, Germany, that was equally unknown to the scientific world. It is strange that I should have stumbled on his name thousands of miles from Erfurt, in the city of Rochester, Minnesota. Today Rochester has itself become an almost symbolic spot to medical circles the world over, because of the labors of Charles and William Mayo. In the spring of 1903 the fame of these brothers, and of their small St. Mary's Hospital in Rochester, was just beginning to spread throughout the United States. And in Rochester itself it was a memorable day when a noted German surgeon, Johannes von Mikulicz, visited the hospital to see for himself what was being done in a place that, to a European's mind, still belonged to the Wild West. Von Mikulicz, on his first and only tour of America, played hob with his schedule in order to make this visit. And I had preceded him to Rochester the day before, to act as a kind of liaison man.

Early in the morning of May 1, 1903, Mikulicz stepped from

the Chicago and Northwestern train—as small, slender, and nervous as ever. It seemed to me that he had scarcely changed in the twenty-three years since I had first become friendly with him in Vienna. Only his face had aged; his blond hair was now silvered. For a man of fifty-three there were almost too many of these gray threads.

Before the day was out Mikulicz, with his restless temperament, had taken in everything the Mayos had to show him. On the one hand there was Rochester itself, an insignificant little town of barely five thousand inhabitants, with muddy streets and unprepossessing architecture of clapboard houses and wooden shacks. There was the unpaved street to St. Mary's Hospital; the hospital itself, with gas lamps installed but no gas supply as yet; with a sewage system that did not function, an empty elevator shaft over which the nurses had to stand guard at night lest anyone fall into it. In the end an itinerant mechanic installed the elevator. On the other hand, in amazing contrast to these primitive conditions, there were the remarkable achievements in diagnosis and surgery of the two Mayo brothers, at that time respectively forty-two and thirty-eight years old, whose reputation attracted to Rochester thousands of patients from all over the country. To outsiders, this enormous popularity was incomprehensible. Yet at bottom there was nothing so remarkable about their secret. It consisted in the first place of an ability to assimilate quickly the successful aspects of progress in surgery. Their father, old Dr. Worrall Mayo, who had started the hospital, had begun by sending his sons to the great centers of surgery "as merchants are sent to fairs to buy the best." They had appropriated the best European and American methods, especially in the fields of abdominal and neural surgery. The two were not especially creative in their gifts, but their skill and courage had combined to bring them extraordinary success in surgery. This, in turn, had attracted droves of patients, the American Northwest being at this time poor in hospitals. Thus the Mayo brothers performed an enormous number of operations, and accordingly acquired vast experience. The necessity for coping with all their work had stimulated the organizational genius of the two brothers. They established the necessary framework for dealing with so many patients, enlisted specialists, and provided the newest in technological aids for the

diagnoses which preceded every operation. Every patient was subjected to a general examination, even if his complaint were local
in nature. The Mayo brothers had discovered what a dispropor-
tionately large number of gastric and gall bladder complaints
arose from disregarded inflammations of the appendix. This discovery also had prompted them to introduce the general examination on a scale practiced nowhere else at the time.

That evening Mikulicz and I were guests at the home of Worrall
Mayo, who at ninety-two was a man of most remarkable vigor.
I can think of no one who more strongly reflected the peculiarities
of our pioneer days in America than he.

He was born in the small English village of Eccles, the son of
a sailing-ship captain. He had studied medicine but had been far
too restive to stick it out and acquire a diploma. In 1845 he moved
from England to America. He became an assistant in the pharmacy
at New York's Bellevue Hospital, which was jointly a charity
hospital and insane asylum. Shortly before his time a prison had
also been housed in the same building, with the convicts acting
as nurses to the patients. Leaving behind this den of misery within
whose walls typhus, yellow fever, and cholera never entirely
subsided, he removed to Lafayette, Indiana. Here he established
a tailor's shop and turned out suits and ladies' coats until cholera
broke out in Lafayette also. Since his medical background was
well known, he was appointed a physician without more ado. For
a few years he actually attended the medical college in La Porte
and helped steal corpses from the cemeteries for anatomy lessons.

Equipped at last with a proper doctor's certificate, he returned
to Lafayette. His subsequent career was as rugged and rich in
adventure as his earlier life. He set up as pharmacist in a drugstore in Lafayette, and practiced on the side as a country doctor.
But he remained so poor that his wife had to open a millinery
shop to make ends meet. Year after year he suffered bouts of
malaria. To escape the fever, he emigrated up the Mississippi as
far as St. Paul, Minnesota. Here his wife again opened a millinery
shop, and Mayo battled with cholera, diphtheria, and the endemic
pneumonia which killed thousands of the inhabitants of the region
during the terrible winters. He also had a spell of fighting the
Sioux Indians, who raised their war cry in Minnesota in 1862.

Since his income from medicine rarely amounted to much, he tried running a newspaper and captaining a river steamer. Finally, during the Civil War, he landed in Rochester as draft-board doctor. Here, in the midst of the broad farmlands, he came to rest at last. For a time he served as mayor, then took up his medical practice again, and at last had begun earning enough not only to keep his family but even to travel to New York in 1869 "in order to learn surgery and gynecology." The folk of Rochester had no great regard for surgeons, considering them mere "belly-slitters," and he had bided his time before he ventured to operate. In 1880 he attempted his first removal of an ovarian tumor. His patient's husband, a blacksmith, had to manufacture the instruments, using parts of an old sewing machine for the purpose. But the operation was a success.

Will and Charlie, the inseparable Mayo brothers, witnessed this sensational operation through a crack in the door. This one operation brought fame to Mayo, now sixty, and surgery became acceptable in Rochester. Mayo's operating table remained, until the founding of St. Mary's Hospital, a living-room table or door taken off its hinges and laid on benches. Nevertheless, his inveterate softheartedness still kept him a poor man. Will and Charlie had to wear cast-off clothes and work as apprentices in drugstores. Mayo was unable to purchase a microscope without mortgaging his house. But both brothers grew up with surgery, and Charlie administered anesthesia before he was twelve years old. Mayo spent his last dollar to send the two to Ann Arbor and Chicago to study medicine.

In August, 1883, Rochester was devastated by a tornado. The plight of the many injured victims of the disaster emphasized so clearly the lack of a hospital that the sisters of the Convent of St. Francis in Rochester resolved to build one. In 1889 St. Mary's Hospital was ready. The sisters offered Mayo, now seventy, the medical directorship. After some hesitation he accepted the post, provided that his sons could gradually take over. There is a story that Will Mayo after completing his medical studies stated: "I intend to stay in Rochester and become the most famous surgeon in the world." Together with his brother he was, by May, 1903, well on his way to becoming just that.

Mikulicz and I stayed overnight at Will Mayo's big house on College Street. Since Mikulicz was one of those nocturnal personalities who are at their best in the wee hours of the night, we sat up talking for a long time. The Mayos had made a tremendous impression upon him; their hospital and methods opened a wholly new world to him. He predicted a great future for them—which, coming from him, meant a good deal, for he was anything but generous in his appreciations of others.

It was approaching one o'clock when I at last came round to asking Mikulicz how he had been in the years since we had last seen one another. I inquired whether he was content, and whether he had accomplished his aims.

"Content?" he repeated thoughtfully. "I suppose that I never shall be content. During my internship my great aim was to attack diseases and malformations of the esophagus, and especially to find a way to use surgery in cancer of the esophagus. To this day I have not succeeded. I have not abandoned the project, but it presents a score of obstacles. As you probably know, the difficulties are not simply the poor healing powers of the esophagus. After excision of the morbid elements, it becomes something of a feat to draw the ends of the wound together. But our chief stumbling-block is still the matter of getting at the esophagus without producing an open pneumothorax."

As we talked, Mikulicz smoked his continual cigarettes. When at last I was taking my leave, he unpacked from his bag a number of offprints from periodicals and stacked them upon the table.

"In spite of the hurly-burly, I have actually had a chance to do some extensive reading on this trip," he said. "Your railroads are more comfortable than ours, and well suited for reading, and at night I read myself to sleep. Here are some of the things I brought along with me from Europe."

I flipped through the offprints, curious to know what sort of thing Mikulicz read. At the top was a paper entitled *Empirical Observations on Intestinal Injuries after Abdominal Contusions, Exemplified by a case of Rupture of the Rectum.*

Mikulicz noticed which title held my eye. "If I were to read everything that is sent to me . . ." he said. "But the young man who wrote that particular paper has been fortunate in that his article reached me during this trip. He seems to have the makings of a scientist. At the moment he is assistant at a hospital in Berlin. I shall try him out in Breslau—as a volunteer, of course. I intend to write him a few lines one of these days soon."

I glanced at the name of the author: Dr. Ferdinand Sauerbruch. At the moment it meant nothing at all to me, and I quickly forgot it. But not a year was to pass before the name was on the lips of thousands of persons, and the memory of that night's conversation in Rochester returned vividly to my mind.

Ferdinand Sauerbruch later told me the story of that summer day, so crucial to his life, when Mikulicz's letter arrived from the United States. An ill-paid assistant at the Berlin-Moabit Hospital, Sauerbruch had for years been unable to afford a vacation. This summer of 1903, as chance would have it, a kindly friend concerned about his health had paid for a holiday journey to Bavaria for him. Mikulicz's letter had therefore reached him at Berchtesgaden, and kindled fantastic pictures of the future in his imagination.

Sauerbruch was at this time twenty-seven years old. His father had died of "galloping consumption" when he was only four, leaving wife and child virtually penniless. Young Sauerbruch had gone through school without distinguishing himself. He had displayed a certain technical facility, but no remarkable talents. However, he went on to the university, studying first in Marburg and then in Leipzig and Jena. In 1901 he passed the regular state medical examination in Germany, and attempted to make his way as a country doctor in a small town in Thuringia. But he soon felt that he was suffocating in the provincial environment. He therefore applied for a post as surgical assistant at the Sisters of Charity Hospital in Kassel—and here he discovered his extraordinary innate gift for the technique of surgery. But within a short time he had quarrelled with the Sisters; they would have denied a sick man admission to the hospital on a Sunday. Thereupon Sauerbruch went to Erfurt as an assistant in surgery, and made a second discovery about himself—that he was more interested in scientific studies to advance the development of surgery than in daily routine. Shortly afterwards he wrote the paper which I had seen in Rochester. For a man with Sauerbruch's restless urge to scientific experimentation, conditions in the Erfurt hospital were cramping. Realizing that he must work in anatomy, he made still another change, becoming assistant to Professor Langerhans —discoverer of the islands in the pancreas which bear his name —in the department of pathology and anatomy at Berlin-Moabit Hospital. Langerhans had advised Sauerbruch to send his paper on intestinal injuries to Mikulicz. From the moment Sauerbruch received Mikulicz's letter there was no question but that he would accept Mikulicz's invitation and go to Breslau to start working for him as a volunteer assistant from October 1, 1903, on.

Mikulicz was a superb surgeon, a great teacher, and a friend to his patients, but in his hospital he was one of the most absolutistic rulers I have ever met. He mercilessly dominated his associates. None of them, as I later discovered, was really happy. What kept them in Breslau was the consciousness that they could learn more from Mikulicz than from most other German or Austrian surgeons.

At this time Mikulicz's sphere of activity extended from Breslau deep into Russia. For an appendicitis or gall bladder operation he might be called to Kharkov, St. Petersburg, or Moscow. Stories were told that when he worked in Russia, the authorities would have the street in front of the house where he was operating covered two feet deep in straw, so that the rattle of passing wagons would not disturb his operation. That, at any rate, was done in Kharkov. Mikulicz's private clinic in Breslau was sought out by patients from all over Europe. In his big, spacious house he entertained international society. All Breslau knew his teams of white and of black horses, which raced his carriage through the streets.

When we met in Rochester I had known Mikulicz for more than two decades. Nevertheless, many more years were to pass before I learned the inside story of what went on at his Breslau clinic and what his relations were with his associates. Thus, for example, I heard that Mikulicz had a lordly way of disregarding time and that it was rare indeed for him to appear at the clinic less than an hour and a half after the time appointed. His operations were constantly being postponed. This was undoubtedly due to his nocturnal habits. Since he would go on receiving private patients at ten and eleven o'clock at night, and would round out

the evening by attending some social function, his mornings
scarcely existed. His assistants and pupils, however, were held to
extreme punctuality, and found the everlasting waiting for him a
torment. The moment he entered his hospital, bells rang on all the
floors, and everyone had to be ready for the great man to appear.
With his restive temperament, he was constantly trying out new
methods and then casting them aside. But when all was told, he
had created a system which could hardly be surpassed. He had
added many refinements to Bergmann's aseptic technique. As a
matter of course, no one ever entered his operating room without
white gown, white trousers, white cap, and rubber gloves. In-
variably, the steam sterilizations were checked by strips of iodized
paper, and all instruments employed in an operation were handled
only with sterile forceps. He had introduced face masks and
forbidden needless talking in the operating room. Moreover, he had
become a veritable drillmaster in sterilization of the hands. He
had first of all demonstrated that it was impossible to make the
skin of the hands really germ-free. He had therefore introduced
sterile mesh gloves which were drawn over hands already cleaned
and cleaned again with soap, alcohol, and sublimate. These gloves
had to be changed frequently, but they permitted far more sterile
work than could be attained with bare hands. After every dis-
infection of the hands, smears were taken, especially from under
the nails, and subjected to microscopic examination. The names
of all the doctors were listed on a public bulletin board, and beside
each name the results of the examinations were unsparingly entered.
During his trip to the United States Mikulicz had learned of
Halsted's rubber gloves, and had promptly introduced them in
Breslau.

In keeping with his temperament, Mikulicz operated with extraordinary speed, and demanded the utmost of his assistants. He
never spoke loudly. But his merest murmur was enough to make
him feared. As I have remarked, he was noted for never praising
anyone. Complacency was abhorrent to him; he insisted on constant progress. In fact, he liked to see a certain amount of battling
among his doctors, for this he thought spurred them to further
efforts. The word "colleague" was banned in his hospital, at least
in his presence. If possible, he avoided telephone conversations
with his doctors, and preferred to send them written messages.

With volunteer assistants, such as Sauerbruch became on October 1, he virtually never spoke. Anyone who had been through an apprenticeship under Mikulicz was undoubtedly "somebody." But it was a harsh and bitter experience, that apprenticeship.

After a few days of this Sauerbruch was tempted to give up. After the first cold, offhand welcome, Mikulicz seemed no longer to see him. In the general frostiness, the newcomer felt himself altogether at a loss. He had no human contact save with one of the assistants named Bardenheuer.

Sauerbruch did not know that Mikulicz was having him carefully observed, and was himself watching him from a distance. After three weeks, which the young man spent between rebellious thoughts of throwing up the sponge and the consciousness that he must hold out for the sake of his scientific career, Mikulicz abruptly sent for him. The meeting was brief, stern in tone, without warmth. For the first time Mikulicz spoke of Sauerbruch's paper, which he had read in the United States. What he wanted from his assistants, he said, was research work. Then he told Sauerbruch what he had told me, though in quite a different manner, that evening in Rochester. He spoke of his lifelong dream of developing surgery of the esophagus, and of the obstacle of open pneumothorax which prevented the fulfillment of this dream. He outlined his experiments on animals in which he had vainly tried to keep the lungs intact by artificial respiration. And finally he presented Sauerbruch with his assignment: to examine still more carefully the physiological conditions of open pneumothorax and to search for a way to prevent collapse of the lung when the thorax had to be opened in surgery.

At this moment Mikulicz surely expected no solution, certainly no final solution, from the young man. He expected at best, as he later told me, some partial result which would lead him a bit further toward the distant goal. And Sauerbruch, who stood dumfounded in the face of so huge a task, was likewise without hope. Never before had he so much as considered the problem. But he could well imagine how many scientists had already vainly sought a solution to it—experienced men with far better equipment for the task.

When Sauerbruch left Mikulicz's office, he could already see himself failing in his attack on a hopeless undertaking. But by next morning, after a sleepless night, his latent determination to rise, to perform some extraordinary feat, had already begun to stir. He realized that here was his chance to climb at a single stroke, to become something and be something—if he found a solution, if he made the impossible possible. And so he went to work, intense ambition combining with his unusual technical gifts.

Mikulicz had given Sauerbruch a recommendation to Privy Councillor Filehne, head of the Pharmacological Institute in Breslau. Here Sauerbruch would be able to work. Ample numbers of dogs and rabbits were at his disposal.

Sauerbruch spent every hour of his free time on his assignment. Mikulicz had not relieved him of his ordinary duties at the hospital. But whenever Sauerbruch could spare a moment, he tore over to the institute and alternated between the cages of the animals and an improvised operating table. At night he read everything that had previously been written on the subject of open pneumothorax. There was a great deal, almost too much to be mastered in a short time. Nevertheless, he recognized that there was not enough. A great many questions were still unclarified.

Sauerbruch tried artificial respiration first. He opened the thoracic cavity of dogs and rabbits while a pump forced air into the lungs and sucked it out again. Like Mikulicz, he soon saw that this procedure could never be applied to operations on the thorax. It was unnatural and led to swelling of the lungs. Circulation was disturbed. Since the air was pumped through an artificial opening in the trachea, there was great difficulty in administering the anesthetic. Another way had to be found.

Sauerbruch began again. He operated on dogs without anesthesia, in order to obtain a completely clear picture of the problem. Perhaps anesthetics inhibited nerve reflexes, which in turn played a part in the phenomenal and fatal effect of open pneumothorax. When he opened both sides of the chest of an animal, the outside air penetrated into the thoracic cavity with a sharp, hissing noise. The lobes of the lungs collapsed, and their bright pink changed to a dirty purple. This was followed by several violent gasps, then arrest of respiration, and the heart ceased to beat.

There was no mystery about the cause of death when both lobes of the lung were stopped by open pneumothorax. But death also

Charles Mayo (left) *and William Mayo* (right). *Together they made the Mayo Clinic world-famous.*

The Mayo Clinic in Rochester, Minnesota, as it looked in the late 1940's.

Ferdinand Sauerbruch (1875–1951), whose low-pressure chamber cleared the way for pulmonary surgery.

Johannes von Mikulicz (1850–1905), Sauerbruch's supporter, and advocate of surgery of the thorax.

Ludolph Brauer (1865–1951), who pioneered the high-pressure method in surgery of the thorax.

ensued when the chest was opened only on one side and only one lobe collapsed. Forlanini's and Murphy's work on artificial pneumothorax had shown that a human being could live quite well with only one lobe of the lung active. Why, then, did death nevertheless follow after opening the chest on one side and cessation of respiration in a single lobe of the lung? Might the cause be the sudden displacement of the mediastinum between the lobes of the lung, thereby disturbing the undamaged part of the lung and displacing the heart, as Murphy had assumed? Was it due to disturbance of the nerves which regulated breathing? Was it due to sudden loss of warmth? Or to changes in blood pressure?

Sauerbruch undertook experiment after experiment upon rabbits and dogs. Working with only two laboratory attendants, the twenty-seven-year-old scientist performed an incredible amount of work. No word, of course, came from Mikulicz. The young man felt that he was further than ever from the solution to his problem of preventing open pneumothorax. But he took heart at discovering that so many of the details regarding the mechanism of pneumothorax were still unclarified. If he could clarify them and describe them, he had reason to hope that Mikulicz would approve his work. Fortunately for him, he was working in Germany, not in England, where the voice of the antivivisectionists was so strong. Innumerable animals died under his hands, with and without anesthesia. At last he achieved a first tentative result. He proved that death in cases of open pneumothorax on one side was not caused by the cessation of respiration on that side, not by disturbed nerve reflexes, not by displacement of the heart, not by change in blood pressure. What happened, rather, was that after sudden collapse of one lobe of the lung, its resistance was so lowered that more blood flowed into it than into the other, noncollapsed lung, which was under steady tension. The result was that only a modicum of the circulating blood could be enriched with oxygen in the still-functioning lobe. Thus, after a few violent, painful breaths, vain efforts to win oxygen, most of the experimental subjects died of asphyxiation.

Sauerbruch's work had reached this point when he suddenly discovered that he had come much closer to his actual goal than he had ever dared to hope. For if it was not the halting of respiration that caused death, then the problem in opening one side of the thoracic cavity was not to maintain respiration. It would suffice if he could maintain enough pressure in the nonfunctioning lung so that it would to some extent resist the circulating blood, thus keeping the normal supply of blood flowing into the functioning lobe where it could be sufficiently enriched with oxygen.

At this point the saving idea occurred to him. If the activity of one lobe of the lung could be dispensed with, if it were enough to prevent the collapse of this lobe, why not create around the lobe the same subatmospheric pressure which existed in the closed thorax? Suppose he enclosed his operating field in a box wherein this subpressure obtained, and did this before opening the thorax.

The interior pressure of the thoracic cavity was known. It was a negative pressure corresponding to a drop of about ten millimeters of mercury. This subpressure should be quite easy to obtain.

Sauerbruch had no real faith in this idea. It seemed to him too simple to be adequate. But he proceeded to construct a "box" which could be kept at a subpressure equal to the pressure within the thoracic cavity. He obtained a glass cylinder wide enough to receive, lengthwise, a dog's chest, and allowing sufficient room for the movement of the surgeon's two hands. The cylinder was closed on the two open ends with airtight gutta-percha paper, so that it looked like a glass drum. Into the paper on one end Sauerbruch cut a large hole, shaped to the upper abdomen of one of his smallest dogs. Into the other drumhead he cut three holes. One of these was large enough to permit the dog's head to pass through. The two other holes were for his forearms. Finally he installed an air pressure gauge in the cylinder, and made a further opening in the paper to admit a rubber tube.

This, then, was the apparatus Sauerbruch had conceived. As he later told me, the time spent patching together this device seemed to him endless. When it was done, it was already late evening, but he was violently tempted not to postpone the test until next day. The two laboratory assistants who had helped gave him an inquiring look. They, too, felt the tension and the ambition of participants in a new experiment. They felt themselves fellow conspirators and allies. Sauerbruch could not resist the temptation. He nodded. One of the attendants rushed off for a dog. He returned with the smallest of the laboratory dogs and placed it on the table. Sauerbruch himself administered anesthesia until the animal lay motionless before him, breathing regularly. The attendant thrust the dog's head and thorax through the larger opening on one end of the cylinder. The other attendant drew the head through the opening on the opposite end, until only the dog's chest was left inside. Then both openings were made airtight with strips of adhesive pasted to the dog's neck and abdomen. Sauerbruch deposited the instruments he would need inside the cylinder. He put both hands through the openings left for that purpose. Then one of the attendants taped up the edges of these openings also, making an airtight seal with the skin of Sauerbruch's arm. The other attendant took the end of the rubber tube into his mouth.

Sauerbruch now stood stooped over the cylinder, the dog's head level with his waist. He must not make a single awkward motion or the paper would tear, the adhesive strips loosen. Over the rims of his glasses he looked at the air pressure gauge while the attendant began sucking out the air. The column of mercury reached minus five, minus eight, then minus ten millimeters. Now the pressure in the cylinder was the same as that in the dog's thoracic cavity.

His back aching, scarcely able to move his forearms, depending largely upon the mobility of wrists and fingers, Sauerbruch opened

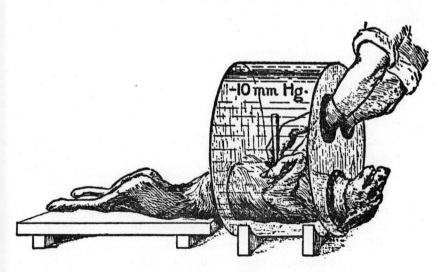

Sauerbruch's first low-pressure cylinder.

the dog's chest with a few big incisions on both sides. The pink lungs were revealed. Now the lung ought to collapse, as had always happened before. But nothing of the sort happened. For all his hopes, for all his theorizing, it still seemed inconceivable to Sauerbruch that he had succeeded. And yet there it was—the lung did not collapse.

But something else was happening—something even more incomprehensible and wonderful. The respiration of the lung continued, although so much of the chest had been incised. There could be only one explanation of this: apparently only small parts of the thorax and a few auxiliary muscles were necessary to keep the lung performing its respiratory movements, so long as its collapse was prevented.

Sauerbruch stood looking down at the animal's chest—for one, then two minutes. There was no change. It was no longer possible to doubt the result. He had been right. In a low-pressure chamber like his cylinder, only many times larger, perhaps large enough for the surgeon to sit inside, chest operations could be performed and the thoracic cavity opened without danger of fatal pneumothorax. With the aid of such a cabinet, one could forestall the deadly collapse which had hitherto made the lung forbidden territory in spite of all the progress of surgery in other fields.

Sauerbruch was still caught up in all these thoughts when he heard a low, whistling sound. Too late, he realized what was happening, what had already happened. Probably the unnatural posture had produced an involuntary movement of his arm. Probably there was a tear in the paper. At any rate, he saw with horror that the column of mercury was rising. Air from outside was entering the cylinder. Before Sauerbruch's eyes the animal's lung collapsed on both sides. There were a few gasping respiratory motions, and before Sauerbruch had time to attempt closing the incision, the animal was dead.

Silently, Sauerbruch withdrew his hands. Innumerable animals had died in this room. But this one need not have died, not at this moment when the saving principle, the very principle by which pneumothorax could be overcome, had already been discovered.

Quickly, however, a sense of the tremendous importance of his discovery banished this brief dismay. The idea was sound. In spite of the unfortunate outcome, there could be no doubt that it was right. The first part of the experiment had already proved this. The only difficulty was that the apparatus was too crude, too susceptible to damage.

During the following days Sauerbruch and his assistants devised a new and improved low-pressure cabinet. The drumhead walls were now made of rubber rather than paper; this was less likely to tear. In the course of the next week the apparatus was built, and Sauerbruch resumed his experiments on dogs and rabbits. Now operation after operation succeeded. Within the shelter of his subpressure cabinet, Sauerbruch opened the thoracic cavities of one animal after the other. None of the lungs collapsed; all continued their respiration. Sauerbruch sewed up the incisions so carefully that no air could penetrate after the animals were removed from the cylinder. The animals awoke from the anesthesia, the wounds healed, and the dogs and rabbits lived on without any detectable disturbance. They ate; they hopped cheerfully about in their cages. The principle was unshakable. The great goal, which at the start had seemed so unattainable, which scientists of vastly greater experience had pursued in vain, had been reached in barely two months. Sauerbruch felt uplifted by a surge of triumph. As yet no one but himself and the attendants knew what had happened. Not even Professor Filehne had been informed. But now Sauerbruch was so sure of himself that he reported to Mikulicz.

Two days later Sauerbruch made his report. In the succinct manner Mikulicz required of his inferiors, he stated that he had found a method for opening the thorax without producing open pneumothorax. Mikulicz stared at his volunteer assistant with frank annoyance. He replied sharply that he had turned the job over to Sauerbruch because he had assumed that Sauerbruch knew how to work scientifically.

In his state of nervousness, Sauerbruch at first did not understand. It took him a long moment to realize that Mikulicz simply did not credit his words. Mikulicz was taking it for granted that Sauerbruch had deceived himself and would now rob him of valuable time with a supposed success which would not stand scientific examination. Pulling himself together, Sauerbruch repeated his statement. This time he added that at the Pharmacological Institute he had built a low-pressure cabinet and opened a dog's thorax inside the cabinet. These words startled Mikulicz and brought him to his feet. With a hasty gesture he asked Sauerbruch to repeat the explanation once more.

Sauerbruch did so. Once more Mikulicz threw a cold, penetrating, mistrustful look at his assistant's face. But the words "subpressure cabinet" had started a train of thought. He asked Sauerbruch to show him this cabinet. The unfulfilled dream of his lifetime was of enough importance to him to justify the sacrifice of fifteen minutes, even at the risk of the whole thing's proving merely a young man's premature enthusiasm. Without wasting another word, in as tearing a hurry as ever, Mikulicz accompanied Sauerbruch to the Pharmacological Institute.

Mikulicz later told me of the events of that morning. He confined himself to the simple, factual comment that Sauerbruch had convinced him by performing a number of truly amazing experiments, and that thereafter all the resources of his hospital were devoted to putting Sauerbruch's idea into practice on a large scale. When Sauerbruch went to Rochester a number of years later to demonstrate his cabinet to the Mayos, he told an entirely different tale. It was as dramatic as Sauerbruch's own temperament. Many of its details sound overdrawn, as though exaggerated for the sake of a good story, the kind of story Sauerbruch loved. Nevertheless, since he himself pictured these crucial hours of his life in such terms, the story must have a core of truth.

According to Sauerbruch, when Mikulicz entered the basement of the Pharmacological Institute the two laboratory assistants were already waiting in the background. The subpressure cabinet, in its new, improved form, stood on the improvised operating table. Everything was ready for the experiment.

Sauerbruch beckoned to the attendants while Mikulicz, with a probing, suspicious air, went up to the glass drum. The attendants brought a rabbit. It was chloroformed and placed in the cabinet. The airtight rubber diaphragms around chest and neck were fastened in place. Sauerbruch thrust his hands and instruments into the cylinder. The openings around his arms were also sealed. Everything went according to plan. Mikulicz did not say a word.

He merely watched. But he watched with increasing alertness and excitement.

One of the assistants took the tube into his mouth and sucked out the air. The pressure inside the cabinet dropped to the proper level. Sauerbruch threw a final nervous glance at Mikulicz's bearded face. He had all he could do to keep his hands from shaking.

At last he made the incision into the rabbit's skin over the chest, severed the musculature and pleura between two ribs—and at that moment heard a familiar, delicate hissing that made him hold his breath. It was the same sound he had heard when his first experimental subject died. For the first few seconds Sauerbruch refused to believe that the mishap could be repeating itself. The new device was so much better. Its material was resistant to tearing. The rubber diaphragms were ideal for the purpose. All previous experiments had turned out well. But even as this indignant, desperate "Impossible!" rang through his mind, the experiment was over. The rabbit's lung had collapsed. The mediastinum fluttered once or twice, for the duration of a few heartbeats. Then the animal was dead. It did not matter where the fault lay, what the causes were—the experiment had failed.

For a long moment there was a frightful silence in the room. Sauerbruch stood stooped, his hands still imprisoned in the cabinet. He did not need to look at Mikulicz's face to know what it expressed. And then he heard his superior's voice, that voice which was never raised even during the tensest moments of an operation, even when he angrily, impatiently reproved an assistant or a nurse. Now it was loud and outraged. Perhaps Sauerbruch was too shattered to hear precisely what Mikulicz was saying. When he told the story in Rochester, he had Mikulicz call him "swindler," and later inveighing against "criminal frivolity." At any rate, Mikulicz forbade Sauerbruch to continue, withdrew the assignment, expelled him from his hospital.

This was too much for a man of Sauerbruch's self-esteem and temperament. His knowledge that he was in the right, his vexation at the unfortunate mischance, his resentment at the treatment he had received from Mikulicz, robbed him of all prudence. Violently he pulled his hands from the drum. Later on, he could no longer know exactly what he had replied. At one time he had himself saying that he could not remain any longer in Mikulicz's prison anyhow. At another time he put even stronger words into his mouth. In any case, he found himself suddenly alone, that December day, with his glass cylinder and two pale, trembling laboratory assistants. Mikulicz had stormed out of the laboratory. Sauerbruch had done the worst thing possible. He had not only had bad luck; he had failed to defend himself in scientific, objective language. Instead, he had shouted at Mikulicz.

That same day Sauerbruch's meager belongings were transferred from the hospital to a furnished room. Sauerbruch thought defiantly of leaving Breslau at once, of beginning anew somewhere else. But after what had happened he would scarcely be able to enter a larger institution where he could develop and test his idea, whose soundness he did not for a moment doubt. Should he apply for a post at some small country hospital or go back to a rural practice once more? Impossible—that would mean the end of his hopes. His ambition did not forsake him, even at this low point. He firmly believed that he held the key to a career, and that he must not let it go. He must prove the validity of his principle so conclusively that if not Mikulicz, some other important medical personality would be convinced and would give him the equipment to continue his work on a generous scale. But how? He had no money, no laboratory, no animals.

In this crisis he was aided by chance. Mikulicz had enemies as well as friends and admirers in Breslau. There were those who envied him; there were those who mocked at him for his idiosyncrasies. Some groups had decided that he was a morphine addict; they adduced his restlessness as proof. Various colleagues made fun of his haste and his unpunctuality, although they also admitted his greatness. Luckily, Sauerbruch met one of the latter sort. This man listened to Sauerbruch's tale and allowed him— not out of scientific interest, but in order to play a trick on Mikulicz—to experiment in his house. The same patron who half a year before had provided Sauerbruch with funds for his vacation to Bavaria now offered to finance the experiments.

Sauerbruch built a third subpressure cabinet. He obtained rabbits, operated again, and had an unbroken series of successes in his experiments, in spite of the fact that he worked without assistants. He developed funnellike openings of rubber which accommodated his arms during the operation. He himself sucked out the air. Never-

theless, there was not a single untoward incident. Rabbits who had
had their chests sewed up inside the drum were hopping about spryly
within a short time after operation. Sauerbruch began making
sketches for a larger subpressure cabinet. He wanted to build a
chamber big enough for himself to sit inside beside the animal.
Only the animal's head would protrude. But such a structure was
too expensive. It would have to be provided with an airtight door.
The requisite subpressure could not be obtained by simply sucking
out the air. He would need an air pump and an assistant to run
it; he would need valves; he would need innumerable things for
which his funds would never suffice.

He could not appeal to his patron again. The doctor in whose
house he was working was not really interested in the problem
as such.

For the second time Sauerbruch faced a crisis, faced the collapse
of all his hopes of an outstanding career in science. And for the
second time chance came to his aid. Sauerbruch met an assistant
from Mikulicz's clinic with whom he had struck up something of
a friendship before his expulsion. This man was Dr. Anschütz,
who was engaged to Mikulicz's eldest daughter. Anschütz asked
how he was getting on, and Sauerbruch, overcoming his stubborn
pride, told Anschütz the whole story.

Anschütz went with him to the room in which he had been
conducting his experiments. And Sauerbruch showed him his
chest operation on a rabbit. Anschütz watched skeptically, but
skepticism vanished as he grasped the significance of what he had
seen. It was overwhelming. The two men came to an agreement.
Sauerbruch would apologize to Mikulicz for his "outburst" if
Anschütz succeeded, in view of his prospective family connection
with Mikulicz, in convincing the despot that he had indeed been
overhasty in his judgment, and persuaded him to witness one more
experiment.

Sauerbruch hoped Mikulicz would come, but he dared not
believe it. Would the arrogant Mikulicz descend from the lofty
heights of his position and deign to pay a call on a dismissed
volunteer assistant? Only one thing could move him to this: the
intensity of his desire to see his life's dream fulfilled, to be able
to undertake surgery of the thorax. This would have to prove
stronger than his pride.

That very day the improbable happened: Mikulicz announced that he was coming. Early in the afternoon Mikulicz stepped into Sauerbruch's cellar laboratory. He seemed composed; only the more rapid twitching of his features betrayed his agitation. Outwardly he was all condescension, all aloofness.

Not a word was said about their last meeting. Mikulicz watched in silence as Sauerbruch, this time aided by Anschütz, made his preparations. He operated on the rabbit. He exposed an entire lobe of the lung. The animal went on breathing. No pneumothorax ensued. Without haste, Sauerbruch sewed up the wound and opened the cylinder. The rabbit came out of the anesthesia, and lived.

Sauerbruch looked at the face of his adversary. He could read nothing in the expression. At last Mikulicz spoke. He asked for a second experiment. This, too, went off well.

From that moment on Mikulicz was a changed man. It was not hard to guess what had startled this cold, aloof person out of his usual reserve. He undoubtedly realized that he had reached the gateway to his lifelong goal. What Sauerbruch had done here with animals must be possible with human beings also. If the apparatus were enlarged, if this ridiculous little drum were converted into a large room which would itself be the operating room . . .

Between the older and the younger man, between Mikulicz at the peak of his career and Sauerbruch struggling to take the first step upwards, an alliance had suddenly come into being such as had never existed between Mickulicz and any of his other assistants.

Placing one of his proud, skilled hands on the humble contrivance his assistant had fashioned, Mikulicz asked Sauerbruch to return to his hospital. He promised that he would place all available equipment at his disposal, would help him to perfect the subpressure cabinet until it could be used for operating on a human being.

The following day, to the amazement of the other volunteers and regular assistants, Sauerbruch returned to the hospital in triumph. But there was little time for celebrating. The very next day he set to work with an intensity beyond anything he had yet manifested.

The construction of a new subpressure cabinet was begun. For the present this was intended only for experiments on animals, but it was to be roomy enough for a surgeon and one assistant. It was six feet long, three feet wide and four and one half feet high, of strong boards and lined inside with sheet metal, the joints soldered to make it airtight. The roof was formed of a large sheet of glass, so that the operations could be observed from outside. The edges of the door were faced with rubber. On one side was an opening with a rubber cowl which permitted the animal's head to extend outside the chamber without breaking the air seal. The whole body of the animal lay on the operating table inside the chamber. On either side of the table were stools for the operator and his assistant. A vacuum pump and valve assured maintenance of pressure at the required low level.

When Sauerbruch first had himself locked into this chamber, with one assistant and an animal, he was still in the dark about the effect of the low pressure upon the operators. Once they were inside the chamber they could no longer communicate with those outside, except by signs. The roar of the pump motor made speech impossible. Whatever instruments were needed for the operation had to be inside the chamber. Otherwise the whole procedure of locking up and establishing the subpressure would have to be repeated.

The first time, Sauerbruch and his assistant remained in the chamber half an hour. The low pressure scarcely troubled them. But the accumulation of heat and moisture was a nuisance. They tried longer and longer stays in the chamber. After an hour, both would come out dripping with perspiration. After two hours they were soaking wet. But it was quite possible to operate for two hours and more. Mikulicz now took part in all the subsequent experiments. Usually he did not find time for this until nine or ten o'clock in the evening, when the rest of the day's work was done. But then he would shut himself up in the chamber with Sauerbruch and operate until eleven.

Mikulicz and Sauerbruch did not have a single accident due to failure of the low-pressure installation. They performed major resections of one and of both sides of the thorax. They opened the mediastinum. And finally Mikulicz succeeded in operating upon the esophagus of a dog. He removed part of the esophagus and sewed the ends together. The animal survived the operation. Another dog survived simultaneous opening of the thoracic cavity, severing and suturing of the esophagus, opening of the mediastinum, and even opening and suturing of the pericardium.

This work went on until the beginning of 1904. Then, for the first time, the cabinet was demonstrated to foreign visitors, including Dr. Scudder of Boston and Dr. Ranzy, an assistant to the Austrian surgeon von Eiselsberg, who, like Mikulicz, had been a pupil of Billroth. In the course of the discussion that followed, a new idea was born, though none of the participants could have stated exactly whose it was. Since the collapse of the lung could be averted as long as its exterior surface was in an artificially engendered low-pressure atmosphere, would it not be even simpler to attain the same goal by increasing the pressure inside the lungs? What would happen if the animal's head instead of its body was enclosed in the chamber, and if, instead of exhausting some of the air in the chamber, a higher-than-atmospheric pressure was created inside? When the animal inhaled the air at higher pressure, would not its lungs likewise be protected from pneumothorax? If this idea were correct, the operators would be freed of their difficult work in the confinement of the chamber. They could then work outside, although an assistant would have to remain inside the chamber to administer the anesthesia.

On January 17, 1904, an experiment of this sort was conducted. The head of the dog remained in the cabinet. Mikulicz's assistant, Dr. Heile, was locked into the room and administered the anesthetic. Mikulicz and Anschütz, outside, opened the dog's thoracic cavity—and the animal went on breathing as normally as in the low-pressure chamber. The method could be reversed. But then it turned out that after twenty minutes inside Dr. Heile was suffering so severely from the effects of the chloroform that he staggered when released from the chamber. Conjointly, Sauerbruch experimented with having the animals breathe through a tracheal cannula, the air being supplied under high pressure by a precision pump. The lungs did not collapse with this method either. But Sauerbruch had the impression that the whole high-pressure method was "unphysiological." Where the thoracic cavity was opened on one side, the unaffected lung was compressed. In Sauerbruch's opinion there were serious disturbances of circulation in the lungs, and the heart was overburdened; a healthy animal's heart might endure this, but not the already overburdened hearts of human patients. Mikulicz and Sauerbruch therefore abandoned as unnatural and useless any further experiments with above-normal pressures.

Mikulicz gave orders for the creation of a pressure cabinet fully equipped with all necessary technical apparatus, including telephonic connection to the rooms outside. It was to be big enough for surgeon and assistants to move about freely, and for an operating table large enough to hold a person. The engineering devices allowed for the possibility of producing high pressure in the chamber. Mikulicz expected that the effect of chloroform in the enlarged space would not be so distressing as it had been in the first experiment. But the idea of hyperpressure was considered only as a very remote variation. The decision on sub-

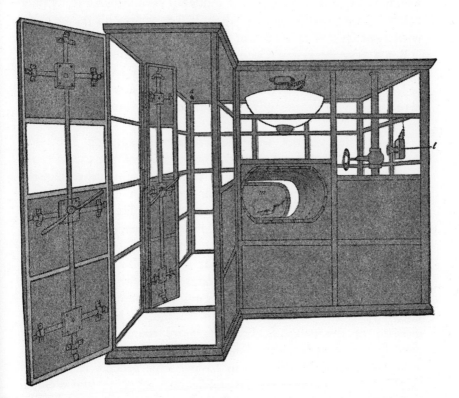

The low-pressure chamber, measuring 14 cubic meters, built to Mikulicz's specifications after Sauerbruch's ideas, in Breslau, 1904.

pressure had already been made. The plans called for completion of this chamber by February 14, 1904. At the same time Mikulicz informed the secretary of the Thirty-third Congress of the German Society for Surgery, which was to meet April 6, that his assistant, Ferdinand Sauerbruch, would address that body on "The Physiological and Physical Bases for Intrathoracic Operations in My Pneumatic Cabinet." At the same time Mikulicz himself announced a lecture on "Surgical Experiences with the Sauerbruch Cabinet."

Sauerbruch was as excited as an actor facing opening night. On January 25 he published, with Mikulicz's aid, his first report on the pressure cabinet in the *Deutsches Zentralblatt für Chirurgie*. Full of suspense, he waited for the first reactions. They were not particularly momentous. Surgeons did not believe that this method, which sounded so simple, could suddenly revolutionize the whole field of chest surgery. Most of them laid Sauerbruch's report aside with a shrug, if they read it at all.

But a few interested visitors called at the clinic. They were received cordially and shown the cabinet. They left Breslau more or less firmly convinced that something wholly new was beginning here, something whose importance for the future might be immeasurable.

Among the visitors was the Heidelberg surgeon Professor Petersen, who had recognized the importance of the experiments at once. Petersen, a young scientist who had distinguished himself in cancer research, personally took part in an operation on an animal in the small chamber, and returned to Heidelberg deeply impressed. This was about the middle of February. Mikulicz and Sauerbruch attached no further importance to his visit. At the moment Mikulicz was battling for a favorable date for Sauerbruch's lecture at the Berlin congress. Sauerbruch's name as yet meant nothing in medical circles and the committee was highly unco-operative. In fact, Sauerbruch had still to be accepted as a member of the congress. His procedure sounded fantastic, especially to the older men. Finally, however, by exerting all his prestige, Mikulicz succeeded in having Sauerbruch's lecture announced for a particularly favorable time—namely, two o'clock in the afternoon on the very first day of the congress. As for Sauerbruch, he may have dreamed of winning glory, but now that it was actually happening, the swiftness of this rise from the insignificance of a volunteer assistant to the status of a preferred speaker at the congress of German surgeons was dizzying.

In the midst of the preparations for the great event, Sauerbruch received from Heidelberg the offprint of an article which had just been published in Strassburg in the *Hoppe-Seylersche Zeitschrift für physiologische Chemie.* Its title was *An Essential Simplification of Sauerbruch's Method of Artificial Respiration.* One of the authors was that same Professor Petersen who had recently visited Breslau. The principal author, however, was Professor Ludolph Brauer, later to become the energetic advocate of artificial pneumothorax. Brauer was the sender of the offprint, and his accompanying note read modestly: "Perhaps this small modification may make some contribution to Sauerbruch's ideas and the Sauerbruch method of operation."

Brauer had read Sauerbruch's first publication at the same time as Petersen, and his own imaginative faculties had been stimulated. It was he who had urged Petersen to visit Breslau. No sooner had Petersen returned and reported on what he had seen than Brauer conceived the idea of reversing the Sauerbruch process, altogether independently of Sauerbruch and Mikulicz, for he knew nothing of their experiments with hyperpressure and their discarding of the idea. Petersen demurred, although no one in Breslau had mentioned the hyperpressure experiments to him. If reversal were so simple, he reasoned, the group in Breslau would long ago have hit upon it. But Brauer would not be discouraged. He began experimenting, at first quite by himself. As it happened, he hit at once upon the right way, that is, the way which was to prove the method of the future and which today has altogether supplanted the Sauerbruch cabinet. Brauer recognized that the cabinet would necessarily remain far too expensive and too involved to be introduced into everyday surgical practice. He therefore thought out and in a short time tested several hyperpressure procedures, some of which approached the experiments of Mikulicz and Sauerbruch, but all of which had special qualities of their own and which, indeed, produced results so good that Brauer, unlike his Breslau predecessors, was not in the least inclined to write off this procedure. On the contrary, he was convinced of its efficacy. Brauer's idea was to construct an airtight mask to enclose the face of an animal or patient. From an oxygen bottle under the desired hyperpressure, a tube would feed oxygen into the mask. Part of the stream of oxygen could traverse a bottle of ether, thereby making possible simultaneous anesthesia.

At first this was only an idea, and Brauer left its careful working out to the near future. This was also true of his second procedure; as yet it was only a proposal. He proposed (as Mikulicz and Sauerbruch had actually already done) placing only the head of an animal in an airtight chamber and creating a hyperpressure inside this chamber. Unlike Mickulicz and Sauerbruch, he would avoid danger to the anesthetist by using a small chamber, just large enough for the head of the subject and the hands of the anesthetist. Here, too, Brauer was aware that a good deal of technical development would be necessary, if only to cope with the problem of vomiting under anesthesia. Consequently, he had for the present performed all his hyperpressure experiments with the aid of tracheotomy. Here again his work was similar to Sauerbruch's, but quite different in result. The decisive factor was that he abandoned completely the use of a pump to generate pressure and substituted an oxygen bottle with its unvarying pressure. In his experimental subjects he had made an incision into the trachea. Through this incision he introduced a T-shaped cannula. To one end of the horizontal pipe of the T he attached the oxygen flask. A branching tube at the neck of the flask led part of the stream of oxygen past a flask of ether. From the other end of the horizontal pipe a rubber tube led through an air chamber, which served to balance the pressure, into a water-filled vessel. By lowering or raising the end of the tube in the water the desired pressure could be simply regulated.

Brauer's subjects breathed under above-normal pressure, and at the same time inhaled the anesthetic.

Brauer had opened the abdominal cavities of animals several times, using this procedure, and had encountered no difficulties. Finally he felt sufficiently sure of himself to demonstrate his work to the skeptical Petersen, whereupon the surgeon became his enthusiastic ally. Petersen continued the operations. He was able to make comparisons with what he had seen in Breslau, and he soon became convinced that the hyperpressure method permitted chest operations quite as successful as those performed in the cabinet, with the advantage that all the complicated apparatus of the chamber could be dispensed with. When Brauer published his report during the second week in March, he undoubtedly had not the slightest intention of challenging Sauerbruch's priority in the discovery of the fundamental process of pressure differential. That was clear from his citing Sauerbruch's name twice in the title of his article. But he wanted to announce an improvement which, so far as he knew, no one in Breslau had thought of. The reasons for his haste are, as he gave them, thoroughly credible: he felt that his announcement should be made before hospitals began building expensive cabinets.

Sauerbruch, however, when he received this offprint of Brauer's article right in the midst of the preparations for the Berlin surgeons' congress, was stunned. True, he and Mikulicz had experimented with hyperpressure before Brauer. But it was also true that he and Mikulicz had abandoned these experiments, and evidently abandoned them too soon. Moreover, the idea of using oxygen was indubitably Brauer's. Sauerbruch was intelligent enough to recognize the weaknesses of his cabinet—its complication and its expense. He was also intelligent enough to foresee that the future belonged to the simplified hyperpressure procedure, if Brauer's belief in it proved justified. It must have been a crushing thought that his cabinet might be outmoded before it was even made known to the medical world. On the eve of his dreamed-of triumph he thought himself victim of the fate of those whose uncontested priority in a great discovery was threatened by a development of greater importance to the future, even before that priority could be established firmly in the eyes of the world. In his first shock he failed to see that in any case he could not be robbed of his credit as discoverer of the method of pressure difference, that he was the pioneer and Brauer only the disciple who had devised a better technique. Even if he could have seen this, he refused to recognize such a division of the glory, and he was convinced that Mikulicz, too, would not accept it. Was the big subpressure cabinet even now being built to be deprived of its significance before it was completed?

On March 26, ten days before the opening of the surgeons' congress the dispute reached the scientific public. Sauerbruch now reacted openly to Brauer's article on the improvement of his procedure, and published his retort in the *Centralblatt für Chirurgie.*

Since he could not claim that Petersen had been informed in Breslau of his own hyperpressure experiments, he had to admit that Brauer had arrived at his idea independently. Nor did he contest the fact that Brauer—unlike Mikulicz and himself—had followed this method through in analysis and in experiment. Even as he granted these points, however, he exposed his bitterness. He took pains to diminish the importance of Brauer's work. "We do not question the fact that Professor Brauer arrived at his idea spontaneously, since, as we have mentioned, most of our colleagues who saw our subpressure-chamber procedure had the same thought." Nor could Sauerbruch pretend that he and Mikulicz had not abandoned the hyperpressure procedure. Therefore he attempted to demonstrate that they were right in doing so. He stuck to his thesis that the hyperpressure method was dangerous, and would not believe that it had any genuine chance of succeeding. For all his outward reasonableness, this dogged attitude could easily be read between the lines.

Meanwhile the congress of the German Society for Surgery was drawing near. On Tuesday, April 5, Mikulicz and Sauerbruch set out for Berlin, taking their small subpressure cabinet with them. For the first time Sauerbruch stayed at one of the big Berlin hotels, the Bristol. For the first time he felt that he belonged in such a place.

At ten o'clock on the morning of April 6 the hundreds of members of the congress assembled in the white-and-gold auditorium of Langenbeck House. Professor Heinrich Braun of Göttingen, the pioneer in local anesthesia, was chairman. The usual introductory speeches must have seemed interminably long to Sauerbruch; unbearably long the papers that were read, and the noon recess. At last two o'clock came. At last the subpressure cabinet was placed behind the lectern—and Sauerbruch stepped up on the platform. Hundreds of eyes were trained upon him, a thin young man of twenty-eight who was now to rise out of obscurity and anonymity.

He plunged straight into his subject: "The principal reasons for the hesitance of surgeons to deal with diseases of the organs of the thorax have been the peculiar physical conditions in the thoracic cavity. . . ." Then followed his report, on the pressure-differential procedure, on his cabinet, its development, the operations on seventy-eight dogs, not a single one of whom had died. Although he was quivering inwardly with excitement, he could sense the astonishment, the incredulity, and also the close attentiveness of his audience. The foremost surgeons of Germany, and many foreigners, were listening to him. He had been given twenty minutes to speak. But all the while he delivered his carefully prepared text, Brauer was on his mind. He had scarcely reached the middle of his address when he turned to the problem of hyperpressure. We may surmise, though there is no way of proving this, that Sauerbruch would never had devoted so much space to this aspect of the matter had it not been for Brauer's publication. At any rate, he now did all in his power to emphasize that the hyperpressure procedure had also been discovered in Breslau. And he likewise attempted to prove that the method was unfeasible and had therefore quite justly been discarded. Then he returned with all the greater earnestness to a description of the subpressure cabinet which stood behind him all the while, and toward the end of his address declared: "On the basis of our experiences with animals we believe we may express the hope that this method will prove practicable for employment with human beings also."

Sauerbruch left the platform. The applause was brief, but considerable for so young a man. Then Mikulicz went up to the lectern to reinforce the impression his pupil had made. The title of his paper was *Surgical Experiences with the Sauerbruch Cabinet under Low and High Pressure*. He gave the term "high pressure" a peculiar emphasis, as if to imply that he was backing Sauerbruch's claim to priority in this procedure also. However, he said very little about the hyperpressure method, beyond reiterating Sauerbruch's thesis that it was unphysiological. Then he turned to the future applications of the pressure procedure.

Mikulicz was not a good speaker. His voice lacked strength, and he glanced down at his manuscript too frequently. He seemed hasty and nervous. But what he had to say, even if its fully revolutionary significance was disputed, was dramatic enough to command the close attention of everyone. Mikulicz painted a picture of a great future for surgery of the chest, based upon Sauerbruch's fundamental discovery. He suggested the possibility of operating upon the heart in the future, perhaps even curing innate or acquired organic defects which no surgeon had hitherto been able to touch. And then he reached his favorite subject: surgery of the esophagus. He discussed the dogs he had already operated on, and proclaimed the dawn of hope for human beings with illnesses of the esophagus which had hitherto been considered inoperable.

Mikulicz's speech made a great impression, in spite of the reservations which were swelled by rumors of the priority dispute in the background. Consequently, the audience was displeased when Brauer and Petersen took the floor immediately after Mikulicz. As was only natural, the general distaste for priority quarrels was directed against the two speakers who were obviously bent on setting forth their position in this altercation.

Petersen took an appeasing tone: Sauerbruch, he said, deserved the priority in discovery of the hyperpressure procedure also. But Brauer was a fighter. He described the fundamental idea of the hyperpressure mask and declared that in the future it would be adopted as the preferred method for chest operations. He concluded with some remarks addressed to Sauerbruch: "Never has progress in medicine been linked in the long run to a single name. Alongside the man who formulated the basic idea, there have always been collaborators and followers. And so Sauerbruch's important discovery will engage the attention of many men in the years to come, and will inevitably lead to a simplification and practical application of his process. It is precisely the work of the many, to which I should like to contribute my modest portion, that makes possible happy progress for medicine as a whole." Certainly this was an acute observation and one which correctly limned the future of Sauerbruch's technique. But Sauerbruch immediately took up the gauntlet. He reiterated his reasons for thinking the hyperpressure method dangerous. Brauer answered, Petersen answered, Sauerbruch, Brauer, Sauerbruch—until at last Braun, the chairman, rang his bell for silence. He put an end to the dispute with the word: "It seems to me that Sauerbruch's procedure opens the way for future progress in operations upon the lung and in the thoracic cavity in general. But I do not believe we shall make any headway in this discussion, and I am convinced that if there is any good in the method, we shall hear more than enough about it in the course of the coming year."

The great scene, the introduction of Sauerbruch's discovery, had played itself out. Brauer had publicly testified his indebtedness to Sauerbruch. Mikulicz made an effort to adjudicate the matter by declaring publicly: "I gladly take this opportunity to state expressly that Professor Brauer independently developed the hyperpressure procedure and has assumed the task of perfecting it technically. There is no doubt that if the hyperpressure procedure should prove its validity not only in experiments upon animals but in operations upon men as well, it will constitute an essential technical simplification of the whole method."

For Mikulicz and Sauerbruch the pressure cabinet under construction became the center of concern. By the early spring of 1904 it stood ready in the Breslau clinic. It was more than six feet in height, and the upper half was entirely sheathed in glass so that spectators, students, and interested doctors could follow the events within. The valves were so constructed that the pressure of the air could be adjusted to fractions of millimeters. A reserve pump was built in, in case the motorized pump should fail, thus endangering the patient's life. In the event that the motor of the second pump should also fail, a hand pump stood ready. The airtight rubber seal which was placed around the patient's neck was constructed with utmost care, in order hermetically to seal off the head, which was outside the chamber, from the interior.

Mikulicz began by operating on more than a dozen large dogs. Without exception, all survived the opening of the thoracic cavity and various types of surgery inside the thorax. Then, at last, Mikulicz decided to venture a first attempt on a human being.

By then it was the end of June. Mikulicz's first patient was a woman, one of those unfortunates whom cancer of the esophagus doomed to slow starvation. News of the impending experiment created a great stir. Doctors and students thronged around the cabinet while the patient was placed inside, and Mikulicz, Sauerbruch, and Anschütz had themselves shut up with her. The air pressure dropped to the necessary level. Outside, the faces of the spectators were pressed against the glass as Mikulicz made his first incisions into the thoracic cavity.

But then the horrible accident occurred. The air pressure in the chamber began to rise. The low pressure could not be maintained. The patient's head fell to one side. All was over before anything could be done to help her. She was already dead. Pneumothorax, which the cabinet was supposed to prevent, had killed her almost instantly.

Neither Mikulicz nor Sauerbruch ever spoke, so far as I know, of the feelings they must have had after this disaster. The cabinet was brand-new and had been tested repeatedly. Its failure remained a mystery. Was this only the workings of some diabolic chance? Would it be repeated? Did they dare expose another patient to the possibility of such an accident?

By the end of the first week in July, Mikulicz and Sauerbruch had recovered from their shock. Mikulicz, at any rate, decided to operate in the cabinet once more. Once again his patient was a woman, this time suffering from a slowly growing tumor under the sternum which could not be removed without opening the thoracic cavity. For the second time the chamber doors closed behind the three doctors. Once again faces pressed against the panes. As he worked Mikulicz glanced rapidly between the operating field and the pressure gauge. He opened the thorax, cut out large parts of the ribs with a rib shears. The lung lay broadly exposed. And this time nothing went wrong. For the first time a tumor under the sternum was extirpated. The wall of the thorax was closed again. Breathing peacefully, the patient was carried out of the cabinet. Ten days later she left the hospital, all unknowing that she had been the first to demonstrate the virtues of the pressure-differential technique. Mikulicz now saw the fulfillment of his lifelong dream drawing near. It was an hour of exaltation.

A few weeks later Sauerbruch saved the life of a third patient, with cancer of the breast. This time, in the course of the deep operation the thoracic cavity was accidentally pierced. Sauerbruch had her rushed into the pressure cabinet before pneumothorax could kill her.

By the time another few weeks had passed sixteen operations had been performed in the cabinet, eight upon the lung and five upon the esophagus. Because of the poor healing qualities of the esophagus, the operations upon this organ showed indifferent results. But that did not reflect upon the pressure-differential procedure, which for the first time had enabled surgery to approach the lung and esophagus. Further work was necessary so that surgeons might acquire experience in this newly opened field, but the road to greater successes, to surgical conquest of the whole area of the thorax, seemed to lie clear and straight ahead.

Then something came to pass that struck Sauerbruch like a bolt from the blue. Mikulicz, the man to whom he owed the initial stimulus, Mikulicz, who had sponsored the whole affair, was suddenly snatched away. The manner in which this happened made Mikulicz one more example of that odd medical tragedy: that doctors die of the diseases they have spent the major part of their lives in fighting.

As I discovered afterwards, it had struck even persons who did not know him too well that Mikulicz had aged very quickly after his return from his visit to the United States. In America I had observed no changes in him, except perhaps for the gray streaks in his hair and the rather sallow cast of his face. But his color had never been especially good.

In Breslau this early aging in a man not yet fifty-five was attributed to the nervous tenor of his life and work. When I saw Mikulicz for the last time at the Berlin surgeons' congress he seemed still extremely vital. Perhaps the development of surgery of the chest and the stir it had aroused in Berlin had given him a last lift.

In the summer of 1904 he suffered from a siege of gastric disorder. He had always had a "nervous" stomach, but this time his complaint was so severe that he went for examination to a colleague specializing in internal medicine. Even after the turn of the century—that is, after the discovery of X-rays—such examinations still consisted chiefly in careful palpation, which on the whole served to identify only advanced gastric disorders. The examination yielded no definite diagnosis, and the symptoms vanished again. But Mikulicz's whole mood underwent a curious change. He, who was foremost of all surgeons in the surgical treatment of cancer of the stomach—he had by then performed some hundred and eighty-five operations for this malady—was undoubtedly seized by a deep, hidden premonition of his fate. With his peculiar sensibility he feared that he had developed a carcinoma of the stomach.

In the autumn of 1904 his appearance rapidly deteriorated. But there was another possible explanation for this. In October he and Sauerbruch had made a trip to Davos, Switzerland, to do a rib resection upon a consumptive patient. Mikulicz had caught cold. A few days later he had gone to Moscow, already in the grip of winter weather, and had returned with a high fever and a severe case of tonsillitis. But he himself gave no credence to these minor illnesses as sufficient explanations for his poor condition.

Many a night he lay awake, his hands probing the pit of his own stomach. Early in December he started into wakefulness in the middle of the night. He had been lying in a kind of half sleep, hands upon his stomach, and had suddenly fancied he felt a hard tumor. In the darkness he probed his stomach once more. He could distinctly feel a movable tumor, about the size of a child's fist, in the left epigastrium.

Mikulicz said nothing to his family or his colleagues for several weeks longer. But his personality underwent more and more changes. He, who long ago as Billroth's assistant had learned that in cases of carcinoma the earliest possible surgery was imperative, put off action because he did not want to spoil Christmas for his family.

On the day after Christmas he sent for his son-in-law and chief resident physician, Professor Kausch. He closed the door, removed his clothes, and showed the horrified young doctor the tumor. He pointed out its unfavorable situation in the posterior part of the stomach, and for the first time pronounced the word "carcinoma." As a surgeon, he declared, he thought it his duty to undergo operation in spite of the poor prognosis, for the prospects of a radical operation were indeed bad. Kausch vainly tried to put a more harmless cast upon the tumor. However, he soon abandoned these efforts. Mikulicz could not be cozened.

Mikulicz wanted Kausch himself to operate. But Kausch refused, and suggested Professor Eiselsberg of Vienna, likewise a pupil of Billroth, who had devoted himself to gastrointestinal surgery. Mikulicz finally agreed. He had long been planning to go off on a hunting trip between Christmas and New Year's Day. If, instead, he went to see Eiselsberg in Vienna, his family would be none the wiser, and he could spare them the bitter truth at least for a short time.

Mikulicz travelled alone. Eiselsberg was just as horrified as Kausch had been. But in the end he could only confirm the diagnosis, and he offered to go to Breslau on January 7 to operate upon Mikulicz in his own hospital.

The evening of January 1 Mikulicz gathered his family around him. With growing apprehension his wife and children noted his unwonted calmness, his resigned solemnity. Mikulicz explained that he was suffering from cancer of the stomach and must undergo an operation in order at least to attempt to remain with them for a while. That same evening, he put his affairs in order. The following day he sent for his chief associates, Kausch, Anschütz, Gottstein, Sauerbruch. Except for Kausch, none of them had as yet the slightest suspicion. They, too, were startled by Mikulicz's grave tranquillity. He told them that he was suffering from gastric carcinoma, and that on January 7 Professor Eiselsberg would attempt a radical operation.

He looked into horror-filled eyes. Sauerbruch most of all felt the collapse of a world; of them all, he could least sustain such a loss just now. Mikulicz himself had to break the stunned silence. He began giving instructions in case he should die during the operation. He urged Sauerbruch not to falter in his work on surgery of the chest and the pressure-differential procedure, no matter what happened.

To the others, it was as if his voice came from far away. The thought that Mikulicz himself, who had carried surgical treatment of gastric carcinoma further than any other living surgeon, should now himself be dying of it—this thought was crushing to his associates. In silence they left the room.

No one besides his family and his closest collaborators was informed of Mikulicz's actual condition. When he entered his own hospital, word was circulated that he was suffering from umbilical hernia, and was to be operated on for that.

Mikulicz checked the aseptic procedures himself. He had himself prepared for the operation exactly as he would have prepared a patient of his own. As soon as the anesthesia took hold, Eiselsberg, with his characteristic speed, incised abdominal walls and stomach. The atmosphere was one of extreme tension. As soon as the big incision in the stomach gaped wide, he turned pale. A grayish, discolored tumor seemed to be growing right up toward his hand. The tumor Mikulicz had felt formed only the foremost tip of an extensive malignant growth which had grown up through the great omentum and deep down into the pancreas.

Eiselsberg's slender shoulders drooped. The word "hopeless" stood written on his face. Kausch and Anschütz, who had staked their hopes on a reprieve of at least a year or two, turned away with ashen faces. Since the pylorus was still unobstructed, there was no necessity for making an artificial connection to the intestine. The abdominal incision was simply closed again.

To Mikulicz, Eiselsberg reported that no operation had been needed since carcinoma was not found, only a severe inflammation of the pancreas. Kausch and Anschütz echoed this statement, and even produced slides which allegedly confirmed the diagnosis. But each of them caught a single penetrating look of Mikulicz's which made them feel that he did not believe a word they said.

From that day on Mikulicz remained taciturn about his illness. He recovered from the operation with apparent swiftness. Eleven days afterwards he was on his feet again. On January 23 he returned home from the hospital. Then he went to Abbazia for a vacation, and on February 15 went back to work as director of the hospital. A good tan concealed the pallor of his skin. His pupils were quite enthralled by the change in his character. The humanitarian impulses which he had always repressed now came to the fore.

Mikulicz resumed his work as a surgeon, and even made a trip to Cracow for a consultation. On March 23 he performed his last operation, an amputation. Then he left for a spring vacation. He brushed aside all questions about his health. He went to Cannes, then to Merano. On April 17 he ordered his carriage to go to the orthopedic congress in Berlin. On the way he suffered a fearful gastric hemorrhage which all but killed him then and there. After that, he insisted on going straight home. He knew that he now had only to wait for death, and wanted to die in the bosom of his family.

After May 16 he did not leave his bedroom. He refused to receive anyone, even his best friends. He had seen so many people die of cancer that he knew precisely what changes they underwent, how the slow death by starvation left only a repellent specter. His pride forbade his being seen in such a state. He refused even to have nurses. Until the last day he attended to his own sponge baths. Only his wife was permitted to help him now and then.

He insisted that she look cheerful. He did not ask after letters or newspapers. But until the last he worked on various essays, and encouraged his pupils, Sauerbruch in particular, not to forget the main goals. When he could no longer eat, scents were his only pleasure: flowers, oranges, eau de cologne.

The last two weeks he deliberately dosed himself with morphine, which had to be administered in increasingly large amounts. The evening of June 13, still fully conscious, he bade his wife farewell. He also wrote a letter to Eiselsberg thanking him for his effort to deceive, but revealing that he had always known the truth. He wrote: "I depart from life without resentment, and content. I have worked to the best of my ability, have had much recognition for my work, and have been happy." Then he composed his own obituary.

The following morning he was in a coma, and died a few hours later.

Mikulicz's successor, Professor Garré of Königsberg, was not particularly interested in surgery of the chest. Moreover, he brought his own closest associates with him from Königsberg. Sauerbruch knew enough to realize that the exceptional position he had achieved under Mikulicz within so short a time would not be retained under the new chief. If he wished to go on working in the field he had made his own, he would have to leave Breslau. He found a place in Greifswald, at the surgical clinic headed by Professor Friedrich. But Friedrich's pioneer work in the field of lung surgery remained restricted to thoracotomy. The meager funds available at the small University of Greifswald did not permit the building of a low-pressure cabinet like that at Breslau. And Sauerbruch still thought of the cabinet as the essential prerequisite for his work. Moreover, the post of first resident was already occupied, and Sauerbruch had to content himself with playing second fiddle. He very soon began to feel himself an exile, banished to an outpost of the surgical world.

In 1907, when Friedrich took over the hospital at Marburg, he suggested to Sauerbruch that he follow him there as first resident surgeon. Sauerbruch did so, hoping that here, under the more expansive conditions of a larger university, he would be able to resume his work with the cabinet. But Marburg, too, failed to offer him the facilities he had lost at Breslau as the result of Mikulicz's death. It was therefore an enormous relief to Sauerbruch when, in 1908, American surgeons appealed to him to go to the United States for a lecture tour, taking with him the small pressure chamber he had built for his experiments on animals. Sauerbruch immediately accepted the invitation. But this tour, too, provided no real outlet for his ambitions. He was only able to demonstrate the kind of experiments upon animals which had already become a matter of routine with him during Mikulicz's lifetime. When I met him in Rochester, he impressed me as a thoroughly discontented man who knew exactly where his abilities lay but was unable to implement them.

Richer in experience, but still discontented, Sauerbruch returned to Germany. He went on working as a surgeon in a variety of fields. Then, in the autumn of 1910, destiny at last gave him his chance to return to the work with which he had begun his first leap to fame. He was invited to Zürich. Physicians in Switzerland's great tuberculosis sanatoria had followed his work in Breslau with close attention. Professor Krönlein, director of the University Hospital in Zürich, was mortally ill. Swiss lung specialists were eager to have as his successor a surgeon who would concern himself with the problems of chest operations, and Sauerbruch seemed obviously to be the man. In spite of his youth, Sauerbruch was appointed professor of surgery in Zürich.

For the first time in six years Sauerbruch had the means to build a large pressure cabinet and resume the work which had been broken off after Mikulicz's death. Thenceforward began his rapid, steep climb, especially in surgery of the chest. It led him to the heights of international fame. Meanwhile, however, the process Ludolph Brauer had predicted at the surgeons' congress in Berlin on April 6, 1904, had long since begun. The problem of the pressure-differential procedure and surgery of the chest was taken up by surgeons throughout the world, and it was their joint work that created modern thoracic surgery. Ultimately, the hyperpressure procedure consigned the subpressure cabinet to oblivion. When Sauerbruch removed to Munich immediately after the World War, he had still another large cabinet built. But it soon stood unused, a memento of the pioneer days in Breslau. Sauerbruch, too, cast his lot in favor of hyperpressure and the hyperpressure mask, which he had once rejected as unphysiological.

Many hurdles had still to be vaulted, many errors corrected. In 1913, eight years after Mikulicz's death, the German surgeon Eugen Enderlen succeeded for the first time in opening the esophagus and extracting a swallowed denture. That same year Franz Torek of New York prolonged the life of a patient for a considerable time with an operation upon a cancerous esophagus. He established an artificial connection between esophagus and stomach. Shortly after the First World War the Swiss surgeon Henschen showed that it was possible to make the incised surface of a severed esophagus grow into the stomach, and Martin Kirschner of Königsberg solved the problem of the gap created by excision of large portions of the esophagus by displacing the stomach upward. All these men completed, step by step, the operative procedures that Mikulicz had once dreamed of.

In 1923 Morriston Davis of London, who had once worked as assistant to Victor Horsley, for the first time accomplished the removal of an entire cancerous lobe of the lung. Harold Brunn in San Francisco the same year made a vital contribution to a difficult field, the excision of parts of the lung, by correcting a misconception that had dominated surgery. This was the idea that no wound in the thoracic area could be drained since the drain would admit exterior air to the thoracic cavity as soon as the hyperpressure mask was removed. Consequently infectious materials would collect inside the cavity, and fatal pneumonia or pleuritis ensue. Brunn introduced drainage tubes which led into glasses of water, thus removing the secretions without admitting air. He was in essence reviving the procedure invented by Bülau of Hamburg half a century before for drainage of secretions. This one detail made a world of difference in the predictable outcome of such operations. In 1931 Rudolf Nissen of Berlin for the first time removed one entire lung of a twelve-year-old child, who made a complete recovery. Nissen was at this time head physician under Sauer-bruch.

Window on the Light

When I reflect on the subsequent chapters of surgery, one in particular always glows in my memory. Perhaps I remember it so well because, like the first surgical intrusions into the mysterious sphere of the brain, it again concerned one of the most delicate and wonderful organs of man: the eye.

In the autumn of 1906 I had suffered a slight heart attack, and had gone to recuperate in the peace of a small village on the Adriatic coast. At the time I arrived, the few hotels were already emptying, so that I had come at the best time of year for my purposes.

After dinner on my third or fourth day in the place, I walked to a completely deserted part of the beach. I sat down on a rock at a spot where the beach sloped up to the road, and watched the brilliant twilight display of colors between sky and sea until the night extinguished the last trace of light. Three days in succession I went to this place without encountering a soul.

The fourth evening I suddenly saw a man and a girl in front of me. The girl was uncommonly slender. A pretty dress brought out the delicacy of her figure. Her companion, on the other hand, seemed strong and vigorous, and his clothing was as poor as that of any of the fishermen who lived in their humble huts to the north of the hotels and the shoreline road. His muscular, tanned hand was clasped around the girl's left arm.

As I drew closer it seemed to me that her way of walking was somehow strange, and that at one point where the path turned she hesitated slightly. Her companion bent his head to her and placed his right arm, with a solicitude and tenderness extraordinary for so strapping a fellow, about her shoulders. Both stopped, and she leaned against him. He drew her into his arms and gave her a long kiss.

The two had not yet noticed me. They moved apart and continued on their way, side by side. When they reached a plank bridging a channel through which one of the sparse mountain streams at this season trickled into the sea, the girl stopped again. As though seeking help, her hand tightened on his arm. He, however, stooped, picked her up, and carried her across the plank. He seemed like a giant carrying a small and fragile burden. Just as he set the girl on her feet again, she turned her head. From where I stood on the slope I saw an extremely attractive face, slim and delicate, with rather Slavic cheekbones and a strange, dreamy expression. For a moment I wondered whether I should turn back. Then a stone my foot had dislodged began to roll.

The two started. Again the girl turned her head in my direction. Then, everything moved with astonishing swiftness. In a flash the young man's face turned toward mine. I had only fractions of a second to note its character, for with an air of terror he seized the girl again, lifted her in his arms, and dashed off to the left. In a moment both had vanished among the low shrubs lining the beach.

I had had a glimpse of a man's face of such unmitigated ugliness as one seldom sees. In this way, too, he was the opposite of the strangely beautiful slip of a girl. The mystery of this odd human relationship preoccupied me throughout my walk home.

Not until that evening, while I was reading a medical journal, did the solution to the puzzle suddenly occur to me. I realized that the girl must have been blind. The idea struck me as I came upon a paper by a physician of whom I had never heard before, Dr. Eduard Zirm, some nonentity, no doubt, who worked in the small town of Olmütz, Germany. He described the surgical transplantation of healthy corneas to diseased eyes. In the past I had occasionally read, with that eagerness that characterized my younger years, reports of attempted transplantation of the cornea; but these accounts had only listed the insuperable difficulties of the project. I was expecting nothing new from an unknown doctor. But the glimpse I had had of that lovely blind girl prompted me to read Zirm's paper with particular care. Fifteen minutes later I was chiding myself for a shallow-minded fool. In spite of a lifetime's experience which should have taught me that pioneering achievements often came precisely from unknown young doctors and surgeons working in small provincial towns, I was still inclined to hasty prejudices. For here, apparently, a young man had solved the problem which hitherto had baffled the greatest of oculists. What I had just read seemed to me of tremendous importance for the future of surgery of the eye. It indubitably belonged alongside the other great discoveries which had raised surgery step by step to its present eminence. If Zirm's account were correct, and if the condition of his first patient had not changed since the writing of the article, Zirm had succeeded—on December 7, 1905—for the first time in successfully transplanting a cornea and thereby giving sight to a blind person by means of a surgical operation. One of Zirm's patients was a day laborer who had been blinded in both eyes by a splash of lime which had burned the corneas. At the time Dr. Zirm had a child patient with a diseased eye which had to be removed. The cornea of this eye was, however, intact. Zirm had implanted parts of the cornea of the child's eye into the laborer's eye. Apparently his operation had succeeded, and at the time of writing the patient had enjoyed sight for nine months. There could be no doubt that this represented one of the great forward leaps of surgery; all my life I had been tracking down such events, and this was one I would not want to miss. I immediately made plans to visit Zirm in Olmütz, and decided that I would leave on November 4.

Four days later I went up the worn steps of the modest Olmütz hospital and followed the sign that pointed to the department of ophthalmology.

Zirm was one of that host of good, steadfast, uninspired medical men who spend their lives and their energies in practical work at hospitals which possess no special reputation in the world of international medicine. At the time I met him he was a man of forty-four, noteworthy for his massive head framed in unusually thick black hair and for his black beard. Born in Vienna, he had received his training in ophthalmology at the Vienna Eye Clinic. Outwardly, the man had taken on the commonplace stamp of all

Eduard Zirm, who in 1905 performed the first successful corneal transplantation.

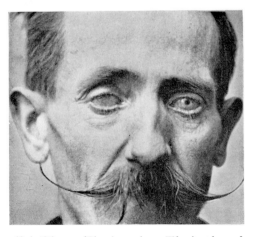

Alois Glogar, Zirm's patient. The implanted corneal disk is visible in the left eye.

Vladimir Petrovich Filatov (1875–1955), who from 1912 on performed more than 1,000 corneal transplantations in Odessa.

the other citizens of Olmütz. But beneath the surface I could sense the spark of that scientific passion which he shared with more fortunate men working at the famous centers of medicine. It was apparent in the manner in which he came forward to meet me. He stood out as a man who had not yet abandoned his dreams and who suffers from the narrowness of his environment both in his work and in his life. He greeted me like a solitary man unexpectedly receiving a messenger from the great world he has longed to enter.

For me, on the other hand, the expectations with which I had come to Olmütz had reached such a pitch that my very first question, full of suspense as it was, might have struck Zirm as slightly offensive. I asked whether the patient he had operated on could still see.

Zirm replied with an unconditional "Yes!" He added with conviction that he believed that the transplanted cornea would serve the man permanently. He went on to say that he had previously suffered so many setbacks that for a long while this fortunate outcome had seemed to him a fluke or miracle which could vanish again at any moment. But the cure had proved lasting. I myself could see his patient.

He offered me a chair beside the window, through which I could see out to the narrow, winding streets of Olmütz. As he began his recital, he asked repeatedly whether I was really interested in the story of his operation. This made me realize how much he craved recognition, how intensely he desired to communicate to others his technique and his knowledge. For my part, nothing came easier than to encourage him to speak. And soon I heard a story—some of which I already knew from the article I had read—which to my mind represents one of the immortal triumphs of surgery.

"I don't know," he began, "whether as a student or a young doctor you too had some particular dream, some special goal you hoped to achieve. For me, the possibility of saving an eye injured by a caustic or acid, or made sightless by trachoma, was fascinating right from the beginning of my medical studies. It was actually chance that led my thoughts that way. . . . But . . ." He broke off and asked once more, with the timidity of a man whose insecurity sprang from isolation, whether he ought to go so far back into the past, and whether this ancient history really interested me.

"You would not wonder if you knew how deeply concerned I am," I replied.

With this reassurance, he continued: "I no longer remember exactly when it was. An issue of the *Baiersche Annalen* fell into my hands. Perhaps you are familiar with this old journal. It was an extremely old volume, dating back to the early decades of the last century—perhaps around 1820. At any rate, it contained an article by Franz Reisinger, who was the professor of surgery and ophthalmology in Bonn, on the fate of those unfortunates with otherwise perfectly sound eyes who have become blind solely because of injury to the cornea. I pored over that article so often that to this day I can recite some of the sentences to you, in their old-fashioned style."

To prove this, he quoted a passage from the article in question. His fluency was astonishing, and I could well believe that he knew it word for word. "I was particularly impressed," he continued, "by one sentence of Reisinger's: 'Discontented with the narrow limits of the art, I considered ways to provide such blinded eyes with a new transparent cornea, that wondrously beautiful little window through which the mind so gloriously enters into relationships with the exterior world. . . .' At first Reisinger probably thought of cutting a windowlike opening in the opaque cornea through which light would once more be admitted to the eye. He also toyed with the thought of inserting a tiny glass window. He abandoned this idea, however, for he wrote: 'Dead, inorganic, even though transparent bodies are unthinkable in connection with so delicate and sensitive an organ, for although a lead bullet will often remain encapsulated without damage in the body, the mobile, irritable eye would never permit an alien guest to be imposed upon it without resentment. I was therefore seized by the idea of placing a living body similar to, and indeed exactly resembling, the transparent human cornea in place of the previously removed opaque cornea . . . and this body could only be the transplanted cornea of a living animal. This idea, which began to occupy me seven years ago, at first only resembled a charming dream.'

"This last sentence of Reisinger's," Zirm continued, "has remained branded upon my memory because the 'charming dream' became my dream also. I suppose there is no determining with certainty whether Reisinger was really the first to light upon the idea of corneal transplantation. One of his contemporaries, Karl Himly, later claimed to have mentioned the idea to Reisinger, who had then appropriated it. But who can judge the question at this late date? Nor does it really matter. In any case, Reisinger was the first to experiment with rabbits' eyes and accumulate practical experience. On a visit to London he learned that the British surgeon Astley Cooper had replaced parts of an injured thumb by pieces of skin taken from a man's sound hand. He wrote concerning this: 'This case gave me excellent encouragement to attempt similar experiments with the cornea.' Reisinger's first efforts in the summer of 1818 failed. But they were interesting enough to prompt Dieffenbach, the most venturesome of the Berlin surgeons of the day, to engage in similar experiments. Dieffenbach attempted to transfer particles of cornea from one chicken's eye to another. He failed, likewise, but characterized corneal transplantation as one of the boldest fantasies of surgery.

"That it certainly was. It was undoubtedly too bold for the times, and was abandoned and forgotten. Anyway, in studying all the literature up to 1872 I came across almost no references to it. In fact, Nepomuk Nussbaum of Munich in 1853 took up the idea that Reisinger had already ruled out, without knowing of Reisinger's work. Nussbaum in all earnestness attempted to implant a transparent crystal something like a collar button into the cornea of rabbits. A less well-known surgeon named Weber, in Darmstadt, made a similar attempt on a blind man two years later. After Weber had inserted the crystal into the cornea, the blind man was actually able to distinguish objects. But a severe hemorrhage put an end to this experiment. A few decades later the English surgeon Baker repeated this experiment. But after a short time the tissue of the operated eye began to degenerate. Von Hippel, the oculist to whom I owe most of my knowledge about this earlier history, likewise had no success with similar efforts. Reisinger had been right. It was impossible to plant inorganic objects into a living eye. The only way to success appeared to be the transplantation of healthy, living cornea."

Zirm turned and pointed toward several framed portraits on the wall of his room. "There," he said, "you see the men who about thirty years ago raised the whole problem out of the oblivion into which it had fallen. The first of them is the Englishman Power, in whom Reisinger's old idea continued to stir. At the International Ophthalmologists' Congress of 1872 in London he reported that he had twice succeeded in implanting pieces of healthy cornea from rabbits' eyes into the morbid cornea of children. These transplants actually took, but, strangely enough, after a short time they completely lost all transparency. They became just as opaque as the cornea surrounding them. Power, however, did not abandon hope, and his hopes were shared by von Hippel, whom you see there in the second picture. Hippel tried using corneas from the eyes of dogs. But in the end he had no more success than Power. The dog cornea also became opaque. In 1877 Hippel published his first report on his experiments, and from then on he worked away at the problem for decades. He was the first to develop a regular technique of transplantation. He also invented the instrument

"Couching a cataract," the oldest known eye operation. From an ancient Roman relief.

which I have been using in recent years, a round trepan with which it is possible to cut a circular spot of cornea out of the defective eye and a patch exactly the same size out of a healthy eye, which can then be placed into the hole in the cornea. Hippel, however, was bent on finding some animal substitute for the defective corneas of human beings. From experiments with canine corneas he went on to experiment with rabbit corneas. About eighteen years ago he succeeded in transplanting a rabbit cornea into the eye of a seventeen-year-old girl, Katharina Schäfer of Kesselbach, in Hessen. This cornea remained transparent for several months and restored a degree of vision to the girl. But here, too, the cornea soon became opaque. Hippel was on the wrong track. This is the man, I would say, who at last found the right one. See there. . . ."

Zirm again lifted his hand—an uncommonly big and heavy hand for an oculist, I thought—and pointed to the third portrait.

"That is Dr. Sellerbeck," he said. "The picture was taken in 1877. I clipped it from a newspaper at the time, and had it framed. Sellerbeck was then working in the ophthalmology department of the Charité in Berlin. Perhaps his name means something to you?"

I said it did not. Although I was familiar with some of the background Zirm was reviewing for me, I had never heard the name of Sellerbeck.

"I thought so," Zirm nodded. "No one knows anything about Sellerbeck, although as far as I know he was the first to recognize the error underlying every attempt to transplant animal corneas to human beings. On June 13, 1878, Sellerbeck for the first time transplanted a cornea from one human being to another: he had come to the conclusion that only tissue of wholly similar nature can really and permanently grow in and heal. He had been treating a young man of twenty-one who had been nearly blinded by a severe case of conjunctivitis. The inflammation of the conjunctiva extended to the cornea. Sellerbeck had been unable to help him by medical therapy, and could only discharge the hapless young man. Then, as it happened, a two-year-old child was brought into the Charité suffering from retinal tumor. There was no help for it; the affected eye would have to be removed. Just before the operation, Sellerbeck remembered the young man whom he had been unable to help. Suppose he took a gamble, Sellerbeck thought, and transplanted a piece of cornea from the child's useless eye to the blind man's? Sellerbeck located the young man, and on June 13 he removed a circular piece of cornea seven millimeters in diameter from the child's eye, cut an opening the same size into the blind man's eye, implanted the healthy cornea, and waited."

Zirm fell silent for a moment. Then he continued: "Today I know what that sort of waiting means. And I know, too, how Sellerbeck must have felt when the transplanted cornea grew into place, healed, and when two weeks after the operation the blind man could read fair-sized print. Try to put yourself in the place of Sellerbeck and his patient. For the first time transplantation of human cornea had been attempted, and gave every indication of having succeeded. But then came the terrible setback. On the twenty-first day the patient reported that he could no longer see so well. The implanted patch of cornea was growing opaque, starting at the edges. Four months later all was lost. The cornea was completely opaque. The experience had been a repetition of the attempts to use animal cornea. Sellerbeck gave up. And everyone else who had undertaken similar experiments likewise abandoned their efforts. Year after year less was heard about corneal transplantation. The few times it was attempted, the aim was no longer to cure blindness, but only to eliminate severe scarifications of the cornea. That was the situation when I started exactly where Sellerbeck had left off. . . ."

Zirm stood up and began pacing back and forth. How often had I seen this same pent-up excitement in scientists as they reached a crucial point in their narratives.

"It would be foolish," Zirm continued, "if I were to assert that I had the slightest notion of how to find the right way. I only had a sort of faith that corneal transplantation from human being to human being should be possible. Naturally, all the progress in anesthesia and asepsis was at my disposal, which meant that I was setting to work under radically different conditions from those of the past. As far as technique was concerned, I regarded Hippel's as the best, and performed my operations accordingly. To cut a round, perfectly smooth opening in the opaque cornea I found Hippel's trepan the best of all instruments." He raised his head and threw a questioning look at me. "Are you familiar with ocular instruments?" he asked.

"In general, yes," I said, "but not with any in this special field."

Zirm went over to a glass case, opened it, and removed a small instrument. It consisted of a styluslike handle, at the lower end of which was a tiny wheel shaped like a crown with a diameter of no more than five millimeters. The lower edge was sharp as a razor. The whole was as fine as the mechanism of a watch. A button on the handle of the instrument controlled the rotation. "This is Hippel's trepan," Zirm said. "If it is placed carefully and perfectly level upon the cornea, and the wheel is rotated, it will cut a perfectly circular disk out of the cornea. The trick is to determine the thickness of the cornea in any given case. The blade must not penetrate any deeper into the eye. As you can see, it is a question of fractions of millimeters. Here, on the side of the revolving wheel, these thin metal plates can be shifted up and down. They prevent the blade from penetrating more than three quarters of a millimeter at the start. If the cornea has not yet been cut through at this depth, the trepan has to be applied again. However, I think it advisable to be able to lift the disk of cornea directly out of the eye with the trepan, without the aid of other instruments, thereby avoiding all raggedness around the edges. The same trepan is then used to cut the disk of the cornea from the healthy eye. Here, too, I should say that everything depends upon avoiding the use of other instruments in lifting out the sound corneal tissue which is to be transplanted. The delicate, slippery cornea is extremely susceptible to injury, which then renders healing more difficult. . . ."

Zirm had been speaking with great rapidity. Now he checked himself and laid the instrument aside. "Well then," he continued, "this is the instrument I used when I began, a number of years ago, to take up Sellerbeck's idea again. As you see, I had no new idea of my own, and no new instrument. All I could do was to use the utmost possible care in excising the tissue. I avoided one mistake my predecessors made, for they treated the opening in the sick eye and the tiny, extremely delicate disk of cornea from the healthy eye, with iodoform and other crude antiseptics which impaired its viability. Nevertheless, I too had nothing but failures for a number of years. I was always having to wait months at a time until by chance some diseased eye had to be removed, which yet retained a cornea sufficiently healthy for my purpose. I experienced many disappointments. But slowly I was able to develop my technique so that I could remove perfectly smooth, clean disks of cornea. I had reached that point when I encountered the case which has brought you here. The day was August 30 two years ago."

Zirm resumed his pacing from one end of the room to the other. "My patient's name was Glogar," he said. "He was forty-five years old, a simple, worn-out day laborer from a small village. On the morning of August 30, while he was slacking lime, some lime had spurted into both eyes. He was in agony. We tried to remove the particles of lime that remained under his lids, and washed the eyes with sal ammoniac solution. But the cornea was already coated with a grayish-white scab. It was a hopeless case. The man was doomed to blindness. When he was discharged on November 17, he could only see a faint glimmer of light. I told him at the time that he should return after a year, when scarification would be completed. Perhaps, I said, there would then be a possibility of aiding him by operation. And so he came to Olmütz once more at the end of November a year ago. By then the corneas of both eyes were completely opaque. I decided, as I had in many previous cases, to attempt the operation, but had to wait until December because no healthy cornea was available. Early in December an eleven-year-old boy was brought in. Some months before, a splinter of iron had entered his right eye. As happens time and again in such cases, the impoverished parents were reluctant to visit a doctor, let alone to travel all the way to Olmütz. They came only when the child's pain had become unbearable. For a long time I tried to remove the splinter with Volkmann's magnet, but in vain. Even after I made incisions and introduced small magnets, the foreign body could not be located. There was nothing for it but to remove the eye. I therefore arranged the operation so that immediately afterwards the healthy cornea could be transplanted to Glogar's eye.

"On December 7 both patients were ready for the operation. In spite of the attendant risks for Glogar, I worked under deep general anesthesia, in both cases, in order to be able to operate without the slightest disturbance. The enucleation of the child's eye proceeded without incident. The eyeball was placed in warm physiological salt solution immediately after removal. Thereupon I operated on Glogar's right eye, removing with Hippel's trepan a disk of cornea five millimeters in diameter. I cut a similar disk from the child's eye, and introduced it into the opening. Unfortunately, I did not succeed in cutting it so precisely that the sound disk corresponded exactly to the opening in the opaque cornea. More-over, it was only after some fussing that I succeeded in fitting it fairly well into its new bed. The inserted piece of cornea was held in place by a strip of conjunctiva from the lower lid, which I folded up over the eye and sutured at the top. Then I operated on the left eye. This time I cut another round disk of healthy cornea out of the child's eye and placed it, with the aid of the trepan, be-tween two pieces of gauze which had been soaked in warm physio-logical salt solution. I had my assistant hold it over the steam from a vessel of boiling water. Then I set about operating on the patient's left eye. To compensate for my clumsiness in handling the right eye, I worked with particular care. I advanced the trepan step by step the tiniest fraction of a millimeter until the cornea was cut through and the excised disk could be lifted out inside the crown-like wheel of the trepan. Then I inserted the disk of healthy cornea, this time without using an instrument, only the dab of gauze to which the disk clung. In this way I succeeded in placing the new cornea without the necessity of shifting it around. My assistant and I exclaimed with one accord: 'How well it fits!' This being so, I did not feel the need to make a bridge of conjunctiva. The trans-planted bit of cornea was held in place only by two crossed threads attached at the ends to the conjunctiva. Then the dressing was applied."

Zirm came to a halt and looked down at his hands. "This was not the first time I had waited for the results of an operation," he said. "It is always like that with eye operations. The oculist can do nothing but wait until the dressing is removed. After so many disappointments I did not dare to expect any miracles. But the fact that the disk of cornea in the left eye had fitted so unusually well had, after all, aroused some hopes in me. A week after the opera-tion the disks of cornea in both eyes were well fixed, and still transparent. But after another ten days the right eye began to give pain. Upon opening the dressing I saw that the unsound cornea was bulging outward in a cone. At the tip of the cone, quite loose, was the bit of cornea I had so painstakingly transplanted. The opera-tion on the right eye, then, had failed. I had to remove the disk again. Perhaps you can imagine my feelings when I proceeded to remove the bandage over the other eye. But then I experienced a great surprise. In the left eye the transplanted disk had already grown into place. Moreover, it was almost perfectly transparent.

Glogar could count fingers and distinguish numbers at a distance of ten feet.

"Nevertheless, I tried to temper my rejoicing. After all, there was no proof that this cure was final. But January of this year began without any sign of relapse. February passed equally well. Glogar's sight constantly improved. In the center of the opaque, grayish-white cornea lay the healthy, transparent disk of cornea like a gleaming black speck. For the first time Glogar began to go about without help. On March 11 he went home to his village, by himself. I did not see him again until June 24. By then his sight had improved still more. He told me that back at home he did all the lighter farm work by himself. In Olmütz he had found his way to the hospital without aid. On June 24 I presented him to our local medical association. By this time six and one-half months had passed since the operation. Yet the implanted cornea was completely transparent. And it has retained that transparency to this day. This, then, is the first time that corneal transplantation has succeeded for anything but the briefest interval. I begin to believe now that he is permanently cured of his blindness."

Zirm paused and took a deep breath. "Of course I don't expect you to believe me without seeing the patient for yourself. I have asked him to come here especially to meet you."

Once again I realized the value Zirm placed on my visit. To him it was an opportunity to reach out beyond his provincial limits, to attain a connection with the greater world of medicine and hear some reverberations of his work. There could be no other explanation for the trouble he had undoubtedly gone to to persuade his patient to come to Olmütz on such short notice.

"Would you like to see Glogar now?" he asked.

I nodded eagerly, and he went to the farther door of his room and opened it wide. I found myself looking down a long corridor which ran perpendicular to the broad corridor I had followed to reach his office. There were a number of benches at the end of the corridor, indicating that it served as a waiting room. At the moment a thin, plainly dressed man was sitting alone on one of the benches.

"That is Alois Glogar," Zirm whispered. "I shall not call him, but only beckon to him. You can judge from his reaction the quality of his sight."

As far as I could see at this distance, the expression in Glogar's eyes seemed lifeless, empty. But it was evident that he could see, for he promptly stood up and approached when Zirm beckoned to him. A moment later he was close enough for me to discern the gleaming black spot in his left eye, contrasting with the scarred, degenerate cornea surrounding it.

"It was good of you to come, Glogar," Zirm said, shaking hands warmly with his patient. "How have you been?"

"Pretty good, Doctor," Glogar said. His whole manner bespoke his utter devotion to this doctor, whom he must have regarded as a light-giving god. As I studied his face and saw the flashing of the small black spot in his eye, I thought of the many other patients I had met in the course of my life, patients who had meekly played their roles in the drama of some new development in surgery, but whose names the world ignored. This hard-working man, too, was one of these.

When Zirm introduced me to him, Glogar shook hands reluctantly, and with a certain timidity. He followed us into the office and Zirm demonstrated to me, with the reading card, how well he saw—this man who had been blind only a year ago—and how normal his range of vision was. After Glogar had left, the doctor sat for a long moment looking expectantly at me.

"I know," he said, "that this one case by no means proves that corneal transplantation will be consistently successful from now on. Undoubtedly there will be more setbacks, fresh errors. But I am now absolutely certain that the operation is feasible and that in a number of years it will be developed into a difficult but conceivable operation. The technique is of the utmost delicacy, that is true, and there are, moreover, two decisive factors to be kept in mind. Both concern the nourishment of the implanted particle of cornea. If the transplant tissue clouded and turned opaque in all previous operations, this was due to its being unable to receive nourishment and sufficient moisture. The nutritive requirements of the transplanted cornea are evidently very low. That explains why such particles of cornea have in many cases remained transparent for some time. They lived on their own resources, so to speak, and required no nourishment from their new surroundings. But as soon as they exhausted their own reserves, they died. Consequently, there is no sense in even undertaking a transplantation unless the injured or diseased old cornea retains, in spite of its opaqueness, remnants of its original structure and an intact system of nourishment. This is frequently the case in acid injury, trachoma, and keratitis, whereas in severe cases of ulceration the nutritional supply is usually destroyed. Further success, therefore, depends largely on choosing the eyes which lend themselves to the operation. It will take long experimentation before we really know. Even with this problem solved, there remains the other which must not be overlooked if corneal transplantations are to succeed."

Zirm looked down at his hands once more, this being evidently a habit of his. He remained for some time lost in thought, so that I had to prompt him. "What is the other problem, then?" I asked.

He started. "Oh yes, the other problem," he said. "We must also be most selective concerning the eyes from which cornea is to be taken. This fact had not been appreciated. It is not only that human eye tissue must be used. The eye must also be free of diseases which effect the nourishment of the cornea. This first success came to me with cornea from a child's eye. The younger the transplanted tissue, the more easily it will adapt to the changed conditions of nourishment in the new eye. That is my firm conviction. Nourishment of the tissue is the central problem, and upon this future work must concentrate."

To hear of sight being restored to the blind, to meet the very man to whom this marvel came to pass—this could not fail to make a unique impression. Though in my life I have seen many feats of surgery that have sometimes seemed like miracles, remembrance of that meeting with Zirm and Alois Glogar stirs me in a way nothing else can. Indeed, it overshadows for me the work of the second great pioneer of corneal transplantation, Anton Elschnig of Prague, who shortly before the outbreak of war in 1914, and during the early years of the war, again succeeded in making the dream of transplantation a reality.

Henry Steven Hartmann lived to see the beginnings of the work of Vladimir Petrovich Filatov, who began transplanting corneas in February, 1912, in Odessa, and who in the course of an unusually long life performed no less than one thousand such operations, thus perfecting the modern technique of creating windows on the light.

List of Sources, Bibliography and Index

LIST OF SOURCES

Numbers refer to the Bibliography at the end of the volume.

Dr. Ferrier's Monkeys

The London congress and its visitors: 419. Situation in cerebral surgery: 186, 115, 114, 322, 152. Antivivisectionism in London: 111, 226, 356, 391. Goltz: 106. Physiology of the brain; Flourens: 186. Broca and the auditory center: 406, 190, 388, 381. Jackson: 296, 329, 279, 289, 291, 290, 292. Fritsch and Hitzig: 240, 321, 207, 306, 264. Ferrier and cerebral localization: 444, 407, 476, 221, 188. Bartholow and his experiments: 119. Broca and prehistoric trepanation: 151, 227, 173, 360, 365, 383, 456, 496, 495. George Squiers and trepanation in Peru. Basic sources: 455, 150, 361, 118, 117, 185, 433. Later history of trepanation, prehistory of cerebral surgery: 213, 412, 132, 466, 95, 102, 168, 283, 133, 493. Goltz and the opposition to functional centers: 218, 106, 241, 220, 250. Program of the congress: 286, 287, 260. Goltz's debrained dog: 287. King's College; Professor Yeo: 203. Opening of the congress; Prince of Wales; German Crown Prince; Mackenzie; Gerhardt: 246, 289, 288, 287. Address of James Paget: 378. Lister and vivisection: 470. Lister and the cerebral abscess: 186. Professor Yeo and Ferrier: 203. Reception in South Kensington: 212, 222. Addresses of Virchow, Foster, Goltz, and Ferrier: 287, 286. Encounter with Charcot. Charcot's personality: 460, 458, 459. Charcot's exclamation: 287, 114. The decision of August 9: 287. Hughes Bennett: 105. Bennett's father and his cerebral tumor: 140, 295, 169. Foster's resolution: 287. Crystal Palace: 222. The charge against Ferrier: 174, 109, 202, 389, 301.

Kocher

Occurrence of goiter in the United States: 208. Medical therapy for goiter; Coindet; iodine: 208, 285, 156, 294, 412, 404, 384. Mystery of the physiology of the thyroid gland: 504, 323, 225. Bigelow: 56. Beginnings of modern goiter surgery: 285, 474, 191, 95, 158. Goiter surgery in antiquity; Celsus; Galen; discovery of the recurrens nerve: 285, 208, 273, 268. Goiter surgery in the Middle Ages and in modern times; Paracelsus; Roland; Desault; Dupuytren; Roux: 285, 261. The cruelty of goiter operations: 154, 354, 330, 262. Rose and total removal of the goiter: 414, 158. Billroth and goiter surgery: 499, 500, 498, 138. Kocher's first goiter operation: 158, 311. Symptoms of tetanus after complete removal of the thyroid gland; Billroth and tetany: 208, 484. Kocher's view of the harmlessness of total removal of the goiter: 312. Kocher's private clinic: 256. Kocher and the old Island Hospital: 137. Sufferers from cachexia at postoperative examinations of Kocher's goiter patients in the Island Hospital: 208, 312, 137. Meeting with Kocher; Kocher's appearance and personality: 137, 256, 485, 157, 206. Kocher's discovery of the dire consequences of total removal of the thyroid gland: 208. The case of Maria Richsel; Dr. Fetscherin's reports: 313. Reverdin: 137, 249, 401. Kocher's postoperative examination of all his goiter patients; changes in Maria Richsel; cachexia strumipriva: 312, 307, 308, 323. Insistence on abandonment of total extirpation: 312. Mixed types of goiter operation; excision and enucleation: 137. The problem of tracheotomy: 159. Reverdin, total removal, and cachexia: 249, 401. Meeting with Jacques Louis and Auguste Reverdin: 345. The Reverdins and the priority dispute with Kocher: 137. Kocher at the congress of surgeons in Berlin: 308, 312. Kocher's comments on anesthesia in goiter operations; his technique of excision: 312, 127, 473. Technique of enucleation; danger of hemorrhage; Billroth's case: 137. Recognition of cachexia strumipriva by surgeons: 308. Goiter operation without anesthesia to protect the recurrens nerve: 137.

Tumor

Charcot; Tuesday evening at home; story about the German official; Takada: 123. Macewen as a personality; characteristic stories: 137, 489, 488, 487, 33. Macewen's operations inside the cranium: 137, 339, 340, 338, 336, 335, 337. Paul Reclus: 328. Reclus and Broca: 252. Ophthalmologists' congress in Heidelberg: 315, 411. Drawbacks of general anesthesia; need for local anesthesia: 260, 432, 156, 163, 187, 258, 435. Reclus's dislike for general anesthesia: 352. Jackson's home, habits: 279. Hughes Bennett, Jackson, and the Henderson case: 468. Henderson's case history; diagnosis of the cerebral tumor; resolve to operate: 124, 219, 125. The National Hospital: 282. Fate of Henderson: 468. Godlee's compunctions: 140. Fate of Hughes Bennett: 105. Preparations for the operation: 468, 124. Jackson's later detachment: 279. Godlee: 453. Course of the operation: 124, 469. Henderson's case history after the operation: 219. Cause of his death: 124. Meeting of the Royal College of Physicians and Surgeons; Macewen's participation: 139, 280. Macewen's greatness and weaknesses: 139, 480.

Marion Sims—John Stough Bobbs—Lawson Tait—Carl Langenbuch

Meeting with Lister; impressions of carbolic antisepsis: 463. Sims in France: 446. Sims's appearance and personality: 211. Bladder stone colic: 463. Trousseau as a diagnostician: 209. Sims's years of apprenticeship and travel: 446. Sims's development as a gynecologist; his sicknesses; his rise to fame: 446, 502, 445, 447. Trousseau; his personality; the donkey's milk: 446, 209. Trousseau's family relationships and prediction of his death: 446. Bobbs; his development; his practice in Indianapolis: 293, 464. Mary Wiggins; her case history; Dr. Newcomer: 464, 149. Bobbs's examination; doubts of ovarian tumor; second examination; decision to operate: 134. The operating room over the drugstore; witnesses of the operation; course of the operation; surprising discharge of the gall bladder: 149, 464, 297. Postoperative treatment; recovery of the patient; death of Bobbs: 149. Sims in Paris again; his disillusionment in New York: 446. Early history of gall bladder surgery; ideas of classical antiquity; first dissections; experiments on animals; opening of gall bladder abscesses; proposed operations: 272, 95, 341. Sims's operation; course and result: 448. Sims on Tait; Tait's first gallstone operation: 341. Lister and Tait; Tait as gynecologist: 341, 327. Lawson Tait, life and personality: 341, 408, 305, 398. Tait's home; his speaking tube; conversation with his secretary; tone with nurses: 421, 348. Tait's appearance; his mode of operating; scalpel between teeth: 348, 304. Slaughterhouse smell; rejection of antisepsis; refusal to use analgesics: 304. Far Eastern curiosities; gifts from Burma: 348. Attitude toward religion: 398. Domestic habits: 348. Tait's first gall bladder operation: 462. His deprecation of the fistula: 302. Friedrich von Esmarch: 215, 216, 108, 413. Langenbuch and gall bladder surgery: 324, 326, 302, 481. Removal of the entire gall bladder: 341. Langenbuch; his personality; his home; the Lazarus Hospital: 224, 377, 217, 347. Langenbuch's first removal of a gall bladder: 325. Cholecystotomy versus cholecystectomy; Tait's stubbornness to the end: 302, 347. Development of gall bladder surgery: 481, 183, 303, 333, 416.

The Blue Almond

Expansion and development of the National Hospital; entry of Victor Horsley; Horsley's way to neurosurgery; first operations; discoveries and impulsiveness: 379, 478, 281. Reports of the illness of the German Crown Prince: 369, 370, 403, 438, 465, 176, 442. Gowers's visit with Jackson; development: 305, 184, 253. Gowers as man and physician: 184. Jenner: 490, 470. Case history of Captain Gilby: 254. Jenner's diagnosis and decision to try an operation: 254, 379. Meeting with Gowers; Park Street; Cavendish Square; Horsley's athleticism, courage, restlessness, excessive energy: 379, 478. The operation; doctors present: 184. Course of the operation: 254. Ballance and his role in the operation: 450, 116, 449. New references to the illness of the German Crown Prince: 342. Captain Gilby after the operation; crises and recovery: 254. Fates of Horsley and Gowers: 184, 379.

Imperial Interlude

Arrival of the Crown Prince in England: 405, 342. Semon and Horsley: 379, 332. Semon's German background; his connections, both with Mackenzie and with doctors in Berlin; his house on Wimpole Street: 438, 451. The Crown Prince and the Crown Princess: 405. Gerhardt's first examination: 318. Development of laryngology: 276, 161. Gerhardt's first diagnosis; attempt at removal of the tumor; Gerhardt's diagnosis of cancer: 318, 440.

Consultation of Bergmann; Dr. Fromm and Zygan: 318, 162, 126. Previous history of laryngeal surgery: 436, 176, 196, 320, 194, 322, 274. Czerny and total extirpation of the larynx: 465. Billroth's extirpation of the larynx; situation in the hospital: 319. Course and outcome of the operation: 263. Total extirpation and partial excision; chances in the latter operation: 438, 318, 440. Bergmann's diagnosis; proposal for immediate operation; comments of the Crown Prince: 318, 162. Wegner; proposal to consult another specialist; intervention of the Crown Princess; her question about an English specialist: 438, 318. Wegner and Mackenzie; Semon's unconscious role; the mission of Reid: 438, 344. Morell Mackenzie; development and personality: 271, 195, 442, 452. Useless sick visit for two guineas: 271. Semon and Mackenzie; Semon's book; consultation of May 18; preparations in the Crown Prince's palace: 438, 162. Arrival of Mackenzie; his rejection of the diagnosis of cancer; his insistence on a sample excision: 342, 318, 440. Mackenzie's earlier comments on the value of microscopic examinations: 440. Mackenzie's tissue sample; Virchow's verdict; triumph over the Germans; close relations with the Crown Prince and Princess: 440, 318, 162, 101. Mackenzie's failure; widening break with the Germans; Mackenzie's promise of a cure in England; decision to go to England: 342, 318, 162, 403. Mackenzie's press campaign; Semon and Butlin; the Emperor's declaration; trip to England: 440, 438. The Jubilee; the Crown Prince in the procession; Mrs. Semon's exclamation; Semon's remark on the Commendatore: 438. In Semon's house; the case of Montagu Williams; Hahn's operation; parallels in the diagnosis; the Crown Prince in front of Mackenzie's house: 439, 491, 438, 248, 368. Dr. Wolfenden: 440. Dr. Landgraf; Mackenzie's contempt for him; Landgraf's abilities: 342, 440. The new tissue sample; Virchow's caution: 440. Norris Castle: 318, 342, 440. Mark Hovell: 362. Semon's urging of Wegner; the Crown Prince's refusal: 438. Braemar; Mackenzie's crucial omissions; the report to Berlin: 440. Conduct of the Crown Princess; trip to Italy: 403. Mackenzie's first vacillation; letter to Oertel: 440, 342. Mackenzie and cancer; his conversation with the Crown Prince in San Remo: 342. Collapse of the Crown Prince; the Crown Princess's stubborn optimism: 405. Mackenzie's insistence on a consultation with the German doctors; call to Krause and Schrötter; dispatch of Prince Wilhelm and Dr. Schmidt; the examination by Schrötter and Krause: 318, 342, 440, 441, 257, 162. Crown Princess's reaction to the arrival of her son: 182. Results of the consultation; hopelessness; Schrötter's report to the Crown Prince; the Crown Prince's written decision: 318. Statement in the *Deutsche Reichsanzeiger;* the German doctors' charges against Mackenzie: 440, 318. Sending of Bramann to San Remo; the Crown Princess's obstinacy; the Crown Prince's attitude toward Schrötter, Mackenzie, and Bramann: 403. Mackenzie's new deception; recantation of the cancer diagnosis in the *British Medical Journal:* 440. Bramann in San Remo: 457, 467. Disputes over the tracheotomy; agony of the Crown Prince; von Kessel's anger; delay of telegram to Bergmann; scenes between Mackenzie, the Crown Princess, and Bramann; the Crown Prince's desperate plea;

performance of the tracheotomy: 162, 467, 318. Sending of Bergmann to San Remo: 162. The Crown Princess on Mackenzie and Bergmann: 182. Discussion of the Crown Princess with Bergmann: 162. Mackenzie's "friendliness of a reptile"; trying conduct of the Crown Princess: 162. The Crown Prince's coughing fits; his valet's statement; cancerous particles under Bergmann's microscope; Mackenzie's dodges; quarrelling over the cannulae; charges against Bergmann; Mackenzie's manipulation of the press; the Crown Prince's decision during the absence of the Crown Princess: 162, 342, 440. Kussmaul in San Remo; Mackenzie's opposition; consultation of Waldeyer: 318. The Crown Princess's opinion of Kussmaul, her attempt to dismiss Bergmann, the Emperor's contrary order: 162. Waldeyer's determination of cancerous cells; Mackenzie's agreement; Bergmann's profound distrust of Mackenzie; Mackenzie's new promises to the Crown Princess: 318, 162, 342. Death of the Emperor; the news comes to San Remo; trip to Berlin; arrival in Berlin; move into the Charlottenburg palace: 405. Mackenzie in Berlin; new dodges; complete deception of the Empress: 182. Note to General Winterfeldt: 162. The growth of the tumor; Mackenzie's appeal to Bergmann for aid; threat of asphyxiation; the second struggle over cannulae; Bergmann's "mistake"; Bergmann and the *Kölnische Zeitung;* Mackenzie and the *British Medical Journal:* 162, 342, 440. Bergmann's withdrawal; the press campaign: 162, 438. Last carriage rides: 405. The *British Medical Journal* report of June 9: 440. Mackenzie and the Emperor on June 10: 342. The Emperor's collapse; visit of King Oscar; death: 162, 405. Bergmann's insistence on an autopsy: 438. Bergmann, Bismarck, Schweninger; the decision on autopsy: 162, 182. Mackenzie's devious statements and the results of the autopsy: 318. Mackenzie's interview with the *Dagblad:* 162. Criticism of the official German publication: 438, 440. Semon's criticism of Mackenzie's pamphlet: 440, 343. Mackenzie's future; his Mediterranean cruise on the *Chimborazo;* his death: 271.

Bassini

Pathology of hernia: 483, 265, 434. The truss: 193, 286. Gallmann's account; conditions in Milan; curtain cord; "Far from it!": 65. Pavia and Bottini: 346. Padua: 197. Bassini: 112. Bassini's 123 cases; Catteneo; military service of patients: 121. Early history of hernia therapy; antiquity; Chinese methods of treatment. The best historical presentation is contained in: 285, 103. Paré: 284, 311, 170, 107, 272, 175. Franco: 394, 107. Taxis, Hood, Czerny, Wood, Socin; relief, not cure: 285, 419, 112. Personality of Bassini; habits; medical and political views: 112, 247, 454. Visiting day in Padua: 355. The patients; the cases of Arturo Malatesta, Ernesto Calzavare, and Aloisi Marchiori: 121, 66. Bassini and the technique of his hernia operations: 121, 504. Bassini's modesty and patriotism: 112, 246, 454. Bassini's students: 355. Course of Bassini's operation; the feather test: 121. Bassini's successes and his first publication: 121, 120. Macewen, Halsted, and inguinal hernia: 284, 269.

Sigmund Freud—Carl Koller—William Halsted—Paul Reclus
Carl Ludwig Schleich—August Bier—Leonard Corning
Heinrich Braun

History of cocaine; Pizarro, von Tschudi, Mariani, Scherzer, Wöhler, Niemann: 166, 164, 472, 497, 350. Koller and Heidelberg: 410, 315. Sigmund Freud; development and personality of Freud in his youth: 298, 235, 390, 399, 418, 494. Freud and Martha Bernays; relation to his interest in cocaine: 298. Aschenbrandt's observation: 110. Freud's first experiences with cocaine; Dr. Bentley: 298. Fleischl: 298. Freud's paper on cocaine: 237. Freud's trip to Hamburg; his remark to Königstein: 298, 235. Koller's studies: 314. Niemann's mention of the analgesic effect of cocaine; comment of Moreno y Maiz: 371, 376, 363. Koller's discovery; Königstein's mistake; Koller's announcement in Heidelberg: 298, 316. Freud's return to Vienna; underestimation of Koller's discovery; Koller's address to the Vienna Medical Society; Königstein's appearance and rejection; Freud's disappointment: 235, 298, 410, 316, 364, 236. Further story of Koller: 395. Halsted: 463. McBride, 25th Street house: 334. Halsted's, Hall's, and Hartley's experiments with cocaine anesthesia; imperceptible alteration of personality; stimulus from account of Moreno y Maiz; discovery of conduction anesthesia; cocaine addiction; fate of Hall; Dr. Monroe and Dr. van der Poel send Halsted to Providence: 334, 502, 363. Halsted's various cures: 334. Burglary of the ship's pharmacy: 502. The complete alteration in Halsted's personality: 334, 223, 275, 351, 490. Welch, Halsted, and Johns Hopkins: 334, 228, 490. Dissemination of cocaine anesthesia; first recognition of the dangers: 214. Kolomnin's suicide: 205. Dr. Brouardel's list of fatalities: 205. Disastrous reports from Philadelphia, Chicago, Paris, etc.: 375, 145, 259. Dr. Hibbs of the Hospital for Orthopedics: 266. Verneuil and Reclus: 475, 328. Reclus and his work in local anesthesia: 328, 402, 160, 145, 396. Trip to Paris, Reclus's personality and family: 328, 243, 244, 387. Reclus's illness and operation upon himself: 387. Reclus and Schleich: 145. Bergmann, private clinic: 162. Hotel Prinz Albrecht: 126. Hedwig Schleich: 431. Carl Ludwig Schleich, his personality and development up to the foundation of his clinic: 431, 145. Schleich's discovery of infiltration anesthesia; his first success: 432, 431. Schleich's appearance at the congress: 465, 431. The word "crime." This was softened in the printed version. The author has received confirmation of Schleich's use of the word from one of the last surviving participants in this congress, *Sanitätsrat* Dr. Schneider, Birkenstein/Obb, in an unpublished communication. Behavior of Schleich's father: 431. Schleich during the years of disregard; testing of his procedure in Bergmann's presence: 466. Origin of Schleich's book; his statement on the superfluity of general anesthesia in most cases: 432, 431. Schleich and Heinrich Braun: 148, 144, 146. Esmarch: see chapter on Marion Sims, etc. Esmarch and Bier; Quincke: 477, 393, 392. Bier; his personality: 477. Bier's idea; his experiments on patients: 128. Decision to experiment on self; the experiment; Hildebrandt's participation;

the consequences: 128. Reverberations of Bier's experiments in France and the United States; Tuffier, Fowler, and Corning: 472, 353, 232, 233, 300. Bier's further experiments; Dr. Eden; eucaine; tropacocaine: 129. Bier and Corning: 130. Corning's work: 181, 179, 180. The priority dispute between Corning and Bier: 477, 155, 397, 267, 410. Bier's further experiments; stoppage of circulation; discovery of novocaine: 129, 270. Heinrich Braun; personality; development of local anesthesia: 259. Adrenalin: 147. Braun and Schleich: 145. Further developments: 187, 270.

Chicago

Murphy's address in Denver: 366. Murphy's development and personality; his own lung disease; his craving for publicity: 463, 189, 204, 56. Early history of thoracic surgery: 273, 422. Pneumothorax; the physical laws of respiration: 422, 273, 380. Bülau: 372, 167. Standstill in research: 273, 422, 366. Gluck, Schmid, and Block: 372, 373, 247, 266. Paget's pessimism: 380. Christian Fenger: 131, 165, 331, 443. *Chicago Tribune:* 189. Effects of newspaper publication; John and Nettie Murphy in Chicago: 189. Senn and Murphy's button: 122, 351, 153, 177. Murphy's Michigan Avenue house: 349. Murphy's despair; Nettie Murphy's attempt to comfort him; large number of letters: 189. August Lemke: 189. Murphy's discovery of artificial pneumothorax: 189. Earlier history of artificial pneumothorax: 238, 425. Murphy's experiments: 366. Cérenville: 242, 172. Murphy's technique of establishing pneumothorax in human patients; his first cases and successes: 366. Murphy and Forlanini: 136, 359. Ospedale degli Incurabili: 355. Forlanini: 198, 508, 113, 230, 229, 231. Murphy's reaction: 189. Ludolph Brauer: 135, 142. Friedrich and the development of thoracic surgery: 240, 382. Further developments: 372, 104.

Sauerbruch

Mikulicz in Rochester: 299, 177. The Mayo Clinic in 1903: 177. Story of Worrall Mayo and his sons: 486. Mikulicz's development since his last meeting with Hartmann; surgery of the esophagus: 299, 317. Mikulicz's letter to Sauerbruch: 424. Receipt of Mikulicz's letter and Sauerbruch's previous career: 424, 92. Sauerbruch in Breslau; Mikulicz's clinic; Mikulicz's personality at that time: 299, 317, 461. Sauerbruch's assignment; his experiments on animals; vivisection; subpressure; construction of the first subpressure cabinet: 429, 427, 424. First experiments on animals in the cabinet; failure; improvement of the cabinet; successful opening of the thoracic cavity: 429, 427, 424. Report to Mikulicz; demonstration of the cabinet to Mikulicz; failure; Mikulicz's reaction; Sauerbruch's dismissal; continuing work in private; successes with new cabinet; Anschütz's role: 424. Reconciliation with Mikulicz; building of the larger subpressure cabinet; successful experiments on animals; operations of the esophagi of animals: 424, 427, 429, 357, 317, 461. Idea of hyperpressure; the experiment of January 17, 1904; abandonment of the idea; plan for a large cabinet: 423. Sauerbruch's publication in the *Centralblatt für Chirurgie;* Petersen's visit; preparations for the surgeons' congress in Berlin; publication of Brauer's article: 427, 423, 428, 143. Brauer, Petersen, and hyperpressure experiments in Heidelberg: 309, 140; and unpublished information about Petersen from Dr. Schneider Berkenstein. The surgeons' congress in Berlin; Sauerbruch's address: 429. Mikulicz as a speaker: 299, 358. Brauer's comments; discussion; concluding words of Heinrich Braun: 474. Mikulicz's declaration to Brauer: 171. The big subpressure cabinet; first operations on human beings; death of the first patient; first operation on the esophagus: 424. Mikulicz's illness, gastric carcinoma, operation by Eiselsberg: 299, 461, 424. Last months of Mikulicz's life; his last statement: 299, 461, 317. Mikulicz's death; the subpressure procedure and Sauerbruch's further career: 424. Sauerbruch and Friedrich: Private communications from the widow of Professor Paul Friedrich, Gauting bei München. Sauerbruch's trip to the United States; Zürich; Sauerbruch's rise: 424, 92. Hyperpressure as preferred procedure; further development of thoracic surgery: 372.

Window on the Light

Zirm's paper: 505. Konrad Eduard Zirm: Unpublished excerpts from the files of the county hospital in Olomouc. In addition to information given in the text, the following may be of interest: Zirm was born on March 18, 1861, in Vienna and was a student at the Schotten Gymnasium. He studied medicine at the University of Vienna. From 1884 to 1887 he was a demonstrator for the anatomic chair of Professor Karl von Lange. From 1887 to 1889 he was assistant to Professor Stellwag, Ophthalmological Clinic in Vienna. Stimulus to corneal transplantation; Franz Reisinger and his early experiments: 505, 277, 400, 43. Himly: 482, 255. Astley Cooper: 118. Dieffenbach: 277, 201, 199, 200. Nussbaum, Weber, Baker: 374, 277, 420. Power: 385. Hippel and the transplantation of dog and rabbit corneas: 277, 278. Sellerbeck: 437. Zirm's start: 505. Hippel's trepan: 277. Zirm's first operations and failures: 505. Postoperative results; Glogar about a year after the operation: 505, 506. Zirm's views on the requirements for successful transplantation: 505, 506. Further development of corneal transplantation; Elschnig; Filatov: 373, 210, 430, 192.

BIBLIOGRAPHY

GENERAL WORKS

1. Abbot, F. C.: "The Life-History of Some Surgical Procedures." *St. Thomas Hospital Reports, 1891.* London, 1892.
2. Albert, E.: *Beiträge zur Geschichte der Chirurgie.* 2 parts. 1877.
3. ———: *Lehrbuch der Chirurgie und Operationslehre.* 4 vols. 1881–83.
4. Andrus, W., and others, ed.: *Advances in Surgery.* 2 vols. New York, 1949–50.
5. Aschoff, L., and P. Diepgen: *Kurze Übersichtstabelle zur Geschichte der Medizin.* Munich, 1945.
6. Baas, H.: *Grundriss der Geschichte der Medizin und des heilenden Standes.* Stuttgart, 1876.
7. Bardeleben, A.: *Lehrbuch der Chirurgie und Operationslehre.* 4 vols. 1863–66.
8. Bauer, K. H.: *Über Fortschritte der modernen Chirurgie.* Berlin, Göttingen, Heidelberg, 1954.
9. Bell, K.: *System der operativen Chirurgie.* German translation by Kosmely. Berlin, 1815.
10. Benedict, T.: *Lehrbuch der allgemeinen Chirurgie und Operationslehre.* Breslau, 1842.
11. Berghoff: "Die Entwicklung der Chirurgie in Wien vor Billroth." *Wiener medizinische Wochenschrift,* 80:1537–69 (1930).
12. Bernstein, J.: *Geschichte der Chirurgie.* 2 vols. 1822–23.
13. Bettmann, O. L.: *A Pictorial History of Medicine.* Springfield, Ill., 1956.
14. Bier, A., H. Braun, and H. Kümmel: *Chirurgische Operationslehre.* Leipzig, 1920.
15. Billings, J. S.: "The History and Literature of Surgery." In F. S. Dennis and J. S. Billings: *A System of Surgery.* Philadelphia, 1895–96.
16. Billroth, T.: *Über das Lehren und Lernen der medizinischen Wissenschaften.* Vienna, 1876.
17. Bland, Sulton: *The Story of a Surgeon.* Boston and New York, 1930.
18. Brown: *Old Masterpieces in Surgery.* Omaha, 1928.
19. Brüning: "Hundert Bände Archiv für klinische Chirurgie." *Archiv für klinische Chirurgie, 100:* Suppl. 1–124 (1913).
20. Brunn, W. von: *Kurze Geschichte der Chirurgie.* Berlin, 1928.

21. ———: "Geschichtliche Einführung in die Chirurgie." In *Die Chirurgie*, ed. by Kirschner-Nordmann, 1924.

22. Brunner, C.: "Geschichte der Wundbehandlung." *Neue deutsche Chirurgie*, 20. Stuttgart, 1926.

23. Buschan, G.: *Über Medizinzauber und Heilkunst im Leben der Völker*. Berlin, 1941.

24. Camac, C. N. B.: *Epoch-making Contributions to Medicine, Surgery and the Allied Sciences*. Philadelphia, 1909.

25. Comrie: *History of Scotch Medicine to 1860*. Research Studies in Medical History, No. 4. London, 1927.

26. Creuz, R., and J. Steudel: *Einführung in die Geschichte der Medizin in Einzeldarstellungen*. Iserlohn, 1948.

27. Czerny, V.: *Über die Entwicklung der Chirurgie während des 19. Jahrhunderts und ihre Beziehung zum Unterricht*. Heidelberg, 1903.

28. Diepgen, P.: *Geschichte der Medizin*. 5 vols. Berlin and Leipzig, 1913–28.

29. ———: *Die Heilkunde und der ärztliche Beruf*. Munich, 1938.

30. Dumesnil: *Histoire illustrée de la médecine*. Paris, 1935.

31. Eve, P. F.: *Remarkable Cases in Surgery*. Philadelphia, 1857.

32. Fischer, G.: *Chirurgie vor 100 Jahren*. Leipzig, 1876.

33. Fischer, J.: *Biographisches Lexikon der hervorragenden Ärzte der letzten fünfzig Jahre*. 2 vols. Berlin and Vienna, 1932–34.

34. Fourmestraux, J. de: *Histoire de la chirurgie française, 1790–1920*. Paris, 1934.

35. Garrison, F. H.: *An Introduction to the History of Medicine*. 4th ed. Philadelphia and London, 1929.

36. Gould, G., and W. Pyle: *Anomalies and Curiosities of Medicine*. New York, 1937.

37. Graham, H.: *The Story of Surgery*. New York, 1939.

38. ———: *Surgeons All*. London, 1939.

39. Gründer, J. W.: *Geschichte der Chirurgie von den Urzeiten bis zum Anfang des 18. Jahrhunderts*. Breslau, 1859.

40. Gurlt, E.: *Geschichte der Chirurgie und ihrer Ausübung*. 3 vols. Berlin, 1898.

41. Guthrie, D.: *A History of Medicine*. London, 1945.

42. Haagensen, C. D., and W. E. B. Lloyd: *A Hundred Years of Medicine*. New York, 1943.

43. Haberling, W., F. Hübotter, and H. Vierordt: *Biographisches Lexikon der hervorragenden Ärzte aller Zeiten und Völker*. 5 vols. Berlin and Vienna, 1929–35.

44. Hacker: *Die geschichtliche Entwicklung der Chirurgie*. Innsbruck, 1899.

45. Haeser, H.: *Übersicht der Geschichte der Chirurgie und des chirurgischen Standes*. 2 vols. 1879.

46. Haggard, E. H. W.: "The Background of the American Surgeon." *Surgery, Gynecology, Obstetrics*, 60:427 (1935).

47. ———: *Devils, Drugs and Doctors*. New York and London, 1929.

48. ———: *The Doctor in History*. New Haven, 1934.
49. ———: "Surgery, the Queen of the Arts." *Surgery, Gynecology, Obstetrics, 58*:410 (1934).
50. Haymaker, W., ed.: *The Founders of Neurology*. Springfield, Ill., 1953.
51. Hecker, J. F. C.: "Geschichte der Chirurgie." In J. Rust: *Theoretisch-praktisches Handbuch der Chirurgie, 4*:613–77 (1831).
52. Helfreich: "Geschichte der Chirurgie." In Pagel, J. L., and M. Neuberger: *Puschmanns Handbuch der Geschichte der Medizin, 3*:1–304. 3 vols. Jena, 1902–5.
53. Hirschberg, J.: *Geschichte der Augenheilkunde*. 4 vols. in 10. Leipzig, 1899–1918.
54. Horrax, G.: *Neurosurgery: An Historical Sketch*. (American Lectures ser. 117: American Lectures in Surgery.) Springfield, Ill., 1952.
55. Isensee, E.: *Die Geschichte der Medicin, Chirurgie und Geburtshülfe*. 4 vols. in 6. Berlin, 1840–45.
56. Kelly, H.: *Dictionary of American Medical Biography*. Philadelphia and London, 1912; 2nd ed., Boston and New York, 1928.
57. Killian, H.:*Hinter uns steht nur der Herrgott. Aufzeichnungen eines Chirurgen*. Munich, 1957.
58. Killian, H., and G. Krämer: *Meister der Chirurgie und die Chirurgenschulen im deutschen Raum*. Stuttgart, 1951.
59. Kümmel, H.: *Die Entwicklung der Chirurgie in den letzten 50 Jahren*. Hamburg, 1922.
60. Küster, E.: "Geschichte der Neueren Deutschen Chirurgie." *Neue Deutsche Chirurgie, 15*. Stuttgart, 1915.
61. Laignel-Lavastine, M.: *Histoire générale de la médecine, de la pharmacie, de l'art dentaire et de l'art vétérinaire* (2 vols. published). Paris, 1936, 1938.
62. Leonardo, R. A.: *History of Surgery*. New York, 1943.
63. Leriche, R.: *Philosophie der Chirurgie*. Zurich, 1954.
64. Lindenberg, W.: *Tragik und Triumph grosser Ärzte*. Ulm, 1948.
65. Majocchi, A.: *Vita di chirurgo*. (German translation, *Das Leben des Chirurgen*, Leipzig, 1939.)
66. Manninger, W.: *Kampf und Sieg der Chirurgie*. Zurich, 1942.
67. Mayrhofer, B.: *Kurzes Wörterbuch zur Geschichte der Medizin*. Jena, 1937.
68. Meyer-Steinegg, T., and K. Sudhoff: *Geschichte der Medizin im Überblick*. Jena, 1922.
69. Meunier, L.: *Histoire de la médecine*. Paris, 1924.
70. Nissen, R.: *Zeitloses und Zeitgebundenes in der Chirurgie*. Stuttgart, 1953.
71. Otis, E.: *Report on Surgery*. Manchester, 1884.
72. Packard, F. R.: *History of Medicine in the United States*. 2 vols. New York, 1931.
73. Pagel, J. L.: *Biographisches Lexikon der hervorragenden Ärzte des XIX. Jahrhunderts*. Berlin, 1901.

74. ———: "Geschichte der Chirurgie." In Kocher and Quervain: *Encyclopädie der gesamten Chirurgie*. Leipzig, 1901.

75. ———: *Historisch-medizinische Bibliographie für die Jahre 1875–1896*. Berlin, 1898.

76. Pagel, J. L., and M. Neuburger: *Puschmanns Handbuch der Geschichte der Medizin*. 3 vols. Jena, 1902–5.

77. Park, R.: "A Lecture on the Evolution of the Surgeon from the Barber." *Janus*, pp. 159–69 (Leiden, 1898).

78. Parker, G.: *The Early History of Surgery in Great Britain*. London, 1920.

79. Portal, M.: *Histoire de l'anatomie et de la chirurgie*. 6 vols. Paris, 1770–73.

80. Power, D'Arcy: "A Century of British Surgery." *British Medical Journal*, 2:134 (1932).

81. ———: "A Mirror for Surgeons." *Selected Readings for Surgeons*. 1935.

82. ———: *A Short History of Surgery*. London, 1933.

83. Quervain: *Der Weg der Chirurgie vom Handwerk zur Wissenschaft*. Bern, 1936.

84. Robinson, V.: *Pathfinders in Medicine*. New York, 1929.

85. Rochard, J.: *Histoire de la chirurgie française au 19ème siècle*. Paris, 1875.

86. Rohlfs, H.: *Die chirurgischen Klassiker Deutschlands*. 1883.

87. Rust, J.: *Theoretisch-praktisches Handbuch der Chirurgie und Augenkrankheiten*. 17 vols. Berlin and Vienna, 1830–36.

88. Sachs, E.: *The History and Development of Neurological Surgery*. New York, 1952.

89. Schönbauer, L.: *Das Medizinische Wien. Geschichte—Werden—Würdigung*. Vienna, 1947.

90. Schwalbe, E.: *Vorlesungen über Geschichte der Medizin*. 3rd ed., Jena, 1919.

91. Siegerist, H. E.: *American Medicine*. New York, 1934.

92. ———: *The Great Doctors, a Biographical History of Medicine*. Tr. by Eden and Cedar Paul. New York, 1933.

93. Sprengel, K., and W. Sprengel: *Geschichte der Chirurgie*. 2 vols. 1805–19.

94. Sudhoff, K.: *Handbuch der Geschichte der Medizin*. Berlin, 1922.

95. Trendelenburg, F.: *Die ersten 25 Jahre der Deutschen Gesellschaft für Chirurgie*. Leipzig, 1923.

96. Treves, F.: *Handbuch der chirurgischen Operationslehre*. German translation by Teuscher. 2 vols. 1892.

97. Vierordt, H.: *Medizingeschichtliches Hilfsbuch*. Tübingen, 1916.

98. Walker, A. Earl: *A History of Neurological Surgery*. Baltimore, 1951.

99. Watson, B. A.: "A Historical Sketch of Surgery, Ancient, Medieval and Modern." *New York Medical Journal* (1890).

100. Wheeler, C.: "Pillars of Surgery." *Surgery, Gynecology, Obstetrics*, 56:257 (1933).

SPECIAL REFERENCES

101. Ackerknecht, E. H.: *Rudolph Virchow, Arzt, Politiker, Anthropologe.* Stuttgart, 1957.
102. Albert, E.: "Die ältere Chirurgie der Kopfverletzung." In his *Beiträge zur Geschichte der Chirurgie.* 2 parts. Vienna, 1877.
103. ——: "Die Herniologie der Alten." *Ibid.*
104. Alexander, J.: "Fifty Years of Thoracic Surgery." *American Journal of Surgery, 51:217–24* (Jan., 1941).
105. "Alexander Hughes Bennett." *British Medical Journal,* Nov. 9, p. 1444 (1901).
106. Anderson, E., and W. Haymaker: "Friedrich Leopold Goltz (1834–1902)." In W. Haymaker, ed.: *The Founders of Neurology.* Springfield, Ill., 1953.
107. Andrews: "A History of the Development of Technique of Herniotomy." *Annals of Medical History,* pp. 450–66 (1935).
108. Anschütz: *Friedrich von Esmarch zum Gedächtnis.* Kiel, 1909.
109. "The Antivivisection Prosecution." *British Medical Journal,* November 11 (1881).
110. Aschenbrandt, T.: "Die physiologische Wirkung und die Bedeutung des Cocains." *Deutsche medizinische Wochenschrift,* December 12 (1883).
111. Austic: "The Vivisection Controversy." *Practitioner,* p. 38 (1874).
112. Austoni, A.: "La vita e le opere di Edoardo Bassini." *Archiv. Ital. di Chirurg.,* pp. 591–620 (1922).
113. Baer, G.: "Nachruf auf Forlanini." *Zeitschrift für Tuberkulose,* fasc. 5 (1918).
114. Ballance, Sir Charles: *A Glimpse into the History of the Surgery of the Brain.* London, 1922.
115. ——: "The History of Brain Surgery." *British Medical Journal,* No. 3181, p. 1041.
116. ——: "Remarks and Reminiscences." *British Medical Journal,* 1:64–67 (1927).
117. Bandeller, A. E.: "Aboriginal Trephining in Bolivia." *American Anthropologist* (1904).
118. Bartels: "Die Ausführung der geradlinigen präkolumbianischen Trepanation." *Deutsche medizinische Wochenschrift,* p. 2311 (1913).
119. Bartholow, R.: "Experimental Investigations into the Functions of the Human Brain." *American Journal of the Medical Sciences* (April, 1874).
120. Bassini, E.: "Die Radikalbehandlung der Hernia inguinale." *Archiv für klinische Chirurgie* (1894).
121. ——: "Über die Behandlung des Leistenbruchs." *Archiv für klinische Chirurgie,* pp. 429–75 (1890).
122. Beck, C.: "Nicholas Senn." *Surgery, Gynecology, Obstetrics,* pp. 398–400 (1923).

123. Beeson, B. B.: "Jean Martin Charcot, A Summary of His Life and Works." *Annals of Medical History, 10:126–32* (1928).

124. Bennett, A. H., and R. S. Godlee: "Case of Cerebral Tumor." *Med. Chir. Transactions, London,* p. 244 (1885).

125. Bergmann, E. von: "Die chirurgische Behandlung der Hirnkrankheiten." *Archiv für klinische Chirurgie* (1887).

126. Bergmann, Gustav von: *Rückschau—Geschehen und Erleben auf meiner Lebensbühne.* Munich, 1953.

127. Bier, Braun, and Kümmel: *Chirurgische Operationslehre.* Leipzig, 1920.

128. Bier, A.: "Versuche über Cocainisierung des Rückenmarks." *Deutsche Zeitschrift für Chirurgie, 51:361* (1899).

129. ———: "Weitere Mitteilungen über Rückenmarksanästhesie. Vortrag, gehalten auf dem 30. Med. Congress am 11. April, 1901." In: *Verhandlungen der Deutschen Gesellschaft für Chirurgie,* 1901.

130. ———: "Zur Geschichte der Rückenmarksanästhesie." *Münchner medizinische Wochenschrift,* pp. 1059–61 (1906).

131. Billings, F.: "Christian Fenger, 1840–1842." *Surgery, Gynecology, Obstetrics,* pp. 365–69 (1922).

132. Bircher: "Schädelverletzungen durch mittelalterliche Nahkampfwaffen." *Archiv für klinische Chirurgie,* 85, No. 2.

133. Bluhn: "Statistik der Trepanation bei Kopfverletzungen." *Archiv für klinische Chirurgie,* pp. 7619 ff. (1875).

134. Bobbs, J. S.: "A Case of Lithotomy of the Gallbladder." *Transactions of the Indiana State Medical Society,* 1868, p. 68.

135. Bochalli, R.: "Das Leben und Wirken Ludolph Brauers." *Beiträge zur Klinik der Tuberkulose,* pp. 190–97 (1950–51).

136. Boni, I.: "Carlo Forlanini." *L'Ospedale Maggiore,* pp. 75–76. Milan, 1918.

137. Bonjour: *Theodor Kocher.* Bern, 1950.

138. Bovet, A.: *Mémoire sur le goitre encysté et son traitement chirurgical.* Zurich, 1864.

139. Bowman, A. K.: *Life and Teaching of Sir William Macewen: a Chapter in the History of Surgery.* London, 1942.

140. Bramwell, E.: "Alexander Hughes Bennett and the First Recorded Case in Which an Intracranial Tumor Was Removed by Operation." *Edinburgh Medical Journal,* p. 312 (1935).

141. Brauer, L.: "Die Ausschaltung der Pneumothoraxfolgen mit Hilfe des Überdruckverfahrens." *Mitteilungen aus den Grenzgebieten der Medizin und Chirurgie,* pp. 398–486 (1904).

142. ———: "Der therapeutische Pneumothorax." *Deutsche medizinische Wochenschrift,* No. 32 (1906).

143. Brauer, L., and Petersen: "Über eine wesentliche Vereinfachung der künstlichen Atmung nach Sauerbruch." *Hoppe-Seylers Zeitschrift für physische Chemie,* pp. 299–303 (1904).

144. Braun, H.: "Experimentelle Untersuchungen und Erfahrungen über Infiltrationsanästhesie." *Archiv für klinische Chirurgie,* vol. 57 (1898).

145. ———: "Geschichte der örtlichen Betäubung." *Der Chirurg*, p. 466 (1929).

146. ———: "Über Infiltrationsanästhesie und regionäre Anästhesie." In: *Volkmanns Sammlung klinischer Vorträge*, 1898.

147. ———: "Über den Einfluss der Vitalität der Gewebe auf die örtliche und allgemeine Giftwirkung lokalanästhesierender Mittel und über die Bedeutung des Adrenalins für die Lokalanästhesie." *Archiv für klinische Chirurgie*, vol. 69 (1903).

148. ——— "Über Infiltrationsanästhesie und regionäre Kokainanästhesis." *Zentralblatt für Chirurgie* (1897).

149. Brayton, W.: "John S. Bobbs of Indianapolis, the Father of Cholecystotomy." *Indiana Medical Journal*, XXIV:21 (1905-6).

150. Broca, P.: "Cas singulier de trépanation chez les Incas." *Bulletin de la Société d'Anthropologie de Paris*, p. 405 (1867).

151. ———: "Sur l'âge des sujets soumis à la trépanation chirurgicale néolithique." *Bulletin de la Société d'Anthropologie de Paris*, p. 572 (1876).

152. Browder: "Advances in Neurological Surgery during the Past 50 Years." *American Journal of Surgery*, pp. 164-85 (1941).

153. Brown, H. M.: "An Anecdotal Sketch of Professor Doctor Nicholas Senn." *Military Surgeon*, pp. 549-63 (1920).

154. Bruberger: "Über die Exstirpation des Kropfes, etc." *Deutsche militairärztliche Zeitschrift*, p. 447 (1876).

155. Brun, V.: "Die Lumbalanästhesie." *Neue Deutsche Chirurgie*, Part 29.

156. Brunn, W. von: "Geschichtliche Einführung in die Chirurgie." In Kirschner and Nordmann, eds., *Die Chirurgie*. 1924.

157. ———: "Theodor Kocher zum Gedächtnis." *Zeitschrift für ärztliche Fortbildung*, p. 439 (1941).

158. Bruns, P. von: "Die Entwicklung der modernen Behandlung des Kropfes." In *Verhandlungen der Deutschen Gesellschaft für Chirurgie, 25. Kongress. Berlin, 1896.*

159. ———: "Zur Äthernarkose." *Berliner klinische Wochenschrift*, p. 1147 (1894).

160. *Bulletin Acad. de Méd.*, Paris, pp. 113-16 (1914).

161. Bryan, J. H.: "The History of Laryngology and Rhinology and the Influence of America in the Development of This Specialty." *Annals of Medical History*, pp. 151-70 (1933).

162. Buchholtz, A.: *Ernst von Bergmann*. Leipzig, 1911.

163. Buess, H.: "Dokumente zur Geschichte der Allgemeinnarkose." *Berliner klinische Wochenschrift*, Nos. 10 ff. (1946).

164. ———: "Über die Anwendung der Koka und des Kokains in der Medizin." *Ciba Zeitschrift*, No. 94 (1944).

165. Buford, C. G.: "Christian Fenger. A Biographical Sketch." *Bulletin of the Society of Medical History*, pp. 196-204 (1913).

166. Bühler, A.: "Zur Erforschung des Kokagenusses." *Ciba Zeitschrift*, No. 94 (1944).

167. Bülau, G.: "Für die Heberdrainage bei Behandlung des Empyen." *Zeitschrift für klinische Medizin*, p. 31 (1891).
168. Busacchi: "La trepanatione del cranio nei popoli preistorici e nei primitivi moderne." *Atti. mem. Acad. Stor. Arte Sanit.*, pp. 64 ff. (1936).
169. Cadge, W.: "The Case of the Late Professor Hughes Bennett." *British Medical Journal*, October 9 (1875).
170. Castiglioni, A.: *Storia della chirurgia di hernia.* Seminario, Padua, 1936.
171. *Centralblatt für Chirurgie*, p. 149 (1904).
172. Cérenville, E. de: *De la Résection des côtes*, etc. Geneva, 1886.
173. Championnière, L.: *Les Origines de la trépanation.* Paris, 1912.
174. "The Charge against Professor Ferrier under the Vivisection Act: Dismissal of the Summons." *British Medical Journal*, November 4 (1881).
175. Chauliac, G.: *La Grande chirurgie.* Paris, 1890.
176. Chiari, Hans: "Chirurgie des Kehlkopfes und der Luftröhre." *Neue Deutsche Chirurgie*, vol. 19. Stuttgart, 1916.
177. Clapesattle, Helen: *The Doctors Mayo.* Minneapolis, University of Minnesota Press, 1941.
178. Cooper, B. B.: *The Life of Sir Astley Cooper.* London, 1843.
179. Corning, L.: "A Further Contribution of Local Medication of the Spinal Cord, with Cases." *Med. Record*, March (1888).
180. ———: *Pain in Its Neuro-pathological, Diagnostic, Medico-legal and Neurotherapeutic Relations.* Philadelphia, 1894.
181. ———: "Spinal Anaesthesia and Local Medication of the Cord." *New York Medical Journal*, October (1885).
182. Corti, E. C.: *Wenn . . . Sendung und Schicksal einer Kaiserin.* Graz, 1954.
183. Courvoisier, L. G.: *Casuistisch-statistische Beiträge zur Pathologie und Chirurgie der Gallenwege.* Leipzig, 1890.
184. Critchley: *Sir William Gowers, 1845–1915. A Biographical Appreciation.* London, 1949.
185. Daland, J.: "Depressed Fracture and Trephining of the Skull by the Incas of Peru." *Annals of Medical History*, p. 549 (1935).
186. Dandy, W. E.: *Gehirnchirurgie.* Leipzig, 1938.
187. Darmstädter: "Ein Überblick über Begründung und Ausbau der Kokain-Lokalanästhesie." *Schmerz, Narkose, Anästhesie*, pp. 169 ff. 1936–38.
188. "David Ferrier." *Prov. Med. Journ.* (London), p. 321 (1876).
189. Davis, Loyal Edward: *J. B. Murphy, Stormy Petrel of Surgery.* New York, G. P. Putnam & Sons, 1938.
190. "Death of Broca." *Edinburgh Medical Journal*, p. 186 (1880).
191. DeCourcy, J. L., and C. B. DeCourcy: *Pathology and Surgery of Thyroid Disease.* Springfield, Ill., 1949.
192. Deineka, I. J.: "Wladimir Petrowitsch Filatow." *Sowjetskaja Medizina*, No. 5 (1955).
193. Delaunay: "Un Chirurgien herniaire de la marine." *Bulletin de la Société Française d'Histoire de la Médecine*, pp. 291–302 (1912).

194. Delavan, B.: "A History of Thyrotomy and Laryngectomy." *Laryngoscope*, No. 2 (1933).

195. ———: *Personal Recollections of a Great Laryngologist, Sir Morell Mackenzie.* 1935.

196. Desault, Pierre: *Chirurgischer Nachlass.* Ed. by Bichat, translated by von Wardenberg. Vol. 2, III, 271.

197. De Vecchi, Paolo: *Modern Italian Surgery and Old Universities of Italy.* New York, Hoeber, 1921.

198. Devoto, L.: "Commemorazione del M. F. prof. Carlo Forlanini." *Gazzetta Medica Lombarda*, pp. 79 ff. (1926).

199. Dieffenbach, J. F.: "Beiträge zur Verpflanzung der Hornhaut." *Ammons Zeitschrift für Ophthalmologie*, p. 172 (1831).

200. ———: *Über den organischen Ersatz.* Berlin, 1830.

201. ———: "Über die Exzision der Zentral-Leukome aus der Hornhaut." *Ammons Zeitschrift für Ophthalmologie* (1830).

202. "Dr. Ferrier's Localisation: For Whose Advantage?" *British Medical Journal*, November 19 (1881).

203. "Dr. Gerald Yeo." *Nature*, p. 314 (1909).

204. "Dr. John B. Murphy—An Appreciation." *Surgery, Gynecology, Obstetrics*, pp. 234–35 (1916).

205. Dumont, F.: *Über den gegenwärtigen Stand der Cocain-Analgesie.* Wiesbaden, 1890.

206. Ebstein: *Ärztereden aus dem 19. Jahrhundert.* Berlin, 1926.

207. "Eduard Hitzig." *Archiv für Psychiatrie und Nervenkrankheiten* (1907).

208. Eiselsberg, A. von: "Die Krankheiten der Schilddrüse." In *Deutsche Chirurgie*, Part 38. Stuttgart, 1901.

209. Eiselt, T.: "Spitäler und Ärzte in Paris." *Allgemeine Wiener medizinische Zeitung* (1858).

210. Elschnig, A., and H. S. Gradle: "History of Keratoplastic Operations to Date." *American Journal of Ophthalmology* (1913).

211. Emmet, T. A.: *A Memoir of Dr. James Marion Sims.* New York, 1884.

212. "The Entertainments." *Lancet*, August 13, 1881.

213. "Die Entwicklung der Hirnchirurgie." *Ciba Zeitschrift*, No. 75.

214. Erlenmeyer: "Über Cocainsucht." *Deutsche medizinische Zeitung* (1886).

215. Esmarch, F. von: "Aus meinen Erinnerungen." *Deutsche Revue*, vol. 27.

216. ———: "Über ganz blutlose Operationen." *Archiv für klinische Chirurgie*, p. 691 (1880).

217. Ewald: "Carl Langenbuch." (Obituary.) *Berliner klinische Wochenschrift*, p. 660 (1901).

218. ———: "Friedrich Goltz." *Pflügers Archiv für Physiologie*, p. 1 (1908).

219. "Excision of a Tumor from the Brain." *Lancet*, November 29 (1884).

220. Fearing, F.: *Reflex Action. A Study in the History of Physiological Psychiatry.* Baltimore, 1930.

221. Ferrier, D.: *The Functions of the Brain.* London, 1876. 2nd ed., 1886.

222. "The Festivities of the Congress." *British Medical Journal*, August 13 (1881).

223. Finney, J. M.: "Personal Appreciation of Dr. Halsted." *Bulletin of the Johns Hopkins Hospital* (1925).

224. Fischer: "Carl Langenbuch." *Deutsche medizinische Wochenschrift*, p. 419 (1901).

225. Fitz: "Certain Aspects of the Medical History of Exophthalmic Goitre." *Boston Medical and Surgical Journal*, p. 675 (1914).

226. Fitzgerald: "The Vivisection Controversy." *Medical Magazine* (London), p. 415 (1882).

227. Fletcher, R.: *On Prehistoric Trephining*. Washington, 1882.

228. Flexner, Simon, and J. T. Flexner: *William Henry Welch and the Heroic Age of American Medicine*. New York, Viking, 1941.

229. Forlanini, C.: "Primo Caso di Tisi Polmonare avanzata curato felicemente col Pneumothorace artificiate." (Communication to the G. Congress for Internal Medicine in Rome in October, 1895.)

230. ———: "Versuche mit künstlichem Pneumothorax, etc." *Münchner medizinische Wochenschrift*, No. 15 (1894).

231. ———: "Zur Behandlung der Lungenschwindsucht durch künstlich erzeugten Pneumothorax." *Deutsche medizinische Wochenschrift*, No. 35 (1906).

232. Fowler: "Cocaine analgesia." *Philadelphia Medical Journal* (1900).

233. ———: "A Study of Eighty-one Cases, etc." *New York Medical News*, January (1901).

234. "Franz Reisinger." In Haberling, W., F. Hübotter, and H. Vierordt: *Biographisches Lexikon der hervorragenden Ärzte aller Zeiten und Völker*. 5 vols. Berlin and Vienna, 1929–35.

235. Freud, S.: *An Autobiographical Study*. Tr. by James Strachey. London, 1935.

236. ———: "Beitrag zur Kenntnis der Cocawirkung." *Wiener medizinische Wochenschrift*, No. 35 (1885).

237. ———: "Über Coca." *Zentralblatt für Therapie*, vol. 2 (1884).

238. Frey: *Der künstliche Pneumothorax*. Leipzig, 1921.

239. Friedrich, P. L.: "Die operative Beeinflussung einseitiger Lungenphthisis durch totale Brustwandmobilisierung und Lungenentspannung (Pleuro-Pneumolysis totalis)." *Archiv für klinische Chirurgie*, No. 87 (1908).

240. Fritsch, G., and E. Hitzig: "Über die elektrische Erregbarkeit des Grosshirns." *Archiv für Anatomie und Physiologie*, p. 308 (1870).

241. Garrison, F. H.: *An Introduction to the History of Medicine*. 4th ed., rev. Philadelphia, 1929.

242. Gautier, L.: "Le Professeur Édouard de Cérenville (1843 à 1915)." *Correspondenzblatt Schweizer Ärzte*, No. 22 (1915).

243. *Gazette des Hôpitaux*, Paris, pp. 69–74 (1919).

244. *Gazette méd. de Paris*, p. 111 (1914).

245. "The General Meetings." *Lancet*, August, 1881.

246. Giordano, D.: "Grande chirurghi italiani del' ultimo secolo." *Boll. ist. stor. Ital. Arte sanit.*, pp. 205–26 (1928).

247. Gluck, T.: "Experimenteller Beitrag zur Frage der Lungenexstirpation." *Berliner klinische Wochenschrift*, No. 18 (1881).

248. Gluck, T., and E. Hahn: *Berliner klinische Wochenschrift*, p. 1087 (1902).

249. Goetz, E.: "Société médicale de Genève. Séance du 13 Sept. 1882." *Revue médicale de la Suisse Romande* (1882).

250. Goldstein, L.: "Beiträge zur Physiologie und Pathologie der Grosshirnrinde." In Schmid's *Jahrbuch der Medizin*, 1879.

251. Goltz, F.: "Discussion on the Localisation of Function in the Cortex Cerebri." In *International Medical Congress, 7th session. Transactions.* London, 1881.

252. Gosset, A.: *Erlebnisse und Erkenntnisse eines Chirurgen.* Stuttgart, 1942.

253. Gowers, W. R.: *A Manual of Diseases of the Nervous System.* London, 1886–88.

254. Gowers, W. R., and V. Horsley: *Ein Fall von Rückenmarksgeschwulst.* Berlin, 1889.

255. Graefe-Saemisch: *Handbuch der Gesamten Augenheilkunde*, vol. 7, p. 437.

256. Gröbly, W.: "Erinnerungen an Theodor Kocher." *Schweizer medizinische Wochenschrift*, p. 1028 (1941).

257. Grossmann, M.: "Leopold von Schrötter." *Monatsschrift für Ohrenheilkunde*, pp. 1–8 (1907).

258. Grossmann, O.: "Die Äthernarkose." *Deutsche medizinische Wochenschrift*, p. 246 (1894).

259. Grote, L. R.: "Heinrich Braun." In *Die Medizin der Gegenwart in Selbstdarstellungen.* Leipzig, 1925.

260. Grysanowski, E.: *Das ärztliche Concil zu London (August 1881).* Hanover, 1881.

261. Günther, G. B.: "Operative Behandlung des Kropfes." In his *Die Lehre von den blutigen Operationen am menschlichen Körper.* Leipzig, 1862–66.

262. Gurlt, E. J.: *Über die Zystengeschwülste des Halses.* Berlin, 1855.

263. Gussenbauer, C.: "Über die erste durch Th. Billroth am Menschen ausgeführte Exstirpation des Kehlkopfes." *Archiv für klinische Chirurgie, 17:*341.

264. "Gustav Fritsch zum 70. Geburtstag." *Deutsche medizinische Wochenschrift* (1908).

265. Gyergyaie: "Kritische Bemerkungen zur Geschichte der Lehre von den Brüchen." *Rohlfs Archiv für Geschichte der Medizin*, vol. 3 (1880).

266. Haagensen, C. D., and W. E. B. Lloyd: *A Hundred Years of Medicine.* New York, 1943.

267. Hahn, E.: "Über subarachnoidale Cocaininjektionen nach Bier." *Centralblatt für die Grenzgebiete der Medizin und Chirurgie*, pp. 310 ff. (1901).

268. Halsted, W. S.: "The Operative Story of Goitre." In *Johns Hopkins Hospital Reports*, XIX, 70–260 (1920).

269. ———: "The Radical Cure of Inguinal Hernia in the Male." *Bulletin of the Johns Hopkins Hospital*, p. 17 (1893).

270. Härtl: "Die Lokalanästhesie." *Deutsche Chirurgie*. Stuttgart, 1916.

271. Haweis, Rev. H. R.: *Sir Morell Mackenzie*. London, 1893.

272. Helfreich, F.: "Chirurgie der Unterleibsbrüche." In M. Neuberger and J. L. Pagel: *Puschmanns Handbuch der Geschichte der Medizin*. 3 vols. Jena, 1902–5.

273. ———: "Geschichte der Chirurgie." *Ibid.*

274. ———: "Laryngo- und Tracheotomie." *Ibid.*

275. Heuer, G. J.: "Dr. Halsted." *Bulletin of the Johns Hopkins Hospital* (1952).

276. Heymann, P.: "Geschichte der Laryngologie und Rhinologie." In M. Neuberger and J. L. Pagel: *Puschmanns Handbuch der Geschichte der Medizin*. 3 vols. Jena, 1902–5.

277. Hippel, A. von: "Über die operative Behandlung totaler stationärer Hornhauttrübungen." *A. von Graefes Archiv für Ophthalmologie*, pp. 78–226 (1877).

278. ———: "Über Transplantation der Hornhaut." *Monatsblatt für Augenheilkunde*, pp. 54–59 (1886).

279. Holmes, Gordon: "John Hughlings Jackson." In K. Kolle: *Grosse Nervenärzte*. Stuttgart, 1956.

280. Horsley, V.: "Discussion of a Paper by A. H. Bennett and R. S. Godlee, 'Case of Cerebral Tumor. The Surgical Treatment.' " *British Medical Journal*, p. 988 (1885).

281. ———: "Remarks on Ten Consecutive Cases of Operations upon the Brain, etc." *British Medical Journal*, p. 863 (1887).

282. "The Hospital for Paralysed and Epileptic." *Illustrated London News*, July 5 (1885).

283. Höveldop: "Die Ansichten über die Verletzungen des Schädels vom Altertum bis zum Beginn der Neuzeit" (medical dissertation). Düsseldorf, 1936.

284. Iason, A. H.: "Historical Evolution of Hernial Surgery." Section I of his *Hernia*. Philadelphia, 1941.

285. Iff, W.: "Die Entwicklung der Kropfbehandlung." *Janus*, p. 69 (1938).

286. International Medical Congress, 7th session held in London, August 2–9, 1881. *Abstracts of the Communications to Be Made in the Various Sections*. Prepared under the direction of Sir William MacCormac. London, 1881.

287. International Medical Congress, 7th session held in London, August 2–9, 1881. *Transactions*. Prepared for publication under the direction of the Executive Committee by Sir William MacCormac, assisted by Henry Makins and the under secretaries of the sections. London, 1881.

288. "The International Medical Congress." *British Medical Journal*, August 6 (1881).

289. Jackson, J. H.: *Neurological Fragments*. London, 1925.

290. ———: "Selected Writings." *Lancet*, p. 307 (1869) and p. 84 (1873).

291. ———: "Selected Writings." *London Hospital Reports*, p. 459 (1864).

292. ———: "Selected Writings." *Transactions St. Andrews Medical Graduates Association*, p. 3 (1870).

293. Jameson, P. H.: "Memorial of Dr. Bobbs." *Indiana Medical Journal, XXIV:*33 (1905–6).

294. "Das Jod." *Ciba Zeitschrift*, no. 118 (1949).

295. "John Hughes Bennett." *Edinburgh Medical Journal*, p. 466 (1876).

296. "John Hughlings Jackson." *Münchner medizinische Wochenschrift*, p. 2797 (1911).

297. "John Stough Bobbs and Lithotomy of the Gallbladder." *Surgery, Gynecology, Obstetrics*, Suppl. 47 (1928).

298. Jones, E.: *The Life and Work of Sigmund Freud.* vol. 1. *The Formative Years and the Great Discoveries.* New York, Basic Books, 1953.

299. Kausch, W.: "Johannes von Mikulicz-Radecki. Sein Leben und seine Bedeutung." *Mitteilungen aus den Grenzgebieten der Medizin und Chirurgie*, 3rd Supplement, pp. 1–65. Jena, 1907.

300. Keen, W. W.: "Large Scrotal Hernia." *Philadelphia Medical Journal*, November (1900).

301. ———: "Vivisection and Brain-Surgery." *Harper's New Monthly Magazine*, p. 128 (1893).

302. Kehr: "Chirurgie der Gallenwege." *Neue Deutsche Chirurgie*, vol. 8 (1913).

303. ———: "Die Praxis der Gallenwegchirurgie." In Grashey: *Die Chirurgie in Einzeldarstellung*. Vol. 1.

304. Kellogg, J. H.: "Lawson Tait." *Surgery, Gynecology, Obstetrics*, pp. 914–19 (1930).

305. Kennedy, F.: "Sir William Richard Gowers (1845–1915)." In W. Haymaker, ed.: *The Founders of Neurology*. Springfield, Ill., 1953.

306. Kirchoff, T.: "Julius Eduard Hitzig." In his *Deutsche Irrenärzte*. Berlin, 1924.

307. Klose, H.: "Die Chirurgie der Basedowschen Krankheit." *Neue deutsche Chirurgie*, vol. 44.

308. Klose, H., and G. Büttner: "Kachexia strumipriva. Historischer Überblick." In Hirsch: *Handbuch der inneren Sekretionen*. Vienna, 1928.

309. Knipping, H. W.: "Ludolph Brauer zum Gedächtnis." *Beiträge zur Klinik der Tuberkulose*, pp. 172–81 (1940).

310. Koch, H.: *Die Geschichte der Herniotomie bis auf Scarpa und Cooper.* Berlin, 1883.

311. Kocher, T.: "Methode der Exstirpatio strumae nebst Bericht über dreizehn Fälle." *Deutsche Zeitschrift für Chirurgie* (1874).

312. ———: "Über die Kropfexstirpation und ihre Folgen." *Archiv für klinische Chirurgie*, p. 254 (1883).

313. ———: "Zur Pathologie und Therapie des Kropfes." *Deutsche Zeitschrift für Chirurgie* (1874).

314. Koller, Carl: "Das Kokain." *Ciba Zeitschrift*, No. 94 (1944).
315. ———: "Historische Notiz über die ersten Anfänge der Lokalanästhesie." *Wiener medizinische Wochenschrift*, p. 601 (1928).
316. ———: "Über die Verwendung des Cocains zur Anästhesierung am Auge." *Wiener medizinische Wochenschrift*, pp. 1276 and 1309 (1884).
317. Kraft, G.: *Erinnerungen an Johannes von Mikulicz und Karl Schönborn aus den Jugendtagen der modernen Chirurgie*. Leipzig, 1926.
318. *Die Krankheit Kaiser Friedrichs III*., dargestellt nach amtlichen Quellen und den im Königlichen Hausministerium niedergelegten Berichten der Ärzte. . . . Kaiserliche Reichsdruckerei, Berlin, 1888.
319. Kronfeld, A.: *Bericht über die Billrothklinik*. n.d.
320. Kühn, J.: "Operationen am Kehlkopf und der Luftröhre. Geschichte." In G. B. Günther: *Die Lehre von den blutigen Operationen am menschlichen Körper*, vol. V. Leipzig, 1862–66.
321. Kuntz, A.: "Eduard Hitzig (1838–1907)." In W. Haymaker, ed.: *The Founders of Neurology*. Springfield, Ill., 1953.
322. Küster, E.: "Geschichte der neueren Deutschen Chirurgie." *Neue Deutsche Chirurgie*, vol. 15, p. 85. Stuttgart, 1915.
323. Labhart, A.: "Die Schilddrüse. Historische Daten." In his *Klinik der inneren Sekretionen*, vol. VI, 1957.
324. Langenbuch, C.: "Chirurgie der Leber und Gallenblase." *Deutsche Chirurgie*, Part 45c.
325. ———: "Ein Fall von Exstirpation der Gallenblase wegen chronischer Cholelithiasis. Heilung." *Berliner klinische Wochenschrift*, No. 48, pp. 725–27 (1882).
326. ———: "Ein Rückblick auf die Entwicklung der Chirurgie des Gallensystems." *Verhandlungen der Deutschen Gesellschaft für Chirurgie*. 1896.
327. "Lawson Tait." (Obituary.) *Lancet*, p. 1736 (1899).
328. Lejars, F.: "Paul Reclus (1847–1914)." *Bulletins et mémoires de la Société de Chirurgie de Paris, 1919*, pp. 148–62.
329. Lennock, W. G.: "John Hughlings Jackson." In W. Haymaker, ed.: *The Founders of Neurology*. Springfield, Ill., 1953.
330. Liston, R.: *Elements of Surgery*. London, 1842.
331. McArthur, L. L.: "Christian Fenger, As I Knew Him." *Bulletin of the Society of Medical History*, pp. 51–57 (1913).
332. McBride: "Sir Felix Semon; sein Lebenswerk und dessen Einfluss auf die Laryngologie. (Die 'Semon Lectures' der Universität London.)" *Semons Internationales Centralblatt für Laryngologie, Rhinologie und verwandte Wissenschaften*, No. 4 (1913).
333. McBurney, Charles: "Removal of Biliary Calculi from the Common Duct." *Annals of Surgery*, p. 480 (1898).
334. McCallum, William George: *William Stewart Halsted, Surgeon*. Baltimore, 1930.
335. Macewen, W.: "An Address on the Surgery of the Brain and Spinal Cord." *British Medical Journal*, p. 302 (1888).

336. ———: "Case of Cerebral Abscess Due to Otitis Media." *Lancet*, p. 616 (1887).

337. ———: "The Case Presentation before the Glasgow Pathological and Clinical Society." *Glasgow Medical Journal*, p. 210 (1886).

338. ———: "Cases Illustrative of Cerebral Surgery." *Lancet*, pp. 881, 934 (1885).

339. ———: "On the Surgery of the Brain and Spinal Cord." *Medical News*, p. 169 (1888).

340. ———: *Pyogenic Diseases of the Brain and Spinal Cord*. New York, 1893.

341. McKay, W. J. S.: *Lawson Tait, His Life and Work*. London and New York, 1922.

342. Mackenzie, M.: *The Fatal Illness of Frederick the Noble*. London, 1888.

343. ———: [Reviews of German and English editions of 318.] *Lancet*, October 20 and October 27 (1888).

344. ———: *Die Krankheiten des Halses und der Nase*. Berlin, 1880.

345. Maillard, H.: "Jacques Louis Reverdin (1882–1929)." *Revue médicale de la Suisse Romande*, No. 1 (1929).

346. Majocchi, A., and G. Galli: "Enrico Bottini." *Münchner medizinische Wochenschrift*, No. 22 (1903).

347. Martin, A.: *Werden und Wirken eines deutschen Frauenarztes*. Berlin, 1914.

348. Martin, C.: "Reminiscences of Lawson Tait." *Journal of Obstetrics and Gynecology*, pp. 117–23 (1929).

349. Martin, F. H.: *Fifty Years of Medicine and Surgery. An Autobiographical Sketch*. Chicago, 1934.

350. Martindale, W.: *Coca, Cocaine and Its Salts: Their History*, etc. London, 1886.

351. Matas, R.: "In Memoriam Nicholas Senn." *Journal of the American Medical Association*, pp. 961–62 (1908).

352. ———: "In Memoriam William Stewart Halsted. An Appreciation." *Bulletin of the Johns Hopkins Hospital* (1925).

353. ———: "Local and Regional Anaesthesis with Cocaine." *Philadelphia Medical Journal*, Nov. 3 (1900).

354. Mayor: *Traité des ligatures en masse*. Paris, 1827.

355. "Med.-chir. Bemerkungen während einer italienischen Reise, 1881–1882." *Berliner klinische Wochenschrift*, pp. 337 ff. (1883).

356. Merbach: "Über die Geschichte der Vivisection." *Jahresbericht der Gesellschaft für Natur- und Heilkunde Dresden*, p. 98 (1878–79).

357. Meyer, W.: "Transthoracic Resection of the Lower End of the Oesophagus in a Dog." *Annals of Surgery*, pp. 666–86 (1905).

358. Mikulicz, J.: "Chirurgische Erfahrungen über die Sauerbruchsche Kammer bei Unter- und bei Überdruck." *Verhandlungen der Deutschen Gesellschaft für Chirurgie, 33. Kongress, Berlin, April 6–9, 1904*.

359. "Mitteilungen von Carlo Forlanini auf dem Internationalen Med. Kongress, Rom, März–April, 1894."

360. Moodie, Roy: "Stone Age Man's Cure for Headache." *Scientific Monthly*, p. 161 (1921).

361. ———: "Surgery in Precolumbian Peru." *Annals of Medical History*, p. 698 (1929).

362. Moore, I.: "Mark Hovell." *Journal of Laryngology*, p. 692 (1925).

363. Moreno y Maiz: *Recherches chimiques et physiologiques sur l'érythraxylon coca du Peru et la cocaïne*. Paris, 1868.

364. Müller, J.: "Gedenkworte zum 50. Jahrestage des Vortrages von Dr. Karl Koller über das Kokain." *Wiener klinische Wochenschrift*, No. 44 (1934).

365. Munro, R.: *On Trepanning the Human Skull in Prehistoric Times*. Edinburgh, 1891.

366. Murphy, J. B.: "Surgery of the Lung." *Journal of the American Medical Association*, pp. 208, 281 (1898).

367. Neuberger, M., and J. L. Pagel: *Puschmanns Handbuch der Geschichte der Medizin*. 3 vols. Jena, 1902–5.

368. Neumann, A., and E. Hahn, in *Zeitschrift für Chirurgie*, No. 3 (1903).

369. New York *Times*, May and June, 1887.

370. New York *Tribune*, May and June, 1887.

371. Niemann, A.: "Über eine neue organische Base in den Cocablättern." (Medical dissertation.) Göttingen, 1860.

372. Nissen, R.: *Erlebtes aus der Thoraxchirurgie*. Stuttgart, 1955.

373. Nizetic, Z.: *Über die Entwicklung und den heutigen Stand der Hornhauttransplantation*. Stuttgart, 1940.

374. Nussbaum, J. N.: *Die Behandlung der Hornhauttrübung, mit besonderer Berücksichtigung der Einsetzung einer künstlichen Hornhaut*. Munich, 1856.

375. Oberst: *Deutsche medizinische Wochenschrift*, p. 287 (1890).

376. Oettingen, F. W. von: "The Earliest Suggestion of the Use of Cocaine for Local Anesthesia." *Annals of Medical History*, pp. 275–80 (1933).

377. Pagel, J. L.: "Langenbuch." (Obituary.) *Die medizinische Wochenschrift*, No. 24 (1901).

378. Paget, Sir James: [Address]. *The Illustrated London News*, August 6 (1881).

379. ———: *Sir Victor Horsley. A Study of His Life and Writings*. London, 1919.

380. ———: *The Surgery of the Chest*. London, 1896.

381. "Paul Broca." *Archiv für Anthropologie*, p. 132 (1880–81).

382. *Paul Leopold Friedrich. Zum Gedächtnis der bevorstehenden 25. Wiederkehr seines Todestages*. Munich, 1940.

383. Perry: "Trephination of the Living Human Skull in Prehistoric Times." *British Medical Journal*, p. 457 (1923).

384. Podach, E.: "Historisches zur Jodmangeltherapie des Kropfes." *Schweizer medizinische Wochenschrift*, p. 794 (1940).

385. Power: "Vortrag auf dem Ophthalmologen-Kongress in London, 1872." *Nagel's Jahrbuch 1873*, p. 275.

386. *Presse méd. Paris*, pp. 408–14 (1912).

387. *Presse méd. Paris*, XII:869 (1914).

388. "Professor Paul Broca." *Lancet*, p. 153 (1880).

389. "The Prosecution or Persecution of Professor David Ferrier by the Antivivisectionists." *Boston Medical and Surgical Journal*, December 8 (1881).

390. Puner, H. W.: *Freud, His Life and His Mind*. New York, 1947.

391. Quail, J.: "The Vivisection Act, 1876." *Transactions National Association for the Promotion of Social Science* (London), p. 309 (1879).

392. Quincke, H. I.: *Die Technik der Lumbalpunktion*. Berlin, 1902.

393. ———: *Über Hydrocephalus. Vortrag, gehalten auf dem X. Kongress für Innere Medizin, 1891*.

394. Raaf, J. E.: "Hernia-Healers." *Annals of Medical History*, pp. 377–89 (1932).

395. Raper, Howard Riley: *Man against Pain: The Epic of Anesthesia*. New York, Prentice Hall, 1945.

396. Reclus, P.: *L'Anesthésie localisée par la cocaïne*. Paris, 1895.

397. ———: "De la Méthode de Bier." *Le Bulletin Méd.*, No. 22 (1901).

398. Reed, A. L.: "The Life and Character of Lawson Tait." *American Journal of Obstetrics*, pp. 840–46 (1899).

399. Reik, T.: *From Thirty Years with Freud*. Tr. by Richard Winston. New York, 1940.

400. Reisinger, F.: "Die Keratoplastik." *Bayer. Annalen der Chirurgie und Augenheilkunde*, pp. 206–15 (1824).

401. Reverdin, J. L.: *Note sur vingt-deux opérations de goitre*. Geneva, 1883.

402. *Revue mensuelle médicale*, IV, 746–64 (1880).

403. Rich, Norman, and M. H. Fisher: *Holstein Papers*, Cambridge University Press, 2 volumes, 1955 and 1957.

404. Richter: "Wer hat zuerst die Spongia usta gegen den Kropf empfohlen?" *Archiv für klinische Chirurgie*, 82 (1907).

405. Richter, W.: *Kaiser Friedrich III*. Zurich and Leipzig, 1938.

406. Riese, W.: "The Early History of Aphasia." *Bulletin of the History of Medicine* (1947).

407. Rioch, D. M.: "Sir David Ferrier." In W. Haymaker, ed.: *The Founders of Neurology*. Springfield, Ill., 1953.

408. Robinson, F. B.: "A Sketch of Lawson Tait and His Work." *Journal of the American Medical Association*, pp. 77 ff. (1892).

409. Robinson, Victor: "Subarachnoid Cocaine Anesthesia." *Medical Record*, November (1901).

410. ———: *Victory over Pain: A History of Anesthesia*. New York, Henry Schuman, 1946.

411. Rodt: "Beitrag zur Geschichte der Schilddrüse." *Deutsche Zeitschrift für Chirurgie*, No. 116, p. 628.

412. Rogers, L.: "The History of Craniotomy. An Account of the Methods Which Have Been Practiced and the Instruments Used for Opening the Human Skull During Life." *Annals of Medical History*, 2 (new series): 495 (1930).

413. Rohlfs: *Die chirurgischen Klassiker Deutschlands. Friedrich von Es-march.* H. 1, 1883.

414. Rose, E.: *Kropftod und die Radikalkur der Kröpfe.* Berlin, 1878.

415. Rosenstein, Paul: *Narben bleiben zurück.* Munich, 1954.

416. Roth: *Chirurgie der Gallenwege.* Berlin, 1885.

417. Sabatier, R. B.: *Handbuch für Wundärzte.* Vienna, 1800.

418. Sachs, H.: *Freud: Master and Friend.* Cambridge, Mass., 1944.

419. Salamon, E.: *London Past and Present,* ed. by Charles Holme. London, 1926.

420. Salzer, E.: *Über den künstlichen Hornhautersatz.* 1898.

421. Sänger: "Lawson Tait." *Monatsschrift für Geburtshilfe,* pp. 224–29 (1899).

422. Sauerbruch, F.: "Aus der Geschichte der Thoraxchirurgie." In: *Chirurgie der Brustorgane.* Berlin, 1920.

423. ———: "Bemerkungen zum Artikel des Herrn Prof. Brauer und Prof. Petersen, Heidelberg: 'Über eine wesentliche Vereinfachung der künstlichen Atmung nach Sauerbruch.'" *Centralblatt für Chirurgie,* pp. 441–47 (1904).

424. ———:*Das war mein Leben.* Bad Wörishofen, 1951.

425. ———: "Die historische Entwicklung der operativen Behandlung der Lungentuberkulose." *Zeitschrift für Tuberkulose,* H. 5 (1930).

426. ———: "Kocher." *Korrespondenzblatt Schweizer Ärzte,* pp. 78–80 (1917).

427. ———: "Über die Ausschaltung der schädlichen Wirkung des Pneumothorax bei intrathorakalen Operationen." *Centralblatt für Chirurgie,* No. 6 (1904).

428. ———: "Über die physiologischen und physikalischen Grundlagen bei intrathorakalen Eingriffen in meiner pneumatischen Kammer." *Verhandlungen der Deutschen Gesellschaft für Chirurgie, 33. Kongress Berlin, April 6–9, 1904.*

429. ———: "Zur Pathologie des offenen Pneumothorax und die Grundlagen meines Verfahrens zu seiner Ausschaltung." *Mitteilungen aus den Grenzgebieten der Medizin und Chirurgie,* pp. 398–486 (1904).

430. Sawaitow, A. S.: "W. P. Filatow." *Sowjetskaja Medizina,* No. 5 (1955).

431. Schleich, C. L.: *Besonnte Vergangenheit. Lebenserinnerungen.* Berlin, 1925.

432. ———: *Schmerzlose Operationen.* Berlin, 1899.

433. Schmid, E.: "Die Schädeltrepanation bei den Inca-Peruanern." *Globus,* p. 177 (1898).

434. Schmidt: "Unterleibsbrüche." In Billroth: *Deutsche Chirurgie,* Part 47.

435. Schönbauer, L.: "Zur Geschichte der Anästhesie." In *Beiträge zur Geschichte der Medizin.* Vienna, 1948.

436. Schüller: "Die Tracheotomie, Laryngotomie und Exstirpation des Kehlkopfes." *Deutsche Chirurgie*, Part 57. Stuttgart, 1880.

437. Sellerbeck: "Über Keratoplastik." *A. von Graefes Archiv für Ophthalmologie*, 4:1–46 (1878).

438. Semon, F.: *The Autobiography of Sir Felix Semon*. Ed. by Henry C. Semon and Thomas A. Macintire. London, 1926.

439: ———: "A Case of Partial Extirpation of the Larynx for Epithelioma of the Left Ventricle of Morgagni; Recovery." *Transactions of the Clinical Society of London*, XX (1887).

440. ———: "Die Krankheit Kaiser Friedrichs III. und die Laryngologie." *Internationales Centralblatt für Laryngologie*, December (1888).

441. ———: "Leopold von Schrötter." *Internationales Centralblatt für Laryngologie, Rhinologie und verwandte Wissenschaften*, No. 6 (1908).

442. ———: "Sir Morell Mackenzie." *Internationales Centralblatt für Laryngologie, Rhinologie und verwandte Wissenschaften*, No. 9 (1892).

443. Senn, N.: "Life and Work of the Late Professor Fenger." *Journal of the American Medical Association*, pp. 4–8 (1902).

444. Sherrington, C. S.: "Sir David Ferrier." In *Dictionary of National Biography*, ed. by Leslie Stephen and Sidney Lee. 22 vols. London, 1908–09. (Reprinted, 1938.)

445. Sims, M. J.: *Clinical Notes on Uterine Surgery*. New York, 1871.

446. ———: *Meine Lebensgeschichte*. Stuttgart, 1885.

447. ———: "On the Treatment of Vesicovaginal Fistula." *American Journal of Medical Sciences* (1852).

448. ———: "Remarks on Cholecystotomy in Dropsy of the Gallbladder." *British Medical Journal*, pp. 811–15 (1878).

449. "Sir Charles Ballance." (Obituary.) *British Medical Journal*, p. 339 (1936).

450. "Sir Charles Ballance." (Obituary.) *Lancet*, p. 450 (1936).

451. "Sir Felix Semon." (Obituary.) *Lancet*, March 12 (1921).

452. "Sir Morell MacKenzie." *Journal of Laryngology, Rhinology and Otology*, No. 3 (1892).

453. "Sir Rickman John Godlee." *British Medical Journal*, April 15 (1925).

454. Spangaro: "Un chirurgo ideale. Edoardo Bassini." *Atti del' Ace di Agricoltura, Verona*, Vol. 2 (1925).

455. Squiers, E. G.: *Incidents of Travel and Exploration in the Land of the Incas*. London, 1877.

456. Stieda, A.: "Über alte trepanierte Schädel." *Wiener medizinsche Wochenschrift*, p. 26 (1911).

457. ———: "Zum Gedächtnis an Fritz Gustav von Bramann." *Archiv für klinische Chirurgie*, pp. 861–71 (1913).

458. Strümpel, A. von: "Charcot." *Deutsche Zeitschrift für Nervenheilkunde* (1893).

459. ———: "Charcot." *Wiener medizinische Wochenschrift*, No. 37 (1893).

460. ———: "Jean Martin Charcot." *Sitzungsbericht der phys. med. Societät zu Erlangen* (1874).

461. Strümpell, A.: *Aus dem Leben eines deutschen Klinikers.* Leipzig, 1925.
462. Tait, L.: "Cholecystotomy for Dropsy of Gallbladder Due to the Impaction of Gallstone." *Lancet,* November 15 (1879).
463. Thorwald, Jürgen: *The Century of the Surgeon.* New York, Pantheon Books, 1957.
464. Tinker, M. B.: "The First Nephrectomy and the First Cholecystotomy, with a Sketch of the Lives of Doctors Erastus B. Walcott and John S. Bobbs." *Johns Hopkins Hospital Bulletin, 12*:247 (1901).
465. Trendelenburg, F.: "Schädel und Gehirn." In his *Die ersten 25 Jahre der Deutschen Gesellschaft für Chirurgie.* Leipzig, 1923.
466. "Die Trepanation seit Beginn der modernen Chirurgie." *Ciba Zeitschrift* (November, 1936).
467. Treskow, H. von: *Von Fürsten und anderen Sterblichen.* Berlin, 1922.
468. Trotter, W.: "A Landmark in Modern Neurology." *Lancet,* p. 1207 (1934).
469. Truax, Rhoda: *British Medical Journal,* June 19 (1897).
470. ———: *Joseph Lister, Father of Modern Surgery.* Indianapolis, 1944.
471. Tschudi, J. von: *Peru. Reminiszenzen aus den Jahren 1832–1842.* St. Gallen, 1846.
472. Tuffier, M. T.: "Analgésie chirurgicale." *Semaine médicale,* No. 49 (1899).
473. Urban, K.: *Die Chirurgie des Kropfes.* Leipzig, 1937.
474. *Verhandlungen der Deutschen Gesellschaft für Chirurgie, 33. Kongress, Berlin, April 6–9, 1904.*
475. "Verneuil." (Obituary.) *Revue de chirurgie,* pp. 555 ff. (1895).
476. Viets, H. R.: "West Riding, 1871–1876." *Bull. Inst. Hist. Med.,* p. 477 (1938).
477. Vogeler, K.: *August Bier, Leben und Werk.* Berlin, 1942.
478. Walker, A. Earl: "Sir Victor Alexander Haden Horsley (1857–1916)." In W. Haymaker, ed.: *The Founders of Neurology.* Springfield, Ill., 1953.
479. ———: "Sir William Macewen." In his *A History of Neurological Surgery.* Baltimore, 1951.
480. ———: "Victor Alexander Haden Horsley." In his *A History of Neurological Surgery.* Baltimore, 1951.
481. Walzel: "Zum 50. Geburtstag der Gallenchirurgie." *Wiener klinische Wochenschrift,* pp. 900–3 (1932).
482. Weber, L. S.: *Dissert. inaug. sist. observationis quaedam in coretodialysim et pupillam in sclerotica aperiendam.* Tübingen, 1817.
483. Wernherr: "Geschichte und Theorie des Mechanismus der Bruchbildung." *Archiv für klinische Chirurgie,* pp. 161–97 (1872).
484. Wernly, M.: "Parathyreoidea." In Hirsch, *Handbuch der inneren Sekretion.* Vienna, 1928.
485. Wiese and Gilbert: "Theodor Kocher." *Annals of Medical History,* pp. 521–29 (1934).
486. Wilder, L.: *The Mayo Clinic.* 2nd ed. Springfield, Ill., 1955.

487. "William Macewen." *British Medical Journal*, p. 1545 (1902).
488. "William Macewen." *Lancet*, pp. 676, 727 (1924).
489. Williams, J. H. H.: *Doctors Differ*. Springfield, Ill., 1952.
490. ———: *The Healing Touch*. London, 1949.
491. Williams, Montagu: *Leaves of a Life*, Vol. 2. London.
492. Willins, Frederick A., comp.: *Aphorisms of Dr. Charles Horace Mayo, 1865–1939, and Dr. William James Mayo, 1861–1939*. Springfield, Ill., 1951.
493. Wilser: "Die Schädelöffnungen in alter und neuer Zeit." *Archiv für Geschichte der Naturwissenschaften*, p. 427 (1913).
494. Wittels, F.: *Sigmund Freud: His Personality, His Teaching, and His School*. Tr. by Eden and Cedar Paul. New York, 1924.
495. Wölfel: "Die Trepanation bei den Naturvölkern." *Wiener klinische Wochenschrift*, p. 131 (1925).
496. ———: "Die Trepanation bei den Urvölkern." *Wiener medizinische Wochenschrift*, p. 294 (1925).
497. Wölfer, P.: "Das Kokain. Seine Bedeutung und seine Geschichte." *Schweizer medizinische Wochenschrift* (1922).
498. Wölffler, A.: "Die Kropfexstirpation an Billroths Klinik von 1877–1881." *Wiener medizinische Wochenschrift*, p. 71 (1882).
499. ———: "Über die Exstirpation der Schilddrüse." *Wiener Med. Presse* (1879).
500. ———: "Weitere Beiträge zur chirurgischen Behandlung des Kropfes." *Wiener medizinische Wochenschrift*, p. 71 (1882).
501. Wyeth, John Allen: *With Sabre and Scalpel*. New York, 1914.
502. Young, A.: *Scalpel: Men Who Made Surgery*. New York, 1956.
503. Zesas: "Ist die Entfernung der Schilddrüse ein physiologisch erlaubter Akt?" *Archiv für klinische Chirurgie*, p. 395 (1884).
504. Zimmermann and Heller: "The Role of Edoardo Bassini in the Development of the Surgery of Hernia." *Surgery, Gynecology, Obstetrics*, p. 971 (1937).
505. Zirm, E.: "Eine erfolgreiche totale Keratoplastik." *Archiv für Ophthalmologie*, pp. 580–94 (1906).
506. ———: "Über Hornhautpfropfung." *Wiener klinische Wochenschrift*, No. 3 (1907).
507. Zoja, L.: "Carlo Forlanini." *Rivista pat. clin. tuberc.*, pp. 321–31 (1928).
508. "Zum 50. Todestag von Joh. v. Mikulicz-Radecki." *Münchner medizinische Wochenschrift*, pp. 772–73 (1955).

INDEX OF NAMES